GREAT BOOKS OF THE WESTERN WORLD

28. GILBERT
    GALILEO
    HARVEY

29. CERVANTES

30. FRANCIS BACON

31. DESCARTES
    SPINOZA

32. MILTON

33. PASCAL

34. NEWTON
    HUYGENS

35. LOCKE
    BERKELEY
    HUME

36. SWIFT
    STERNE

37. FIELDING

38. MONTESQUIEU
    ROUSSEAU

39. ADAM SMITH

40. GIBBON I

41. GIBBON II

42. KANT

43. AMERICAN STATE
    PAPERS
    THE FEDERALIST
    J. S. MILL

44. BOSWELL

45. LAVOISIER
    FOURIER
    FARADAY

46. HEGEL

47. GOETHE

48. MELVILLE

49. DARWIN

50. MARX
    ENGELS

51. TOLSTOY

52. DOSTOEVSKY

53. WILLIAM JAMES

54. FREUD

GREAT BOOKS
OF THE WESTERN WORLD

ROBERT MAYNARD HUTCHINS, *EDITOR IN CHIEF*

10.

HIPPOCRATES

GALEN

HIPPOCRATIC WRITINGS

ON
THE NATURAL FACULTIES
BY GALEN

WILLIAM BENTON, *Publisher*

ENCYCLOPÆDIA BRITANNICA, INC.

CHICAGO · LONDON · TORONTO

The text of *On the Natural Faculties,* translated
by Arthur John Brock, M.D., is reprinted by arrangement with the
HARVARD UNIVERSITY PRESS.

THE UNIVERSITY OF CHICAGO

*The Great Books
is published with the editorial advice of the faculties
of The University of Chicago*

GENERAL CONTENTS

✦✦✦✦✦✦✦✦✦✦✦✦✦✦✦✦✦✦✦

✦✦✦✦✦✦✦✦✦✦✦✦✦✦✦✦✦✦✦

HIPPOCRATIC WRITINGS

BIOGRAPHICAL NOTE

Hippocrates, *fl.* 400 B.C.

Our knowledge of the historical Hippocrates is almost completely dependent upon Plato. From the *Protagoras* and the *Phædrus* we learn that Hippocrates was a contemporary of Socrates, that he was a native of Cos, and an Asclepiad, a member, that is, of a family or guild that traced its origin to the God of Healing. He was well known both as a practitioner and a teacher of medicine, and he held that knowledge of the body depends upon the knowledge of the whole man. There is also the implication in Plato's words that Hippocrates travelled from city to city and that, like the great sophists and rhetoricians, he came to Athens to practise and to teach his art.

The figure of the legendary Father of Medicine soon replaced the historical Hippocrates. Although there is no evidence from his own time that he left any writings, within a century medical works were being attributed to him, especially those emanating from the famous medical school of Cos. The writings which now go by the name of the Hippocratic Collection consist for the most part of the early Greek medical treatises which were brought together by the Alexandrian scholars of the third century. The Collection is large and heterogeneous and although all were attributed to Hippocrates, the genuineness of some of them was questioned even in antiquity.

The Alexandrian accounts of the life of Hippocrates are rich in detail. He was born in the year 460 B.C., descended from Hercules as well as from Æsculapius. He studied medicine and philosophy from famous teachers and travelled over the whole Greek world, curing a Macedonian tyrant of the malady of love, driving out the plague from Athens by lighting fires in the public squares, refusing to go to Persia to treat the King, and dying at a great age—the dates range from 375 to 351 B.C.—at Larissa in Thessaly, where his tomb could still be seen in the second century, A.D. The honey of the bees that swarmed there was said to be healing to the mouth, a tribute to the man who, according to Celsus, was as eminent for eloquence as for knowledge.

For succeeding generations Hippocrates has been, as he was for Galen, the legislator of medicine, the ideal physician "who with purity and with holiness lived his life and practised his art."

Contents

The Oath

I SWEAR by Apollo the physician, and Æsculapius, and Health, and All-heal, and all the gods and goddesses, that, according to my ability and judgment, I will keep this Oath and this stipulation—to reckon him who taught me this Art equally dear to me as my parents, to share my substance with him, and relieve his necessities if required; to look upon his offspring in the same footing as my own brothers, and to teach them this art, if they shall wish to learn it, without fee or stipulation; and that by precept, lecture, and every other mode of instruction, I will impart a knowledge of the Art to my own sons, and those of my teachers, and to disciples bound by a stipulation and oath according to the law of medicine, but to none others. I will follow that system of regimen which, according to my ability and judgment, I consider for the benefit of my patients, and abstain from whatever is deleterious and mischievous. I will give no deadly medicine to any one if asked, nor suggest any such counsel; and in like manner I will not give to a woman a pessary to produce abortion. With purity and with holiness I will pass my life and practice my Art. I will not cut persons laboring under the stone, but will leave this to be done by men who are practitioners of this work. Into whatever houses I enter, I will go into them for the benefit of the sick, and will abstain from every voluntary act of mischief and corruption; and, further from the seduction of females or males, of freemen and slaves. Whatever, in connection with my professional practice or not, in connection with it, I see or hear, in the life of men, which ought not to be spoken of abroad, I will not divulge, as reckoning that all such should be kept secret. While I continue to keep this Oath unviolated, may it be granted to me to enjoy life and the practice of the art, respected by all men, in all times! But should I trespass and violate this Oath, may the reverse be my lot!

HIPPOCRATIC WRITINGS

On Ancient Medicine

WHOEVER having undertaken to speak or write on Medicine, have first laid down for themselves some hypothesis to their argument, such as hot, or cold, or moist, or dry, or whatever else they choose (thus reducing their subject within a narrow compass, and supposing only one or two original causes of diseases or of death among mankind), are all clearly mistaken in much that they say; and this is the more reprehensible as relating to an art which all men avail themselves of on the most important occasions, and the good operators and practitioners in which they hold in especial honor. For there are practitioners, some bad and some far otherwise, which, if there had been no such thing as Medicine, and if nothing had been investigated or found out in it, would not have been the case, but all would have been equally unskilled and ignorant of it, and everything concerning the sick would have been directed by chance. But now it is not so; for, as in all the other arts, those who practise them differ much from one another in dexterity and knowledge, so is it in like manner with Medicine. Wherefore I have not thought that it stood in need of an empty hypothesis, like those subjects which are occult and dubious, in attempting to handle which it is necessary to use some hypothesis; as, for example, with regard to things above us and things below the earth; if any one should treat of these and undertake to declare how they are constituted, the reader or hearer could not find out, whether what is delivered be true or false; for there is nothing which can be referred to in order to discover the truth.

2. But all these requisites belong of old to Medicine, and an origin and way have been found out, by which many and elegant discoveries have been made, during a length of time, and others will yet be found out, if a person possessed of the proper ability, and knowing those discoveries which have been made, should proceed from them to prosecute his investigations. But whoever, rejecting and despising all these, attempts to pursue another course and form of inquiry, and says he has discovered anything, is deceived himself and deceives others, for the thing is impossible. And for what reason it is impossible, I will now endeavor to explain, by stating and showing what the art really is. From this it will be manifest that discoveries cannot possibly be made in any other way. And most especially, it appears to me, that whoever treats of this art should treat of things which are familiar to the common people. For of nothing else will such a one have to inquire or treat, but of the diseases under which the common people have labored, which diseases and the causes of their origin and departure, their increase and decline, illiterate persons cannot easily find out themselves, but still it is easy for them to understand these things when discovered and expounded by others. For it is nothing more than that every one is put in mind of what had occurred to himself. But whoever does not reach the capacity of the illiterate vulgar and fails to make them listen to him, misses his mark. Wherefore, then, there is no necessity for any hypothesis.

3. For the art of Medicine would not have been invented at first, nor would it have been made a subject of investigation (for there would have been no need of it), if when men are indisposed, the same food and other articles of regimen which they eat and drink when in good health were proper for them, and if no others were preferable to these. But now necessity itself made medicine to be sought out and discovered by men, since the same things when administered to the sick, which agreed with them when in good health, neither did nor do agree with them. But to go still further back, I hold that the diet and food which people in health now use would not have been discovered, provided it had suited with man to eat

and drink in like manner as the ox, the horse, and all other animals, except man, do of the productions of the earth, such as fruits, weeds, and grass; for from such things these animals grow, live free of disease, and require no other kind of food. And, at first, I am of opinion that man used the same sort of food, and that the present articles of diet had been discovered and invented only after a long lapse of time, for when they suffered much and severely from this strong and brutish diet, swallowing things which were raw, unmixed, and possessing great strength, they became exposed to strong pains and diseases, and to early deaths. It is likely, indeed, that from habit they would suffer less from these things then than we would now, but still they would suffer severely even then; and it is likely that the greater number, and those who had weaker constitutions, would all perish; whereas the stronger would hold out for a longer time, as even nowadays some, in consequence of using strong articles of food, get off with little trouble, but others with much pain and suffering. From this necessity it appears to me that they would search out the food befitting their nature, and thus discover that which we now use: and that from wheat, by macerating it, stripping it of its hull, grinding it all down, sifting, toasting, and baking it, they formed bread; and from barley they formed cake(maza), performing many operations in regard to it; they boiled, they roasted, they mixed, they diluted those things which are strong and of intense qualities with weaker things, fashioning them to the nature and powers of man, and considering that the stronger things Nature would not be able to manage if administered, and that from such things pains, diseases, and death would arise, but such as Nature could manage, that from them food, growth, and health, would arise. To such a discovery and investigation what more suitable name could one give than that of Medicine? since it was discovered for the health of man, for his nourishment and safety, as a substitute for that kind of diet by which pains, diseases, and deaths were occasioned.

4. And if this is not held to be an art, I do not object. For it is not suitable to call any one an artist of that which no one is ignorant of, but which all know from usage and necessity. But still the discovery is a great one, and requiring much art and investigation. Wherefore those who devote themselves to gymnastics and training, are always making some new discovery, by pursuing the same line of inquiry, where, by eating and drinking certain things, they are improved and grow stronger than they were.

5. Let us inquire then regarding what is admitted to be Medicine; namely, that which was invented for the sake of the sick, which possesses a name and practitioners, whether it also seeks to accomplish the same objects, and whence it derived its origin. To me, then, it appears, as I said at the commencement, that nobody would have sought for medicine at all, provided the same kinds of diet had suited with men in sickness as in good health. Wherefore, even yet, such races of men as make no use of medicine, namely, barbarians, and even certain of the Greeks, live in the same way when sick as when in health; that is to say, they take what suits their appetite, and neither abstain from, nor restrict themselves in anything for which they have a desire. But those who have cultivated and invented medicine, having the same object in view as those of whom I formerly spoke, in the first place, I suppose, diminished the quantity of the articles of food which they used, and this alone would be sufficient for certain of the sick, and be manifestly beneficial to them, although not to all, for there would be some so affected as not to be able to manage even small quantities of their usual food, and as such persons would seem to require something weaker, they invented soups, by mixing a few strong things with much water, and thus abstracting that which was strong in them by dilution and boiling. But such as could not manage even soups, laid them aside, and had recourse to drinks, and so regulated them as to mixture and quantity, that they were administered neither stronger nor weaker than what was required.

6. But this ought to be well known, that soups do not agree with certain persons in their diseases, but, on the contrary, when administered both the fevers and the pains are exacerbated, and it becomes obvious that what was given has proved food and increase to the disease, but a wasting and weakness to the body. But whatever persons so affected partook of solid food, or cake, or bread, even in small quantity, would be ten times and more decidedly injured than those who had taken soups, for no other reason than from the strength of the food in reference to the affection; and to whomsoever it is proper to take soups and not eat solid food, such a one will be much more injured if he eat much than if he eat little, but even little food will be injurious to him. But all the causes

of the sufferance refer themselves to this rule, that the strongest things most especially and decidedly hurt man, whether in health or in disease.

7. What other object, then, had he in view who is called a physician, and is admitted to be a practitioner of the art, who found out the regimen and diet befitting the sick, than he who originally found out and prepared for all mankind that kind of food which we all now use, in place of the former savage and brutish mode of living? To me it appears that the mode is the same, and the discovery of a similar nature. The one sought to abstract those things which the constitution of man cannot digest, because of their wildness and intemperature, and the other those things which are beyond the powers of the affection in which any one may happen to be laid up. Now, how does the one differ from the other, except that the latter admits of greater variety, and requires more application, whereas the former was the commencement of the process?

8. And if one would compare the diet of sick persons with that of persons in health, he will find it not more injurious than that of healthy persons in comparison with that of wild beasts and of other animals. For, suppose a man laboring under one of those diseases which are neither serious and unsupportable, nor yet altogether mild, but such as that, upon making any mistake in diet, it will become apparent, as if he should eat bread and flesh, or any other of those articles which prove beneficial to healthy persons, and that, too, not in great quantity, but much less than he could have taken when in good health; and that another man in good health, having a constitution neither very feeble, nor yet strong, eats of those things which are wholesome and strengthening to an ox or a horse, such as vetches, barley, and the like, and that, too, not in great quantity, but much less than he could take; the healthy person who did so would be subjected to no less disturbance and danger than the sick person who took bread or cake unseasonably. All these things are proofs that Medicine is to be prosecuted and discovered by the same method as the other.

9. And if it were simply, as is laid down, that such things as are stronger prove injurious, but such as are weaker prove beneficial and nourishing, both to sick and healthy persons, it were an easy matter, for then the safest rule would be to circumscribe the diet to the lowest point. But then it is no less mistake, nor one that injures a man less, provided a deficient diet, or one consisting of weaker things than what are proper, be administered. For, in the constitution of man, abstinence may enervate, weaken, and kill. And there are many other ills, different from those of repletion, but no less dreadful, arising from deficiency of food; wherefore the practice in those cases is more varied, and requires greater accuracy. For one must aim at attaining a certain measure, and yet this measure admits neither weight nor calculation of any kind, by which it may be accurately determined, unless it be the sensation of the body; wherefore it is a task to learn this accurately, so as not to commit small blunders either on the one side or the other, and in fact I would give great praise to the physician whose mistakes are small, for perfect accuracy is seldom to be seen, since many physicians seem to me to be in the same plight as bad pilots, who, if they commit mistakes while conducting the ship in a calm do not expose themselves, but when a storm and violent hurricane overtake them, they then, from their ignorance and mistakes, are discovered to be what they are, by all men, namely, in losing their ship. And thus bad and commonplace physicians, when they treat men who have no serious illness, in which case one may commit great mistakes without producing any formidable mischief (and such complaints occur much more frequently to men than dangerous ones): under these circumstances, when they commit mistakes, they do not expose themselves to ordinary men; but when they fall in with a great, a strong, and a dangerous disease, then their mistakes and want of skill are made apparent to all. Their punishment is not far off, but is swift in overtaking both the one and the other.

10. And that no less mischief happens to a man from unseasonable depletion than from repletion, may be clearly seen upon reverting to the consideration of persons in health. For, to some, with whom it agrees to take only one meal in the day, and they have arranged it so accordingly; whilst others, for the same reason, also take dinner, and this they do because they find it good for them, and not like those persons who, for pleasure or from any casual circumstance, adopt the one or the other custom: and to the bulk of mankind it is of little consequence which of these rules they observe, that is to say, whether they make it a practice to take one or two meals. But there are certain persons who cannot readily change their diet with impunity; and if they make any alteration in it for one day, or even for a part of a day, are greatly injured thereby. Such persons,

provided they take dinner when it is not their wont, immediately become heavy and inactive, both in body and mind, and are weighed down with yawning, slumbering, and thirst; and if they take supper in addition, they are seized with flatulence, tormina, and diarrhea, and to many this has been the commencement of a serious disease, when they have merely taken twice in a day the same food which they have been in the custom of taking once. And thus, also, if one who has been accustomed to dine, and this rule agrees with him, should not dine at the accustomed hour, he will straightway feel great loss of strength, trembling, and want of spirits, the eyes of such a person will become more pallid, his urine thick and hot, his mouth bitter; his bowels will seem, as it were, to hang loose; he will suffer from vertigo, lowness of spirit, and inactivity,—such are the effects; and if he should attempt to take at supper the same food which he was wont to partake of at dinner, it will appear insipid, and he will not be able to take it off; and these things, passing downwards with tormina and rumbling, burn up his bowels; he experiences insomnolency or troubled and disturbed dreams; and to many of them these symptoms are the commencement of some disease.

11. But let us inquire what are the causes of these things which happened to them. To him, then, who was accustomed to take only one meal in the day, they happened because he did not wait the proper time, until his bowels had completely derived benefit from and had digested the articles taken at the preceding meal, and until his belly had become soft, and got into a state of rest, but he gave it a new supply while in a state of heat and fermentation; for such bellies digest much more slowly, and require more rest and ease. And as to him who had been accustomed to dinner, since, as soon as the body required food, and when the former meal was consumed, and he wanted refreshment, no new supply was furnished to it, he wastes and is consumed from want of food. For all the symptoms which I describe as befalling to this man I refer to want of food. And I also say that all men who, when in a state of health, remain for two or three days without food, experience the same unpleasant symptoms as those which I described in the case of him who had omitted to take dinner.

12. Wherefore, I say, that such constitutions as suffer quickly and strongly from errors in diet, are weaker than others that do not; and that a weak person is in a state very nearly approaching to one in disease; but a person in disease is the weaker, and it is, therefore, more likely that he should suffer if he encounters anything that is unseasonable. It is difficult, seeing that there is no such accuracy in the Art, to hit always upon what is most expedient, and yet many cases occur in medicine which would require this accuracy, as we shall explain. But on that account, I say, we ought not to reject the ancient Art, as if it were not, and had not been properly founded, because it did not attain accuracy in all things, but rather, since it is capable of reaching to the greatest exactitude by reasoning, to receive it and admire its discoveries, made from a state of great ignorance, and as having been well and properly made, and not from chance.

13. But I wish the discourse to revert to the new method of those who prosecute their inquiries in the Art by hypothesis. For if hot, or cold, or moist, or dry, be that which proves injurious to man, and if the person who would treat him properly must apply cold to the hot, hot to the cold, moist to the dry, and dry to the moist—let me be presented with a man, not indeed one of a strong constitution, but one of the weaker, and let him eat wheat, such as it is supplied from the thrashing-floor, raw and unprepared, with raw meat, and let him drink water. By using such a diet I know that he will suffer much and severely, for he will experience pains, his body will become weak, and his bowels deranged, and he will not subsist long. What remedy, then, is to be provided for one so situated? Hot? or cold? or moist? or dry? For it is clear that it must be one or other of these. For, according to this principle, if it is one of the which is injuring the patient, it is to be removed by its contrary. But the surest and most obvious remedy is to change the diet which the person used, and instead of wheat to give bread, and instead of raw flesh, boiled, and to drink wine in addition to these; for by making these changes it is impossible but that he must get better, unless completely disorganized by time and diet. What, then, shall we say? whether that, as he suffered from cold, these hot things being applied were of use to him, or the contrary? I should think this question must prove a puzzler to whomsoever it is put. For whether did he who prepared bread out of wheat remove the hot, the cold, the moist, or the dry principle in it?—for the bread is consigned both to fire and to water, and is wrought with many things, each of which has its peculiar property and nature, some of which it loses,

and with others it is diluted and mixed.

14. And this I know, moreover, that to the human body it makes a great difference whether the bread be fine or coarse; of wheat with or without the hull, whether mixed with much or little water, strongly wrought or scarcely at all, baked or raw—and a multitude of similar differences; and so, in like manner, with the cake (maza); the powers of each, too, are great, and the one nowise like the other. Whoever pays no attention to these things, or, paying attention, does not comprehend them, how can he understand the diseases which befall a man? For, by every one of these things, a man is affected and changed this way or that, and the whole of his life is subjected to them, whether in health, convalescence, or disease. Nothing else, then, can be more important or more necessary to know than these things. So that the first inventors, pursuing their investigations properly, and by a suitable train of reasoning, according to the nature of man, made their discoveries, and thought the Art worthy of being ascribed to a god, as is the established belief. For they did not suppose that the dry or the moist, the hot or the cold, or any of these are either injurious to man, or that man stands in need of them, but whatever in each was strong, and more than a match for a man's constitution, whatever he could not manage, that they held to be hurtful, and sought to remove. Now, of the sweet, the strongest is that which is intensely sweet; of the bitter, that which is intensely bitter; of the acid, that which is intensely acid; and of all things that which is extreme, for these things they saw both existing in man, and proving injurious to him. For there is in man the bitter and the salt, the sweet and the acid, the sour and the insipid, and a multitude of other things having all sorts of powers both as regards quantity and strength. These, when all mixed and mingled up with one another, are not apparent, neither do they hurt a man; but when any of them is separate, and stands by itself, then it becomes perceptible, and hurts a man. And thus, of articles of food, those which are unsuitable and hurtful to man when administered, every one is either bitter, or intensely so, or saltish or acid, or something else intense and strong, and therefore we are disordered by them in like manner as we are by the secretions in the body. But all those things which a man eats and drinks are devoid of any such intense and well-marked quality, such as bread, cake, and many other things of a similar nature which man is accustomed to use for

food, with the exception of condiments and confectionaries, which are made to gratify the palate and for luxury. And from those things, when received into the body abundantly, there is no disorder nor dissolution of the powers belonging to the body; but strength, growth, and nourishment result from them, and this for no other reason than because they are well mixed, have nothing in them of an immoderate character, nor anything strong, but the whole forms one simple and not strong substance.

15. I cannot think in what manner they who advance this doctrine, and transfer the Art from the cause I have described to hypothesis, will cure men according to the principle which they have laid down. For, as far as I know, neither the hot nor the cold, nor the dry, nor the moist, has ever been found unmixed with any other quality; but I suppose they use the same articles of meat and drink as all we other men do. But to this substance they give the attribute of being hot, to that cold, to that dry, and to that moist. Since it would be absurd to advise the patient to take something hot, for he would straightway ask what it is? so that he must either play the fool, or have recourse to some one of the well-known substances; and if this hot thing happen to be sour, and that hot thing insipid, and this hot thing has the power of raising a disturbance in the body (and there are many other kinds of heat, possessing many opposite powers), he will be obliged to administer some one of them, either the hot and the sour, or the hot and the insipid, or that which, at the same time, is cold and sour (for there is such a substance), or the cold and the insipid. For, as I think, the very opposite effects will result from either of these, not only in man, but also in a bladder, a vessel of wood, and in many other things possessed of far less sensibility than man; for it is not the heat which is possessed of great efficacy, but the sour and the insipid, and other qualities as described by me, both in man and out of man, and that whether eaten or drunk, rubbed in externally, and otherwise applied.

16. But I think that of all the qualities heat and cold exercise the least operation in the body, for these reasons: as long time as hot and cold are mixed up with one another they do not give trouble, for the cold is attempered and rendered more moderate by the hot, and the hot by the cold; but when the one is wholly separate from the other, then it gives pain; and at that season when cold is applied it creates some pain to a man, but quickly, for that very reason, heat spontaneously arises in him with-

out requiring any aid or preparation. And these things operate thus both upon men in health and in disease. For example, if a person in health wishes to cool his body during winter, and bathes either in cold water or in any other way, the more he does this, unless his body be fairly congealed, when he resumes his clothes and comes into a place of shelter, his body becomes more heated than before. And thus, too, if a person wish to be warmed thoroughly either by means of a hot bath or strong fire, and straightway having the same clothing on, takes up his abode again in the place he was in when he became congealed, he will appear much colder, and more disposed to chills than before. And if a person fan himself on account of a suffocating heat, and having procured refrigeration for himself in this manner, cease doing so, the heat and suffocation will be ten times greater in his case than in that of a person who does nothing of the kind. And, to give a more striking example, persons travelling in the snow, or otherwise in rigorous weather, and contracting great cold in their feet, their hands, or their head, what do they not suffer from inflammation and tingling when they put on warm clothing and get into a hot place? In some instances, blisters arise as if from burning with fire, and they do not suffer from any of those unpleasant symptoms until they become heated. So readily does either of these pass into the other; and I could mention many other examples. And with regard to the sick, is it not in those who experience a rigor that the most acute fever is apt to break out? And yet not so strongly neither, but that it ceases in a short time, and, for the most part, without having occasioned much mischief; and while it remains, it is hot, and passing over the whole body, ends for the most part in the feet, where the chills and cold were most intense and lasted longest; and, when sweat supervenes, and the fever passes off, the patient is much colder than if he had not taken the fever at all. Why then should that which so quickly passes into the opposite extreme, and loses its own powers spontaneously, be reckoned a mighty and serious affair? And what necessity is there for any great remedy for it?

17. One might here say—but persons in ardent fevers, pneumonia, and other formidable diseases, do not quickly get rid of the heat, nor experience these rapid alterations of heat and cold. And I reckon this very circumstance the strongest proof that it is not from heat simply that men get into the febrile state, neither is it the sole cause of the mischief, but that this species of heat is bitter, and that acid, and the other saltish, and many other varieties; and again there is cold combined with other qualities. These are what proves injurious; heat, it is true, is present also, possessed of strength as being that which conducts, is exacerbated and increased along with the other, but has no power greater than what is peculiar to itself.

18. With regard to these symptoms, in the first place those are most obvious of which we have all often had experience. Thus, then, in such of us as have a coryza and defluxion from the nostrils, this discharge is much more acrid than that which formerly was formed in and ran from them daily; and it occasions swelling of the nose, and it inflames, being of a hot and extremely ardent nature, as you may know, if you apply your hand to the place; and, if the disease remains long, the part becomes ulcerated although destitute of flesh and hard; and the heat in the nose ceases, not when the defluxion takes place and the inflammation is present, but when the running becomes thicker and less acrid, and more mixed with the former secretion, then it is that the heat ceases. But in all those cases in which this decidedly proceeds from cold alone, without the concourse of any other quality, there is a change from cold to hot, and from hot to cold, and these quickly supervene, and require no coction. But all the others being connected, as I have said, with acrimony and intemperance of humors, pass off in this way by being mixed and concocted.

19. But such defluxions as are determined to the eyes being possessed of strong and varied acrimonies, ulcerate the eyelids, and in some cases corrode the cheeks and parts below the eyes upon which they flow, and even occasion rupture and erosion of the tunic which surrounds the eyeball. But pain, heat, and extreme burning prevail until the defluxions are concocted and become thicker, and concretions form about the eyes, and the coction takes place from the fluids being mixed up, diluted, and digested together. And in defluxions upon the throat, from which are formed hoarseness, cynanche, crysipelas, and pneumonia, all these have at first saltish, watery, and acrid discharges, and with these the diseases gain strength. But when the discharges become thicker, more concocted, and are freed from all acrimony, then, indeed, the fevers pass away, and the other symptoms which annoyed the patient; for we must account those things the cause of each complaint, which, being present in a certain fashion, the complaint exists,

but it ceases when they change to another combination. But those which originate from pure heat or cold, and do not participate in any other quality, will then cease when they undergo a change from cold to hot, and from hot to cold; and they change in the manner I have described before. Wherefore, all the other complaints to which man is subject arise from powers (qualities?). Thus, when there is an overflow of the bitter principle, which we call yellow bile, what anxiety, burning heat, and loss of strength prevail! but if relieved from it, either by being purged spontaneously, or by means of a medicine seasonably administered, the patient is decidedly relieved of the pains and heat; but while these things float on the stomach, unconcocted and undigested, no contrivance could make the pains and fever cease; and when there are acidities of an acrid and æruginous character, what varieties of frenzy, gnawing pains in the bowels and chest, and inquietude, prevail! and these do not cease until the acidities be purged away, or are calmed down and mixed with other fluids. The coction, change, attenuation, and thickening into the form of humors, take place through many and various forms; therefore the crises and calculations of time are of great importance in such matters; but to all such changes hot and cold are but little exposed, for these are neither liable to putrefaction nor thickening. What then shall we say of the change? that it is a combination (crasis) of these humors having different powers toward one another. But the hot does not loose its heat when mixed with any other thing except the cold; nor again, the cold, except when mixed with the hot. But all other things connected with man become the more mild and better in proportion as they are mixed with the more things besides. But a man is in the best possible state when they are concocted and at rest, exhibiting no one peculiar quality; but I think I have said enough in explanation of them.

20. Certain sophists and physicians say that it is not possible for any one to know medicine who does not know what man is [and how he was made and how constructed], and that whoever would cure men properly, must learn this in the first place. But this saying rather appertains to philosophy, as Empedocles and certain others have described what man in his origin is, and how he first was made and constructed. But I think whatever such has been said or written by sophist or physician concerning nature has less connection with the art of medicine than with the art of painting. And I think

that one cannot know anything certain respecting nature from any other quarter than from medicine; and that this knowledge is to be attained when one comprehends the whole subject of medicine properly, but not until then; and I say that this history shows what man is, by what causes he was made, and other things accurately. Wherefore it appears to me necessary to every physician to be skilled in nature, and strive to know, if he would wish to perform his duties, what man is in relation to the articles of food and drink, and to his other occupations, and what are the effects of each of them to every one. And it is not enough to know simply that cheese is a bad article of food, as disagreeing with whoever eats of it to satiety, but what sort of disturbance it creates, and wherefore, and with what principle in man it disagrees; for there are many other articles of food and drink naturally bad which affect man in a different manner. Thus, to illustrate my meaning by an example, undiluted wine drunk in large quantity renders a man feeble; and everybody seeing this knows that such is the power of wine, and the cause thereof; and we know, moreover, on what parts of a man's body it principally exerts its action; and I wish the same certainty to appear in other cases. For cheese (since we used it as an example) does not prove equally injurious to all men, for there are some who can take it to satiety without being hurt by it in the least, but, on the contrary, it is wonderful what strength it imparts to those it agrees with; but there are some who do not bear it well, their constitutions are different, and they differ in this respect, that what in their body is incompatible with cheese, is roused and put in commotion by such a thing; and those in whose bodies such a humor happens to prevail in greater quantity and intensity, are likely to suffer the more from it. But if the thing had been pernicious to the whole nature of man, it would have hurt all. Whoever knows these things will not suffer from it.

21. During convalescence from diseases, and also in protracted diseases, many disorders occur, some spontaneously, and some from certain things accidentally administered. I know that the common herd of physicians, like the vulgar, if there happen to have been any innovation made about that day, such as the bath being used, a walk taken, or any unusual food eaten, all which were better done than otherwise, attribute notwithstanding the cause of these disorders, to some of these things, being ignorant of the true cause but proscribing what may have

been very proper. Now this ought not to be so; but one should know the effects of a bath or a walk unseasonably applied; for thus there will never be any mischief from these things, nor from any other thing, nor from repletion, nor from such and such an article of food. Whoever does not know what effect these things produce upon a man, cannot know the consequences which result from them, nor how to apply them.

22. And it appears to me that one ought also to know what diseases arise in man from the powers, and what from the structures. What do I mean by this? By powers, I mean intense and strong juices; and by structures, whatever conformations there are in man. For some are hollow, and from broad contracted into narrow; some expanded, some hard and round, some broad and suspended, some stretched, some long, some dense, some rare and succulent, some spongy and of loose texture. Now, then, which of these figures is the best calculated to suck to itself and attract humidity from another body? Whether what is hollow and expanded, or what is solid and round, or what is hollow, and from broad, gradually turning narrow? I think such as from hollow and broad are contracted into narrow: this may be ascertained otherwise from obvious facts: thus, if you gape wide with the mouth you cannot draw in any liquid; but by protruding, contracting, and compressing the lips, and still more by using a tube, you can readily draw in whatever you wish. And thus, too, the instruments which are used for cupping are broad below and gradually become narrow, and are so constructed in order to suck and draw in from the fleshy parts. The nature and construction of the parts within a man are of a like nature; the bladder, the head, the uterus in woman; these parts clearly attract, and are always filled with a juice which is foreign to them. Those parts which are hollow and expanded are most likely to receive any humidity flowing into them, but cannot attract it in like manner. Those parts which are solid and round could not attract a humidity, nor receive it when it flows to them, for it would glide past, and find no place of rest on them. But spongy and rare parts, such as the spleen, the lungs, and the breasts, drink up especially the juices around them, and become hardened and enlarged by the accession of juices. Such things happen to these organs especially. For it is not with the spleen as with the stomach, in which there is a liquid, which it contains and evacuates every day; but when it (the spleen) drinks

up and receives a fluid into itself, the hollow and lax parts of it are filled, even the small interstices; and, instead of being rare and soft, it becomes hard and dense, and it can neither digest nor discharge its contents: these things it suffers, owing to the nature of its structure. Those things which engender flatulence or tormina in the body, naturally do so in the hollow and broad parts of the body, such as the stomach and chest, where they produce rumbling noises; for when they do not fill the parts so as to be stationary, but have changes of place and movements, there must necessarily be noise and apparent movements from them. But such parts as are fleshy and soft, in these there occur torpor and obstructions, such as happen in apoplexy. But when it (the flatus?) encounters a broad and resisting structure, and rushes against such a part, and this happens when it is by nature not strong so as to be able to withstand it without suffering injury; nor soft and rare, so as to receive or yield to it, but tender, juicy, full of blood, and dense, like the liver, owing to its density and broadness, it resists and does not yield. But flatus, when it obtains admission, increases and becomes stronger, and rushes toward any resisting object; but owing to its tenderness, and the quantity of blood which it (the liver) contains, it cannot be without uneasiness; and for these reasons the most acute and frequent pains occur in the region of it, along with suppurations and chronic tumors (phymata). These symptoms also occur in the site of the diaphragm, but much less frequently; for the diaphragm is a broad, expanded, and resisting substance, of a nervous (tendinous?) and strong nature, and therefore less susceptible of pain; and yet pains and chronic abscesses do occur about it.

23. There are both within and without the body many other kinds of structure, which differ much from one another as to sufferings both in health and disease; such as whether the head be small or large; the neck slender or thick, long or short; the belly long or round; the chest and ribs broad or narrow; and many others besides, all which you ought to be acquainted with, and their differences; so that knowing the causes of each, you may make the more accurate observations.

24. And, as has been formerly stated, one ought to be acquainted with the powers of juices, and what action each of them has upon man, and their alliances towards one another. What I say is this: if a sweet juice change to another kind, not from any admixture, but be-

cause it has undergone a mutation within itself; what does it first become?—bitter? salt? austere? or acid? I think acid. And hence, an acid juice is the most improper of all things that can be administered in cases in which a sweet juice is the most proper. Thus, if one should succeed in his investigations of external things, he would be the better able always to select the best; for that is best which is farthest removed from that which is unwholesome.

On Airs, Waters, and Places

WHOEVER wishes to investigate medicine properly, should proceed thus: in the first place to consider the seasons of the year, and what effects each of them produces for they are not at all alike, but differ much from themselves in regard to their changes. Then the winds, the hot and the cold, especially such as are common to all countries, and then such as are peculiar to each locality. We must also consider the qualities of the waters, for as they differ from one another in taste and weight, so also do they differ much in their qualities. In the same manner, when one comes into a city to which he is a stranger, he ought to consider its situation, how it lies as to the winds and the rising of the sun; for its influence is not the same whether it lies to the north or the south, to the rising or to the setting sun. These things one ought to consider most attentively, and concerning the waters which the inhabitants use, whether they be marshy and soft, or hard, and running from elevated and rocky situations, and then if saltish and unfit for cooking; and the ground, whether it be naked and deficient in water, or wooded and well watered, and whether it lies in a hollow, confined situation, or is elevated and cold; and the mode in which the inhabitants live, and what are their pursuits, whether they are fond of drinking and eating to excess, and given to indolence, or are fond of exercise and labor, and not given to excess in eating and drinking.

2. From these things he must proceed to investigate everything else. For if one knows all these things well, or at least the greater part of them, he cannot miss knowing, when he comes into a strange city, either the diseases peculiar to the place, or the particular nature of common diseases, so that he will not be in doubt as to the treatment of the diseases, or commit mistakes, as is likely to be the case provided one had not previously considered these matters. And in particular, as the season and the year advances, he can tell what epidemic diseases will attack the city, either in summer or in winter, and what each individual will be in danger of experiencing from the change of regimen. For knowing the changes of the seasons, the risings and settings of the stars, how each of them takes place, he will be able to know beforehand what sort of a year is going to ensue. Having made these investigations, and knowing beforehand the seasons, such a one must be acquainted with each particular, and must succeed in the preservation of health, and be by no means unsuccessful in the practice of his art. And if it shall be thought that these things belong rather to meteorology, it will be admitted, on second thoughts, that astronomy contributes not a little, but a very great deal, indeed, to medicine. For with the seasons the digestive organs of men undergo a change.

3. But how each of the aforementioned things should be investigated and explained, I will now declare in a clear manner. A city that is exposed to hot winds (these are between the wintry rising, and the wintry setting of the sun), and to which these are peculiar, but which is sheltered from the north winds; in such a city the waters will be plenteous and saltish, and as they run from an elevated source, they are necessarily hot in summer, and cold in winter; the heads of the inhabitants are of a humid and pituitous constitution, and their bellies subject to frequent disorders, owing to the phlegm running down from the head; the forms of their bodies, for the most part, are rather flabby; they do not eat nor drink much; drinking wine in particular, and more especially if carried to intoxication, is oppressive to them; and the following diseases are peculiar to the district: in the first place, the women are sickly and subject to excessive menstruation; then many are unfruitful from disease, and not from nature, and they have frequent miscarriages; infants are subject to attacks of convulsions and asthma, which they consider to be connected with infancy, and hold to be a sacred disease (epilepsy). The men are subject to attacks of dysentery, diarrhea, hepialus,[1] chronic

[1] The Hepialus is a species of intermittent fever, very common in warm climates.

fevers in winter, of epinyctis,[1] frequently, and of hemorrhoids about the anus. Pleurisies, peripneumonies, ardent fevers, and whatever diseases are reckoned acute, do not often occur, for such diseases are not apt to prevail where the bowels are loose. Ophthalmies occur of a humid character, but not of a serious nature, and of short duration, unless they attack epidemically from the change of the seasons. And when they pass their fiftieth year, defluxions supervening from the brain, render them paralytic when exposed suddenly to strokes of the sun, or to cold. These diseases are endemic to them, and, moreover, if any epidemic disease connected with the change of the seasons, prevail, they are also liable to it.

4. But the following is the condition of cities which have the opposite exposure, namely, to cold winds, between the summer settings and the summer risings of the sun, and to which these winds are peculiar, and which are sheltered from the south and the hot breezes. In the first place the waters are, for the most part, hard and cold. The men must necessarily be well braced and slender, and they must have the discharges downwards of the alimentary canal hard, and of difficult evacuation, while those upwards are more fluid, and rather bilious than pituitous. Their heads are sound and hard, and they are liable to burstings (of vessels?) for the most part. The diseases which prevail epidemically with them, are pleurisies, and those which are called acute diseases. This must be the case when the bowels are bound; and from any causes, many become affected with suppurations in the lungs, the cause of which is the tension of the body, and hardness of the bowels; for their dryness and the coldness of the water dispose them to ruptures (of vessels?). Such constitutions must be given to excess of eating, but not of drinking; for it is not possible to be gourmands and drunkards at the same time. Ophthalmies, too, at length supervene; these being of a hard and violent nature, and soon ending in rupture of the eyes; persons under thirty years of age are liable to severe bleedings at the nose in summer; attacks of epilepsy are rare but severe. Such people are likely to be rather long-lived; their ulcers are not attended with serious discharges, nor of a malignant character; in disposition they are rather ferocious than gentle. The diseases I have mentioned are peculiar to the men, and besides they are liable to any common complaint which may be prevailing from the changes of the seasons. But the women, in the first place, are

[1] A disease of the skin.

of a hard constitution, from the waters being hard, indigestible, and cold; and their menstrual discharges are not regular, but in small quantity, and painful. Then they have difficult parturition, but are not very subject to abortions. And when they do bring forth children, they are unable to nurse them; for the hardness and indigestable nature of the water puts away their milk. Phthisis frequently supervenes after childbirth, for the efforts of it frequently bring on ruptures and strains. Children while still little are subject to dropsies in the testicle, which disappear as they grow older; in such a town they are late in attaining manhood. It is, as I have now stated, with regard to hot and cold winds and cities thus exposed.

5. Cities that are exposed to winds between the summer and the winter risings of the sun, and those the opposite to them, have the following characters:—Those which lie to the rising of the sun are all likely to be more healthy than such as are turned to the North, or those exposed to the hot winds, even if there should not be a furlong between them. In the first place, both the heat and cold are more moderate. Then such waters as flow to the rising sun, must necessarily be clear, fragrant, soft, and delightful to drink, in such a city. For the sun in rising and shining upon them purifies them, by dispelling the vapors which generally prevail in the morning. The persons of the inhabitants are, for the most part, well colored and blooming, unless some disease counteract. The inhabitants have clear voices, and in temper and intellect are superior to those which are exposed to the north, and all the productions of the country in like manner are better. A city so situated resembles the spring as to moderation between heat and cold, and the diseases are few in number, and of a feeble kind, and bear a resemblance to the diseases which prevail in regions exposed to hot winds. The women there are very prolific, and have easy deliveries. Thus it is with regard to them.

6. But such cities as lie to the west, and which are sheltered from winds blowing from the east, and which the hot winds and the cold winds of the north scarcely touch, must necessarily be in a very unhealthy situation: in the first place the waters are not clear, the cause of which is, because the mist prevails commonly in the morning, and it is mixed up with the water and destroys its clearness, for the sun does not shine upon the water until he be considerably raised above the horizon. And in summer, cold breezes from the east blow and dews fall; and in the

latter part of the day the setting sun particularly scorches the inhabitants, and therefore they are pale and enfeebled, and are partly subject to all the aforesaid diseases, but no one is peculiar to them. Their voices are rough and hoarse owing to the state of the air, which in such a situation is generally impure and unwholesome, for they have not the northern winds to purify it; and these winds they have are of a very humid character, such being the nature of the evening breezes. Such a situation of a city bears a great resemblance to autumn as regards the changes of the day, inasmuch as the difference between morning and evening is great. So it is with regard to the winds that are conducive to health, or the contrary.

7. And I wish to give an account of the other kinds of waters, namely, of such as are wholesome and such as are unwholesome, and what bad and what good effects may be derived from water; for water contributes much towards health. Such waters then as are marshy, stagnant, and belong to lakes, are necessarily hot in summer, thick, and have a strong smell, since they have no current; but being constantly supplied by rain-water, and the sun heating them, they necessarily want their proper color, are unwholesome and form bile; in winter, they become congealed, cold, and muddy with the snow and ice, so that they are most apt to engender phlegm, and bring on hoarseness; those who drink them have large and obstructed spleens, their bellies are hard, emaciated, and hot; and their shoulders, collar-bones, and faces are emaciated; for their flesh is melted down and taken up by the spleen, and hence they are slender; such persons then are voracious and thirsty; their bellies are very dry both above and below, so that they require the strongest medicines. This disease is habitual to them both in summer and in winter, and in addition they are very subject to dropsies of a most fatal character; and in summer dysenteries, diarrheas, and protracted quartan fevers frequently seize them, and these diseases when prolonged dispose such constitutions to dropsies, and thus prove fatal. These are the diseases which attack them in summer; but in winter younger persons are liable to pneumonia, and maniacal affections; and older persons to ardent fevers, from hardness of the belly. Women are subject to œdema and leucophlegmasiæ;[1] when pregnant they have difficult deliveries; their infants are large and swelled, and then during nursing they become wasted and sickly, and the lochial

[1] A species of dropsy.

discharge after parturition does not proceed properly with the women. The children are particularly subject to hernia, and adults to varices and ulcers on their legs, so that persons with such constitutions cannot be long-lived, but before the usual period they fall into a state of premature old age. And further, the women appear to be with child, and when the time of parturition arrives, the fulness of the belly disappears, and this happens from dropsy of the uterus. Such waters then I reckon bad for every purpose. The next to them in badness are those which have their fountains in rocks, so that they must necessarily be hard, or come from a soil which produces thermal waters, such as those having iron, copper, silver, gold, sulphur, alum, bitumen, or nitre (soda) in them; for all these are formed by the force of heat. Good waters cannot proceed from such a soil, but those that are hard and of a heating nature, difficult to pass by urine, and of difficult evacuation by the bowels. The best are those which flow from elevated grounds, and hills of earth; these are sweet, clear, and can bear a little wine; they are hot in summer and cold in winter, for such necessarily must be the waters from deep wells. But those are most to be commended which run to the rising of the sun, and especially to the summer sun; for such are necessarily more clear, fragrant, and light. But all such as are salty, crude, and harsh, are not good for drink. But there are certain constitutions and diseases with which such waters agree when drunk, as I will explain presently. Their characters are as follows: the best are such as have their fountains to the east; the next, those between the summer risings and settings of the sun, and especially those to the risings; and third, those between the summer and winter settings; but the worst are those to the south, and the parts between the winter rising and setting, and those to the south are very bad, but those to the north are better. They are to be used as follows: whoever is in good health and strength need not mind, but may always drink whatever is at hand. But whoever wishes to drink the most suitable for any disease, may accomplish his purpose by attending to the following directions: To persons whose bellies are hard and easily burnt up, the sweetest, the lightest, and the most limpid waters will be proper; but those persons whose bellies are soft, loose, and pituitous, should choose the hardest, those kinds that are most crude, and the saltiest, for thus will they be most readily dried up; for such waters as are adapted for boiling, and are of a very solvent nature, naturally loosen readily and melt down the bowels; but such as are intractable, hard, and by no means proper for boiling, these rather bind and dry up the bowels. People have deceived themselves with regard to salt waters, from inexperience, for they think these waters purgative, whereas they are the very reverse; for such waters are crude, and ill adapted for boiling, so that the belly is more likely to be bound up than loosened by them. And thus it is with regard to the waters of springs.

8. I will now tell how it is with respect to rain-water, and water from snow. Rain waters, then, are the lightest, the sweetest, the thinnest, and the clearest; for originally the sun raises and attracts the thinnest and lightest part of the water, as is obvious from the nature of salts; for the saltish part is left behind owing to its thickness and weight, and forms salts; but the sun attracts the thinnest part, owing to its lightness, and he abstracts this not only from the lakes, but also from the sea, and from all things which contain humidity, and there is humidity in everything; and from man himself the sun draws off the thinnest and lightest part of the juices. As a strong proof of this, when a man walks in the sun, or sits down having a garment on, whatever parts of the body the sun shines upon do not sweat, for the sun carries off whatever sweat makes its appearance; but those parts which are covered by the garment, or anything else, sweat, for the particles of sweat are drawn and forced out by the sun, and are preserved by the cover so as not to be dissipated by the sun; but when the person comes into the shade the whole body equally perspires, because the sun no longer shines upon it. Wherefore, of all kinds of water, these spoil the soonest; and rain water has a bad smell, because its particles are collected and mixed together from most objects, so as to spoil the soonest. And in addition to this, when attracted and raised up, being carried about and mixed with the air, whatever part of it is turbid and darkish is separated and removed from the other, and becomes cloud and mist, but the most attenuated and lightest part is left, and becomes sweet, being heated and concocted by the sun, for all other things when concocted become sweet. While dissipated then and not in a state of consistence it is carried aloft. But when collected and condensed by contrary winds, it falls down wherever it happens to be most condensed. For this is likely to happen when the clouds being carried along and moving with a wind which does not allow them to rest, suddenly encounters another wind and other clouds from the opposite direction: there it is first condensed, and what is behind is carried up to the spot, and thus it thickens, blackens, and is conglomerated, and by its weight it falls down and becomes rain. Such, to all appearance, are the best of waters, but they require to be boiled and strained; for otherwise they have a bad smell, and occasion hoarseness and thickness of the voice to those who drink them. Those from snow and ice are all bad, for when once congealed, they never again recover their former nature; for whatever is clear, light, and sweet in them, is separated and disappears; but the most turbid and weightiest part is left behind. You may ascertain this in the following manner: If in winter you will pour water by measure into a vessel and expose it to the open air until it is all frozen, and then on the following day bring it into a warm situation where the ice will thaw, if you will measure the water again when dissolved you will find it much less in quantity. This is a proof that the lightest and thinnest part is dissipated and dried up by the congelation, and not the heaviest and thickest, for that is impossible: wherefore I hold that waters from snow and ice, and those allied to them, are the worst of any for all purposes whatever. Such are the characters of rain-water, and those from ice and snow.

9. Men become affected with the stone, and are seized with diseases of the kidneys, strangury, sciatica, and become ruptured, when they drink all sorts of waters, and those from great rivers into which other rivulets run, or from a lake into which many streams of all sorts flow, and such as are brought from a considerable distance. For it is impossible that such waters can resemble one another, but one kind is sweet, another saltish and aluminous, and some flow from thermal springs; and these being all mixed up together disagree, and the strongest part always prevails; but the same kind is not always the strongest, but sometimes one and sometimes another, according to the winds, for the north wind imparts strength to this water, and the south to that, and so also with regard to the others. There must be deposits of mud and sand in the vessels from such waters, and the aforesaid diseases must be engendered by them when drunk, but why not to all I will now explain. When the bowels are loose and in a healthy state, and when the bladder is not hot, nor the neck of the bladder very contracted, all such persons pass water freely, and no concretion forms in the bladder; but those in whom the

belly is hot, the bladder must be in the same condition; and when preternaturally heated, its neck becomes inflamed; and when these things happen, the bladder does not expel the urine, but raises its heat excessively. And the thinnest part of it is secreted, and the purest part is passed off in the form of urine, but the thickest and most turbid part is condensed and concreted, at first in small quantity, but afterwards in greater; for being rolled about in the urine, whatever is of a thick consistence it assimilates to itself, and thus it increases and becomes indurated. And when such persons make water, the stone forced down by the urine falls into the neck of the bladder and stops the urine, and occasions intense pain; so that calculous children rub their privy parts and tear at them, as supposing that the obstruction to the urine is situated there. As a proof that it is as I say, persons affected with calculus have very limpid urine, because the thickest and foulest part remains and is concreted. Thus it generally is in cases of calculus. It forms also in children from milk, when it is not wholesome, but very hot and bilious, for it heats the bowels and bladder, so that the urine being also heated undergoes the same change. And I hold that it is better to give children only the most diluted wine, for such will least burn up and dry the veins. Calculi do not form so readily in women, for in them the urethra is short and wide, so that in them the urine is easily expelled; neither do they rub the pudendum with their hands, nor handle the passage like males; for the urethra in women opens direct into the pudendum, which is not the case with men, neither in them is the urethra so wide, and they drink more than children do. Thus, or nearly so, is it with regard to them.

10. And respecting the seasons, one may judge whether the year will prove sickly or healthy from the following observations:—If the appearances connected with the rising and setting stars be as they should be; if there be rains in autumn; if the winter be mild, neither very tepid nor unseasonably cold, and if in spring the rains be seasonable, and so also in summer, the year is likely to prove healthy. But if the winter be dry and northerly, and the spring showery and southerly, the summer will necessarily be of a febrile character, and give rise to ophthalmies and dysenteries. For when suffocating heat sets in all of a sudden, while the earth is moistened by the vernal showers, and by the south wind, the heat is necessarily doubled from the earth, which is thus soaked by rain and heated by a burning sun, while, at the same time, men's bellies are not in an orderly state, nor the brain properly dried; for it is impossible, after such a spring, but that the body and its flesh must be loaded with humors, so that very acute fevers will attack all, but especially those of a phlegmatic constitution. Dysenteries are also likely to occur to women and those of a very humid temperament. And if at the rising of the Dogstar rain and wintery storms supervene, and if the etesian winds blow, there is reason to hope that these diseases will cease, and that the autumn will be healthy; but if not, it is likely to be a fatal season to children and women, but least of all to old men; and that convalescents will pass into quartans, and from quartans into dropsies; but if the winter be southerly, showery and mild, but the spring northerly, dry, and of a wintry character, in the first place women who happen to be with child, and whose accouchement should take place in spring, are apt to miscarry; and such as bring forth, have feeble and sickly children, so that they either die presently or are tender, feeble, and sickly, if they live. Such is the case with the women. The others are subject to dysenteries and dry ophthalmics, and some have catarrhs beginning in the head and descending to the lungs. Men of a phlegmatic temperament are likely to have dysenteries; and women, also, from the humidity of their nature, the phlegm descending downwards from the brain; those who are bilious, too, have dry ophthalmies from the heat and dryness of their flesh; the aged, too, have catarrhs from their flabbiness and melting of the veins, so that some of them die suddenly and some become paralytic on the right side or the left. For when, the winter being southerly and the body hot, the blood and veins are not properly constringed; a spring that is northerly, dry, and cold, having come on, the brain when it should have been expanded and purged, by the coryza and hoarseness is then constringed and contracted, so that the summer and the heat occurring suddenly, and a change supervening, these diseases fall out. And such cities as lie well to the sun and winds, and use good waters, feel these changes less, but such as use marshy and pooly waters, and lie well both as regards the winds and the sun, these all feel it more. And if the summer be dry, those diseases soon cease, but if rainy, they are protracted; and there is danger of any sore that there is becoming phagedenic from any cause; and lienteries and dropsies supervene at the conclusion of diseases; for the bowels are not readily dried up. And if the summer be rainy and southerly,

and next the autumn, the winter must, of necessity, be sickly, and ardent fevers are likely to attack those that are phlegmatic, and more elderly than forty years, and pleurisies and peripneumonies those that are bilious. But if the summer is parched and northerly, but the autumn rainy and southerly, headache and sphacelus of the brain are likely to occur; and in addition hoarseness, coryza, coughs, and in some cases, consumption. But if the season is northerly and without water, there being no rain, neither after the Dogstar nor Arcturus; this state agrees best with those who are naturally phlegmatic, with those who are of a humid temperament, and with women; but it is most inimical to the bilious; for they become much parched up, and ophthalmies of a dry nature supervene, fevers both acute and chronic, and in some cases melancholy; for the most humid and watery part of the bile being consumed, the thickest and most acrid portion is left, and of the blood likewise, when these diseases come upon them. But all these are beneficial to the phlegmatic, for they are thereby dried up, and reach winter not oppressed with humors, but with them dried up.

11. Whoever studies and observes these things may be able to foresee most of the effects which will result from the changes of the seasons; and one ought to be particularly guarded during the greatest changes of the seasons, and neither willingly give medicines, nor apply the cautery to the belly, nor make incisions there until ten or more days be past. Now, the greatest and most dangerous are the two solstices, and especially the summer, and also the two equinoxes, but especially the autumnal. One ought also to be guarded about the rising of the stars, especially of the Dogstar, then of Arcturus, and then the setting of the Pleiades; for diseases are especially apt to prove critical in those days, and some prove fatal, some pass off, and all others change to another form and another constitution. So it is with regard to them.

12. I wish to show, respecting Asia and Europe, how, in all respects, they differ from one another, and concerning the figure of the inhabitants, for they are different, and do not at all resemble one another. To treat of all would be a long story, but I will tell you how I think it is with regard to the greatest and most marked differences. I say, then, that Asia differs very much from Europe as to the nature of all things, both with regard to the productions of the earth and the inhabitants, for everything is produced much more beautiful and large in Asia; the country is milder, and the dispositions of the inhabitants also are more gentle and affectionate. The cause of this is the temperature of the seasons, because it lies in the middle of the risings of the sun towards the east, and removed from the cold (and heat), for nothing tends to growth and mildness so much as when the climate has no predominant quality, but a general equality of temperature prevails. It is not everywhere the same with regard to Asia, but such parts of the country as lie intermediate between the heat and the cold, are the best supplied with fruits and trees, and have the most genial climate, and enjoy the purest waters, both celestial and terrestrial. For neither are they much burnt up by the heat, nor dried up by the drought and want of rain, nor do they suffer from the cold; since they are well watered from abundant showers and snow, and the fruits of the season, as might be supposed, grow in abundance, both such as are raised from seed that has been sown, and such plants as the earth produces of its own accord, the fruits of which the inhabitants make use of, training them from their wild state and transplanting them to a suitable soil; the cattle also which are reared there are vigorous, particularly prolific, and bring up young of the fairest description; the inhabitants too, are well fed, most beautiful in shape, of large stature, and differ little from one another either as to figure or size; and the country itself, both as regards its constitution and mildness of the seasons, may be said to bear a close resemblance to the spring. Manly courage, endurance of suffering, laborious enterprise, and high spirit, could not be produced in such a state of things either among the native inhabitants or those of a different country, for there pleasure necessarily reigns. For this reason, also, the forms of wild beasts there are much varied. Thus it is, as I think, with the Egyptians and Libyans.

13. But concerning those on the right hand of the summer risings of the sun as far as the Palus Mæotis (for this is the boundary of Europe and Asia), it is with them as follows: the inhabitants there differ far more from one another than those I have treated of above, owing to the differences of the seasons and the nature of the soil. But with regard to the country itself, matters are the same there as among all other men; for where the seasons undergo the greatest and most rapid changes, there the country is the wildest and most unequal; and you will find the greatest variety of mountains, forests, plains, and meadows; but where the sea-

sons do not change much there the country is the most even; and, if one will consider it, so is it also with regard to the inhabitants; for the nature of some is like to a country covered with trees and well watered; of some, to a thin soil deficient in water; of others, to fenny and marshy places; and of some again, to a plain of bare and parched land. For the seasons which modify their natural frame of body are varied, and the greater the varieties of them the greater also will be the differences of their shapes.

14. I will pass over the smaller differences among the nations, but will now treat of such as are great either from nature, or custom; and, first, concerning the Macrocephali. There is no other race of men which have heads in the least resembling theirs. At first, usage was the principal cause of the length of their head, but now nature cooperates with usage. They think those the most noble who have the longest heads. It is thus with regard to the usage: immediately after the child is born, and while its head is still tender, they fashion it with their hands, and constrain it to assume a lengthened shape by applying bandages and other suitable contrivances whereby the spherical form of the head is destroyed, and it is made to increase in length. Thus, at first, usage operated, so that this constitution was the result of force: but, in the course of time, it was formed naturally; so that usage had nothing to do with it; for the semen comes from all parts of the body, sound from the sound parts, and unhealthy from the unhealthy parts. If, then, children with bald heads are born to parents with bald heads; and children with blue eyes to parents who have blue eyes; and if the children of parents having distorted eyes squint also for the most part; and if the same may be said of other forms of the body, what is to prevent it from happening that a child with a long head should be produced by a parent having a long head? But now these things do not happen as they did formerly, for the custom no longer prevails owing to their intercourse with other men. Thus it appears to me to be with regard to them.

15. As to the inhabitants of Phasis, their country is fenny, warm, humid, and wooded; copious and severe rains occur there at all seasons; and the life of the inhabitants is spent among the fens; for their dwellings are constructed of wood and reeds, and are erected amidst the waters; they seldom practice walking either to the city or the market, but sail about, up and down, in canoes constructed out of single trees, for there are many canals there. They drink the hot and stagnant waters, both when rendered putrid by the sun, and when swollen with rains. The Phasis itself is the most stagnant of all rivers, and runs the smoothest; all the fruits which spring there are unwholesome, of feeble and imperfect growth, owing to the redundance of water, and on this account they do not ripen, for much vapor from the waters overspreads the country. For these reasons the Phasians have shapes different from those of all other men; for they are large in stature, and of a very gross habit of body, so that not a joint nor vein is visible; in color they are sallow, as if affected with jaundice. Of all men they have the roughest voices, from their breathing an atmosphere which is not clear, but misty and humid; they are naturally rather languid in supporting bodily fatigue. The seasons undergo but little change either as to heat or cold; their winds for the most part are southerly, with the exception of one peculiar to the country, which sometimes blows strong, is violent and hot, and is called by them the wind *cenchron*. The north wind scarcely reaches them, and when it does blow it is weak and gentle. Thus it is with regard to the different nature and shape of the inhabitants of Asia and Europe.

16. And with regard to the pusillanimity and cowardice of the inhabitants, the principal reason the Asiatics are more unwarlike and of gentler disposition than the Europeans is, the nature of the seasons, which do not undergo any great changes either to heat or cold, or the like; for there is neither excitement of the understanding nor any strong change of the body whereby the temper might be ruffled and they be roused to inconsiderate emotion and passion, rather than living as they do always in the same state. It is changes of all kinds which arouse the understanding of mankind, and do not allow them to get into a torpid condition. For these reasons, it appears to me, the Asiatic race is feeble, and further, owing to their laws; for monarchy prevails in the greater part of Asia, and where men are not their own masters nor independent, but are the slaves of others, it is not a matter of consideration with them how they may acquire military discipline, but how they may seem not to be warlike, for the dangers are not equally shared, since they must serve as soldiers, perhaps endure fatigue, and die for their masters, far from their children, their wives, and other friends; and whatever noble and manly actions they may perform lead only to the aggrandizement of their masters, whilst the fruits which they reap are dangers and death; and, in addition to all this, the lands of such persons

must be laid waste by the enemy and want of culture. Thus, then, if any one be naturally warlike and courageous, his disposition will be changed by the institutions. As a strong proof of all this, such Greeks or barbarians in Asia as are not under a despotic form of government, but are independent, and enjoy the fruits of their own labors, are of all others the most warlike; for these encounter dangers on their own account, bear the prizes of their own valor, and in like manner endure the punishment of their own cowardice. And you will find the Asiatics differing from one another, for some are better and others more dastardly; of these differences, as I stated before, the changes of the seasons are the cause. Thus it is with Asia.

17. In Europe there is a Scythian race, called Sauromatæ, which inhabits the confines of the Palus Mæotis, and is different from all other races. Their women mount on horseback, use the bow, and throw the javelin from their horses, and fight with their enemies as long as they are virgins; and they do not lay aside their virginity until they kill three of their enemies, nor have any connection with men until they perform the sacrifices according to law. Whoever takes to herself a husband, gives up riding on horseback unless the necessity of a general expedition obliges her. They have no right breast; for while still of a tender age their mothers heat strongly a copper instrument constructed for this very purpose, and apply it to the right breast, which is burnt up, and its development being arrested, all the strength and fullness are determined to the right shoulder and arm.

18. As the other Scythians have a peculiarity of shape, and do not resemble any other, the same observation applies to the Egyptians, only that the latter are oppressed by heat and the former by cold. What is called the Scythian desert is a prairie, rich in meadows, high-lying, and well watered; for the rivers which carry off the water from the plains are large. There live those Scythians which are called Nomades, because they have no houses, but live in wagons. The smallest of these wagons have four wheels, but some have six; they are covered in with felt, and they are constructed in the manner of houses, some having but a single apartment, and some three; they are proof against rain, snow, and winds. The wagons are drawn by yokes of oxen, some of two and others of three, and all without horns, for they have no horns, owing to the cold. In these wagons the women live, but the men are carried about on horses, and the sheep, oxen, and horses accompany them; and they remain on any spot as long as there is provender for their cattle, and when that fails they migrate to some other place. They eat boiled meat, and drink the milk of mares, and also eat *hippace,* which is cheese prepared from the milk of the mare. Such is their mode of life and their customs.

19. In respect of the seasons and figure of body, the Scythian race, like the Egyptian, have a uniformity of resemblance, different from all other nations; they are by no means prolific, and the wild beasts which are indigenous there are small in size and few in number, for the country lies under the Northern Bears, and the Rhiphæan mountains, whence the north wind blows; the sun comes very near to them only when in the summer solstice, and warms them but for a short period, and not strongly; and the winds blowing from the hot regions of the earth do not reach them, or but seldom, and with little force; but the winds from the north always blow, congealed, as they are, by the snow, ice, and much water, for these never leave the mountains, which are thereby rendered uninhabitable. A thick fog covers the plains during the day, and amidst it they live, so that winter may be said to be always present with them; or, if they have summer, it is only for a few days, and the heat is not very strong. Their plains are high-lying and naked, not crowned with mountains, but extending upwards under the Northern Bears. The wild beasts there are not large, but such as can be sheltered underground; for the cold of winter and the barrenness of the country prevent their growth, and because they have no covert nor shelter. The changes of the seasons, too, are not great nor violent, for, in fact, they change gradually; and therefore their figures resemble one another, as they all equally use the same food, and the same clothing summer and winter, respiring a humid and dense atmosphere, and drinking water from snow and ice; neither do they make any laborious exertions, for neither body nor mind is capable of enduring fatigue when the changes of the seasons are not great. For these reasons their shapes are gross and fleshy, with ill-marked joints, of a humid temperament, and deficient in tone: the internal cavities, and especially those of the intestines, are full of humors; for the belly cannot possibly be dry in such a country, with such a constitution and in such a climate; but owing to their fat, and the absence of hairs from their bodies, their shapes resemble one another, the males being all alike, and so also with the women; for the seasons being of a uniform temperature, no

corruption or deterioration takes place in the concretion of the semen, unless from some violent cause, or from disease.

20. I will give you a strong proof of the humidity (laxity?) of their constitutions. You will find the greater part of the Scythians, and all the Nomades, with marks of the cautery on their shoulders, arms, wrists, breasts, hip-joints, and loins, and that for no other reason but the humidity and flabbiness of their constitution, for they can neither strain with their bows, nor launch the javelin from their shoulder owing to their humidity and atony: but when they are burnt, much of the humidity in their joints is dried up, and they become better braced, better fed, and their joints get into a more suitable condition. They are flabby and squat at first, because, as in Egypt, they are not swathed (?); and then they pay no attention to horsemanship, so that they may be adepts at it; and because of their sedentary mode of life; for the males, when they cannot be carried about on horseback, sit the most of their time in the wagon, and rarely practise walking, because of their frequent migrations and shiftings of situation; and as to the women, it is amazing how flabby and sluggish they are. The Scythian race are tawny from the cold, and not from the intense heat of the sun, for the whiteness of the skin is parched by the cold, and becomes tawny.

21. It is impossible that persons of such a constitution could be prolific, for, with the man, the sexual desires are not strong, owing to the laxity of his constitution, the softness and coldness of his belly, from all which causes it is little likely that a man should be given to venery; and besides, from being jaded by exercise on horseback, the men become weak in their desires. On the part of the men these are the causes; but on that of the women, they are embonpoint and humidity; for the womb cannot take in the semen, nor is the menstrual discharge such as it should be, but scanty and at too long intervals; and the mouth of the womb is shut up by fat and does not admit the semen; and, moreover, they themselves are indolent and fat, and their bellies cold and soft. From these causes the Scythian race is not prolific. Their female servants furnish a strong proof of this; for they no sooner have connection with a man than they prove with child, owing to their active course of life and the slenderness of body.

22. And, in addition to these, there are many eunuchs among the Scythians, who perform female work, and speak like women. Such persons are called effeminates. The inhabitants of the country attribute the cause of their impotence to a god, and venerate and worship such persons, every one dreading that the like might befall himself; but to me it appears that such affections are just as much divine as all others are, and that no one disease is either more divine or more human than another, but that all are alike divine, for that each has its own nature, and that no one arises without a natural cause. But I will explain how I think that the affection takes its rise. From continued exercise on horseback they are seized with chronic defluxions in their joints owing to their legs always hanging down below their horses; they afterwards become lame and stiff at the hip-joint, such of them, at least, as are severely attacked with it. They treat themselves in this way: when the disease is commencing, they open the vein behind either ear, and when the blood flows, sleep, from feebleness, seizes them, and afterwards they awaken, some in good health and others not. To me it appears that the semen is altered by this treatment, for there are veins behind the ears which, if cut, induce impotence; now, these veins would appear to me to be cut. Such persons afterwards, when they go in to women and cannot have connection with them, at first do not think much about it, but remain quiet; but when, after making the attempt two, three, or more times, they succeed no better, fancying they have committed some offence against the god whom they blame for the affection, they put on female attire, reproach themselves for effeminacy, play the part of women, and perform the same work as women do. This the rich among the Scythians endure, not the basest, but the most noble and powerful, owing to their riding on horseback; for the poor are less affected, as they do not ride on horses. And yet, if this disease had been more divine than the others, it ought not to have befallen the most noble and the richest of the Scythians alone, but all alike, or rather those who have little, as not being able to pay honors to the gods, if, indeed, they delight in being thus rewarded by men, and grant favors in return; for it is likely that the rich sacrifice more to the gods, and dedicate more votive offerings, inasmuch as they have wealth, and worship the gods; whereas the poor, from want, do less in this way, and, moreover, upbraid the gods for not giving them wealth, so that those who have few possessions were more likely to bear the punishments of these offences than the rich. But, as I formerly said, these affections are divine just as much as others, for each springs from a natural cause, and this dis-

ease arises among the Scythians from such a cause as I have stated. But it attacks other men in like manner, for whenever men ride much and very frequently on horseback, then many are affected with rheums in the joints, sciatica, and gout, and they are inept at venery. But these complaints befall the Scythians, and they are the most impotent of men for the aforesaid causes, and because they always wear breeches, and spend the most of their time on horseback, so as not to touch their privy parts with the hands, and from the cold and fatigue they forget the sexual desire, and do not make the attempt until after they have lost their virility. Thus it is with the race of the Scythians.

23. The other races in Europe differ from one another, both as to stature and shape, owing to the changes of the seasons, which are very great and frequent, and because the heat is strong, the winters severe, and there are frequent rains, and again protracted droughts, and winds, from which many and diversified changes are induced. These changes are likely to have an effect upon generation in the coagulation of the semen, as this process cannot be the same in summer as in winter, nor in rainy as in dry weather; wherefore, I think, that the figures of Europeans differ more than those of Asiatics; and they differ very much from one another as to stature in the same city; for vitiations of the semen occur in its coagulation more frequently during frequent changes of the seasons, than where they are alike and equable. And the same may be said of their dispositions, for the wild, and unsociable, and the passionate occur in such a constitution; for frequent excitement of the mind induces wildness, and extinguishes sociableness and mildness of disposition, and therefore I think the inhabitants of Europe more courageous than those of Asia; for a climate which is always the same induces indolence, but a changeable climate, laborious exertions both of body and mind; and from rest and indolence cowardice is engendered, and from laborious exertions and pains, courage. On this account the inhabitants of Europe are more warlike than the Asiatics, and also owing to their institutions, because they are not governed by kings like the latter, for where men are governed by kings there they must be very cowardly, as I have stated before; for their souls are enslaved, and they will not willingly, or readily undergo dangers in order to promote the power of another; but those that are free undertake dangers on their own account, and not for the sake of others; they court hazard and go out to meet it, for they themselves bear off the rewards of victory, and thus their institutions contribute not a little to their courage.

Such is the general character of Europe and Asia.

24. And there are in Europe other tribes, differing from one another in stature, shape, and courage: the differences are those I formerly mentioned, and will now explain more clearly. Such as inhabit a country which is mountainous, rugged, elevated, and well watered, and where the changes of the seasons are very great, are likely to have great variety of shapes among them, and to be naturally of an enterprising and warlike disposition; and such persons are apt to have no little of the savage and ferocious in their nature; but such as dwell in places which are low-lying, abounding in meadows and ill ventilated, and who have a larger proportion of hot than of cold winds, and who make use of warm waters—these are not likely to be of large stature nor well proportioned, but are of a broad make, fleshy, and have black hair; and they are rather of a dark than of a light complexion, and are less likely to be phlegmatic than bilious; courage and laborious enterprise are not naturally in them, but may be engendered in them by means of their institutions. And if there be rivers in the country which carry off the stagnant and rain water from it, these may be wholesome and clear; but if there be no rivers, but the inhabitants drink the waters of fountains, and such as are stagnant and marshy, they must necessarily have prominent bellies and enlarged spleens. But such as inhabit a high country, and one that is level, windy, and well-watered, will be large of stature, and like to one another; but their minds will be rather unmanly and gentle. Those who live on thin, ill-watered, and bare soils, and not well attempered in the changes of the seasons, in such a country they are likely to be in their persons rather hard and well braced, rather of a blond than a dark complexion, and in disposition and passions haughty and self-willed. For, where the changes of the seasons are most frequent, and where they differ most from one another, there you will find their forms, dispositions, and nature the most varied. These are the strongest of the natural causes of difference, and next the country in which one lives, and the waters; for, in general, you will find the forms and dispositions of mankind to correspond with the nature of the country; for where the land is fertile, soft, and well-watered, and supplied with waters from very elevated situations, so as to be hot in summer and cold

in winter, and where the seasons are fine, there the men are fleshy, have ill-formed joints, and are of a humid temperament; they are not disposed to endure labor, and, for the most part, are base in spirit; indolence and sluggishness are visible in them, and to the arts they are dull, and not clever nor acute. When the country is bare, not fenced, and rugged, blasted by the winter and scorched by the sun, there you may see the men hardy, slender, with well-shaped joints, well-braced, and shaggy; sharp industry and vig-

ilance accompany such a constitution; in morals and passions they are haughty and opinionative, inclining rather to the fierce than to the mild; and you will find them acute and ingenious as regards the arts, and excelling in military affairs; and likewise all the other productions of the earth corresponding to the earth itself. Thus it is with regard to the most opposite natures and shapes; drawing conclusions from them, you may judge of the rest without any risk of error.

The Book of Prognostics

IT APPEARS to me a most excellent thing for the physician to cultivate Prognosis; for by foreseeing and foretelling, in the presence of the sick, the present, the past, and the future, and explaining the omissions which patients have been guilty of,[1] he will be the more readily believed to be acquainted with the circumstances of the sick; so that men will have confidence to intrust themselves to such a physician. And he will manage the cure best who has foreseen what is to happen from the present state of matters. For it is impossible to make all the sick well; this, indeed, would have been better than to be able to foretell what is going to happen; but since men die, some even before calling the physician, from the violence of the disease, and some die immediately after calling him, having lived, perhaps, only one day or a little longer, and before the physician could bring his art to counteract the disease; it therefore becomes necessary to know the nature of such affections, how far they are above the powers of the constitution; and, moreover, if there be anything divine in the diseases, and to learn a foreknowledge of this also. Thus a man will be the more esteemed to be a good physician, for he will be the better able to treat those aright who can be saved, from having long anticipated everything; and by seeing and announcing beforehand those who will live and those who will die, he will thus escape censure.

2. He should observe thus in acute diseases: first, the countenance of the patient, if it be like those of persons in health, and more so, if like itself, for this is the best of all; whereas the most

opposite to it is the worst, such as the following; *a sharp nose, hollow eyes, collapsed temples; the ears cold, contracted, and their lobes turned out; the skin about the forehead being rough, distended, and parched; the color of the whole face being green, black, livid, or lead-colored.* If the countenance be such at the commencement of the disease, and if this cannot be accounted for from the other symptoms, inquiry must be made whether the patient has long wanted sleep; whether his bowels have been very loose; and whether he has suffered from want of food; and if any of these causes be confessed to, the danger is to be reckoned so far less; and it becomes obvious, in the course of a day and a night, whether or not the appearance of the countenance proceeded from these causes. But if none of these be said to exist, and if the symptoms do not subside in the aforesaid time, it is to be known for certain that death is at hand. And, also, if the disease be in a more advanced stage either on the third or fourth day, and the countenance be such, the same inquiries as formerly directed are to be made, and the other symptoms are to be noted, those in the whole countenance, those on the body, and those in the eyes; for if they shun the light, or weep involuntarily, or squint, or if the one be less than the other, or if the white of them be red, livid, or has black veins in it; if there be a gum upon the eyes, if they are restless, protruding, or are become very hollow; and if the countenance be squalid and dark, or the color of the whole face be changed—all these are to be reckoned bad and fatal symptoms. The physician should also observe the appearance of the eyes from below the eyelids in sleep; for when a portion of the white appears, owing to the eyelids not being closed together, and when this is not connected with diarrhea or purgation from medicine, or

---

[1] Galen, in his Commentary on this clause of the sentence, remarks that patients are justly disposed to form a high opinion of a physician who points out to them symptoms of their complaint which they themselves had omitted to mention to him.

when the patient does not sleep thus from habit, it is to be reckoned an unfavorable and very deadly symptom; but if the eyelid be contracted, livid, or pale, or also the lip, or nose, along with some of the other symptoms, one may know for certain that death is close at hand. It is a mortal symptom, also, when the lips are relaxed, pendent, cold, and blanched.

3. It is well when the patient is found by his physician reclining upon either his right or his left side, having his hands, neck, and legs slightly bent, and the whole body lying in a relaxed state, for thus the most of persons in health recline, and these are the best of postures which most resemble those of healthy persons. But to lie upon one's back, with the hands, neck, and the legs extended, is far less favorable. And if the patient incline forward, and sink down to the foot of the bed, it is a still more dangerous symptom; but if he be found with his feet naked and not sufficiently warm, and the hands, neck, and legs tossed about in a disorderly manner and naked, it is bad, for it indicates aberration of intellect. It is a deadly symptom, also, when the patient sleeps constantly with his mouth open, having his legs strongly bent and plaited together, while he lies upon his back; and to lie upon one's belly, when not habitual to the patient to sleep thus while in good health, indicates delirium, or pain in the abdominal regions. And for the patient to wish to sit erect at the acme of a disease is a bad symptom in all acute diseases, but particularly so in pneumonia. To grind the teeth in fevers, when such has not been the custom of the patient from childhood, indicates madness and death, both which dangers are to be announced beforehand as likely to happen; and if a person in delirium do this it is a very deadly symptom. And if the patient had an ulcer previously, or if one has occurred in the course of the disease, it is to be observed; for if the man be about to die the sore will become livid and dry, or yellow and dry before death.

4. Respecting the movement of the hands I have these observations to make: When in acute fevers, pneumonia, phrenitis, or headache, the hands are waved before the face, hunting through empty space, as if gathering bits of straw, picking the nap from the coverlet, or tearing chaff from the wall—all such symptoms are bad and deadly.

5. Respiration, when frequent, indicates pain or inflammation in the parts above the diaphragm: a large respiration performed at a great interval announces delirium; but a cold respiration at nose or mouth is a very fatal symptom. Free respiration is to be looked upon as contributing much to the safety of the patient in all acute diseases, such as fevers, and those complaints which come to a crisis in forty days.

6. Those sweats are the best in all acute diseases which occur on the critical days, and completely carry off the fever. Those are favorable, too, which taking place over the whole body, show that the man is bearing the disease better. But those that do not produce this effect are not beneficial. The worst are cold sweats, confined to the head, face, and neck; these in an acute fever prognosticate death, or in a milder one, a prolongation of the disease; and sweats which occur over the whole body, with the characters of those confined to the neck, are in like manner bad. Sweats attended with a miliary eruption, and taking place about the neck, are bad; sweats in the form of drops and of vapour are good. One ought to know the entire character of sweats, for some are connected with prostration of strength in the body, and some with intensity of the inflammation.

7. That state of the hypochondrium is best when it is free from pain, soft, and of equal size on the right side and the left. But if inflamed, or painful, or distended; or when the right and left sides are of disproportionate sizes;—all these appearances are to be dreaded. And if there be also pulsation in the hypochondrium, it indicates perturbation or delirium; and the physician should examine the eyes of such persons; for if their pupils be in rapid motion, such persons may be expected to go mad. A swelling in the hypochondrium, that is hard and painful, is very bad, provided it occupy the whole hypochondrium; but if it be on either side, it is less dangerous when on the left. Such swellings at the commencement of the disease prognosticate speedy death; but if the fever has passed twenty days, and the swelling has not subsided, it turns to a suppuration. A discharge of blood from the nose occurs to such in the first period, and proves very useful; but inquiry should be made if they have headache or indistinct vision; for if there be such, the disease will be determined thither. The discharge of blood is rather to be expected in those who are younger than thirty-five years. Such swellings as are soft, free from pain, and yield to the finger, occasion more protracted crises, and are less dangerous than the others. But if the fever continue beyond sixty days, without any subsidence of the swelling, it indicates that empyema is about to take place; and a swelling in any other part of the cavity will terminate in like manner. Such,

then, as are painful, hard, and large, indicate danger of speedy death; but such as are soft, free of pain, and yield when pressed with the finger, are more chronic than these. Swellings in the belly less frequently form abscesses than those in the hypochondrium; and seldomest of all, those below the navel are converted into suppuration; but you may rather expect a hemorrhage from the upper parts. But the suppuration of all protracted swellings about these parts is to be anticipated. The collections of matter there are to be thus judged of: such as are determined outwards are the best when they are small, when they protrude very much, and swell to a point; such as are large and broad, and which do not swell out to a sharp point, are the worst. Of such as break internally, the best are those which have no external communication, but are covered and indolent; and when the whole place is free from discoloration. That pus is best which is white, homogeneous, smooth, and not at all fetid; the contrary to this is the worst.

8. All dropsies arising from acute diseases are bad; for they do not remove the fever, and are very painful and fatal. The most of them commence from the flanks and loins, but some from the liver; in those which derive their origin from the flanks and loins the feet swell, protracted diarrhœas supervene, which neither remove the pains in the flanks and loins, nor soften the belly, but in dropsies which are connected with the liver there is a tickling cough, with scarcely any perceptible expectoration, and the feet swell; there are no evacuations from the bowels, unless such as are hard and forced; and there are swellings about the belly, sometimes on the one side and sometimes on the other, and these increase and diminish by turns.

9. It is a bad symptom when the head, hands, and feet are cold, while the belly and sides are hot; but it is a very good symptom when the whole body is equally hot. The patient ought to be able to turn round easily, and to be agile when raised up; but if he appear heavy in the rest of his body as well as in his hands and feet, it is more dangerous; and if, in addition to the weight, his nails and fingers become livid, immediate death may be anticipated; and if the hands and feet be black it is less dangerous than if they be livid, but the other symptoms must be attended to; for if he appear to bear the illness well, and if certain of the salutary symptoms appear along with these there may be hope that the disease will turn to a deposition, so that the man may recover; but the blackened parts of the body will drop off. When the testicles and members are retracted upwards, they indicate strong pains and danger of death.

10. With regard to sleep—as is usual with us in health, the patient should wake during the day and sleep during the night. If this rule be anywise altered it is so far worse: but there will be little harm provided he sleep in the morning for the third part of the day; such sleep as takes place after this time is more unfavorable; but the worst of all is to get no sleep either night or day; for it follows from this symptom that the insomnolency is connected with sorrow and pains, or that he is about to become delirious.

11. The excrement is best which is soft and consistent, is passed at the hour which was customary to the patient when in health, in quantity proportionate to the ingesta; for when the passages are such, the lower belly is in a healthy state. But if the discharges be fluid, it is favorable that they are not accompanied with a noise, nor are frequent, nor in great quantity; for the man being oppressed by frequently getting up, must be deprived of sleep; and if the evacuations be both frequent and large, there is danger of his falling into deliquium animi. But in proportion to the ingesta he should have evacuations twice or thrice in the day, once at night and more copiously in the morning, as is customary with a person in health. The fæces should become thicker when the disease is tending to a crisis; they ought to be yellowish and not very fetid. It is favorable that round worms be passed with the discharges when the disease is tending to a crisis. The belly, too, through the whole disease, should be soft and moderately distended; but excrements that are very watery, or white, or green, or very red, or frothy, are all bad. It is also bad when the discharge is small, and viscid, and white, and greenish, and smooth; but still more deadly appearances are the black, or fatty, or livid, or verdigris-green, or fetid. Such as are of varied characters indicate greater duration of the complaint, but are no less dangerous; such as those which resemble scrapings, those which are bilious, those resembling leeks, and the black; these being sometimes passed together, and sometimes singly. It is best when wind passes without noise, but it is better that flatulence should pass even thus than that it should be retained; and when it does pass thus, it indicates either that the man is in pain or in delirium, unless he gives vent to the wind spontaneously. Pains in the hypochondria, and swellings, if recent, and not accompanied with inflammation, are relieved by borborygmi super-

vening in the hypochondrium, more especially if it pass off with fæces, urine, and wind; but even although not, it will do good by passing along, and it also does good by descending to the lower part of the belly.

12. The urine is best when the sediment is white, smooth, and consistent during the whole time, until the disease come to a crisis, for it indicates freedom from danger, and an illness of short duration; but if deficient, and if it be sometimes passed clear, and sometimes with a white and smooth sediment, the disease will be more protracted, and not so void of danger. But if the urine be reddish, and the sediment consistent and smooth, the affection, in this case, will be more protracted than the former, but still not fatal. But farinaceous sediments in the urine are bad, and still worse are the leafy; the white and thin are very bad, but the furfuraceous are still worse than these. Clouds carried about in the urine are good when white, but bad if black. When the urine is yellow and thin, it indicates that the disease is unconcocted; and if it (the disease) should be protracted, there may be danger lest the patient should not hold out until the urine be concocted. But the most deadly of all kinds of urine are the fetid, watery, black, and thick; in adult men and women the black is of all kinds of urine the worst, but in children, the watery. In those who pass thin and crude urine for a length of time, if they have otherwise symptoms of convalescence, an abscess may be expected to form in the parts below the diaphragm. And fatty substances floating on the surface are to be dreaded, for they are indications of melting. And one should consider respecting the kinds of urine, which have clouds, whether they tend upwards or downwards, and the colors which they have and such as fall downwards, with the colors as described, are to be reckoned good and commended; but such as are carried upwards, with the colors as described, are to be held as bad, and are to be distrusted. But you must not allow yourself to be deceived if such urine be passed while the bladder is diseased; for then it is a symptom of the state, not of the general system, but of a particular viscus.

13. That vomiting is of most service which consists of phlegm and bile mixed together, and neither very thick nor in great quantity; but those vomitings which are more unmixed are worse. But if that which is vomited be of the color of leeks or livid, or black, whatever of these colors it be, it is to be reckoned bad; but if the same man vomit all these colors, it is to be reckoned a very fatal symptom. But of all the vomitings, the livid indicates the most imminent danger of death, provided it be of a fetid smell. But all the smells which are somewhat putrid and fetid, are bad in all vomitings.

14. The expectoration in all pains about the lungs and sides, should be quickly and easily brought up, and a certain degree of yellowness should appear strongly mixed up with the sputum. But if brought up long after the commencement of the pain, and of a yellow or ruddy color, or if it occasions much cough, or be not strongly mixed, it is worse; for that which is intensely yellow is dangerous, but the white, and viscid, and round, do no good. But that which is very green and frothy is bad; but if so intense as to appear black, it is still more dangerous than these; it is bad if nothing is expectorated, and the lungs discharge nothing, but are gorged with matters which boil (as it were) in the airpassages. It is bad when coryza and sneezing either precede or follow affections of the lungs, but in all other affections, even the most deadly, sneezing is a salutary symptom. A yellow spittle mixed up with not much blood in cases of pneumonia, is salutary and very beneficial if spit up at the commencement of the disease, but if on the seventh day, or still later, it is less favorable. And all sputa are bad which do not remove the pain. But the worst is the black, as has been described. Of all others the sputa which remove the pain are the best.

15. When the pains in these regions do not cease, either with the discharge of the sputa, nor with alvine evacuations, nor from venesection, purging with medicine, nor a suitable regimen, it is to be held that they will terminate in suppurations. Of empyemata such as are spit up while the sputum is still bilious, are very fatal, whether the bilious portion be expectorated separate, or along with the other; but more especially if the empyema begin to advance after this sputum on the seventh day of the disease. It is to be expected that a person with such an expectoration shall die on the fourteenth day, unless something favorable supervene. The following are favorable symptoms: to support the disease easily, to have free respiration, to be free from pain, to have the sputa readily brought up, the whole body to appear equally warm and soft, to have no thirst, the urine, and fæces, sleep, and sweats to be all favorable, as described before; when all these symptoms concur, the patient certainly will not die; but if some of these be present and some not, he will not survive longer than the fourteenth day. The bad symptoms are the opposite of these, namely, to bear

the disease with difficulty, respiration large and dense, the pain not ceasing, the sputum scarcely coughed up, strong thirst, to have the body unequally affected by the febrile heat, the belly and sides intensely hot, the forehead, hands, and feet cold; the urine, and excrements, the sleep, and sweats, all bad, agreeably to the characters described above; if such a combination of symptoms accompany the expectoration, the man will certainly die before the fourteenth day, and either on the ninth or eleventh. Thus then one may conclude regarding this expectoration, that it is very deadly, and that the patient will not survive until the fourteenth day. It is by balancing the concomitant symptoms whether good or bad, that one is to form a prognosis; for thus it will most probably prove to be a true one. Most other suppurations burst, some on the twentieth, some on the thirtieth, some on the fortieth, and some as late as the sixtieth day.

16. One should estimate when the commencement of the suppuration will take place, by calculating from the day on which the patient was first seized with fever, or if he had a rigor, and if he says, that there is a weight in the place where he had pain formerly, for these symptoms occur in the commencement of suppurations. One then may expect the rupture of the abscesses to take place from these times according to the periods formerly stated. But if the empyema be only on either side, one should turn him and inquire if he has pain on the other side; and if the one side be hotter than the other, and when laid upon the sound side, one should inquire if he has the feeling of a weight hanging from above, for if so, the empyema will be upon the opposite side to that on which the weight was felt.

17. Empyema may be recognized in all cases by the following symptoms: In the first place, the fever does not go off, but is slight during the day, and increases at night, and copious sweats supervene, there is a desire to cough, and the patients expectorate nothing worth mentioning, the eyes become hollow, the cheeks have red spots on them, the nails of the hands are bent, the fingers are hot especially their extremities, there are swellings in the feet, they have no desire of food, and small blisters (phlyctænæ) occur over the body. These symptoms attend chronic empyemata, and may be much trusted to; and such as are of short standing are indicated by the same, provided they be accompanied by those signs which occur at the commencement, and if at the same time the patient has some difficulty of breathing. Whether they will

break earlier or later may be determined by these symptoms; if there be pain at the commencement, and if the dyspnœa, cough, and ptyalism be severe, the rupture may be expected in the course of twenty days or still earlier; but if the pain be more mild, and all the other symptoms in proportion, you may expect from these the rupture to be later; but pain, dyspnœa, and ptyalism, must take place before the rupture of the abscess. Those patients recover most readily whom the fever leaves the same day that the abscess bursts,—when they recover their appetite speedily, and are freed from the thirst,—when the alvine discharges are small and consistent, the matter white, smooth, uniform in color, and free of phlegm, and if brought up without pain or strong coughing. Those die whom the fever does not leave, or when appearing to leave them it returns with an exacerbation; when they have thirst, but no desire of food, and there are watery discharges from the bowels; when the expectoration is green or livid, or pituitous and frothy; if all these occur they die, but if certain of these symptoms supervene, and others not, some patients die and some recover, after a long interval. But from all the symptoms taken together one should form a judgment, and so in all other cases.

18. When abscesses form about the ears, after peripneumonic affections, or depositions of matter take place in the inferior extremities and end in fistula, such persons recover. The following observations are to be made upon them: if the fever persist, and the pain do not cease, if the expectoration be not normal, and if the alvine discharges be neither bilious, nor free and unmixed; and if the urine be neither copious nor have its proper sediment, but if, on the other hand, all the other salutary symptoms be present, in such cases abscesses may be expected to take place. They form in the inferior parts when there is a collection of phlegm about the hypochondria; and in the upper when the hypochondria continue soft and free of pain, and when dyspnœa having been present for a certain time, ceases without any obvious cause. All deposits which take place in the legs after severe and dangerous attacks of pneumonia, are salutary, but the best are those which occur at the time when the sputa undergo a change; for if the swelling and pain take place while the sputa are changing from yellow and becoming of a purulent character, and are expectorated freely, under these circumstances the man will recover most favorably and the abscess becoming free of pain, will soon cease; but if the expectora-

tion is not free, and the urine does not appear to have the proper sediment, there is danger lest the limb should be maimed, or that the case otherwise should give trouble. But if the abscesses disappear and go back, while expectoration does not take place, and fever prevails, it is a bad symptom; for there is danger that the man may get into a state of delirium and die. Of persons having empyema after peripneumonic affections, those that are advanced in life run the greatest risk of dying; but in the other kinds of empyema younger persons rather die. In cases of empyema treated by the cautery or incision, when the matter is pure, white, and not fetid, the patient recovers; but if of a bloody and dirty character, he dies.

19. Pains accompanied with fever which occur about the loins and lower parts, if they attack the diaphragm, and leave the parts below, are very fatal. Wherefore one ought to pay attention to the other symptoms, since if any unfavorable one supervene, the case is hopeless; but if while the disease is determined to the diaphragm, the other symptoms are not bad, there is great reason to expect that it will end in empyema. When the bladder is hard and painful, it is an extremely bad and mortal symptom, more especially in cases attended with continued fever; for the pains proceeding from the bladder alone are enough to kill the patient; and at such a time the bowels are not moved, or the discharges are hard and forced. But urine of a purulent character, and having a white and smooth sediment, relieves the patient. But if no amendment takes place in the characters of the urine, nor the bladder become soft, and the fever is of the continual type, it may be expected that the patient will die in the first stages of the complaint. This form attacks children more especially, from their seventh to their fifteenth year.

20. Fevers come to a crisis on the same days as to number on which men recover and die. For the mildest class of fevers, and those originating with the most favorable symptoms, cease on the fourth day or earlier; and the most malignant, and those setting in with the most dangerous symptoms, prove fatal on the fourth day or earlier. The first class of them as to violence ends thus: the second is protracted to the seventh day, the third to the eleventh, the fourth to the fourteenth, the fifth to the seventeenth, and the sixth to the twentieth. Thus these periods from the most acute disease ascend by fours up to twenty. But none of these can be truly calculated by whole days, for neither the year nor the months can be numbered by entire days. After these in the same manner, according to the same progression, the first period is of thirty-four days, the second of forty days, and the third of sixty days. In the commencement of these it is very difficult to determine those which will come to a crisis after a long interval; for these beginnings are very similar, but one should pay attention from the first day, and observe further at every additional tetrad, and then one cannot miss seeing how the disease will terminate. The constitution of quartans is agreeable to the same order. Those which will come to a crisis in the shortest space of time, are the easiest to be judged of; for the differences of them are greatest from the commencement, thus those who are going to recover breathe freely, and do not suffer pain, they sleep during the night, and have the other salutary symptoms, whereas those that are to die have difficult respiration, are delirious, troubled with insomnolency, and have other bad symptoms. Matters being thus, one may conjecture, according to the time, and each additional period of the diseases, as they proceed to a crisis. And in women, after parturition, the crises proceed agreeably to the same ratio.

21. Strong and continued headaches with fever, if any of the deadly symptoms be joined to them, are very fatal. But if without such symptoms the pain be prolonged beyond twenty days, a discharge of blood from the nose or some abscess in the inferior parts may be anticipated; but while the pain is recent, we may expect in like manner a discharge of blood from the nose, or a suppuration, especially if the pain be seated above the temples and forehead; but the hemorrhage is rather to be looked for in persons younger than thirty years, and the suppuration in more elderly persons.

22. Acute pain of the ear, with continual and strong fever, is to be dreaded; for there is danger that the man may become delirious and die. Since, then, this is a hazardous spot, one ought to pay particular attention to all these symptoms from the commencement. Younger persons die of this disease on the seventh day, or still earlier, but old persons much later; for the fevers and delirium less frequently supervene upon them, and on that account the ears previously come to a suppuration, but at these periods of life, relapses of the disease coming on generally prove fatal. Younger persons die before the ear suppurates; only if white matter run from the ear, there may be hope that a younger person will recover, provided any other favorable symptom be combined.

23. Ulceration of the throat with fever, is a serious affection, and if any other of the symptoms formerly described as being bad, be present, the physician ought to announce that his patient is in danger. Those quinsies are most dangerous, and most quickly prove fatal, which make no appearance in the fauces, nor in the neck, but occasion very great pain and difficulty of breathing; these induce suffocation on the first day, or on the second, the third, or the fourth. Such as, in like manner, are attended with pain, are swelled up, and have redness (erythema) in the throat, are indeed very fatal, but more protracted than the former, provided the redness be great. Those cases in which both the throat and the neck are red, are more protracted, and certain persons recover from them, especially if the neck and breast be affected with erythema, and the erysipelas be not determined inwardly. If neither the erysipelas disappear on the critical day, nor any abscess form outwardly, nor any pus be spit up, and if the patient fancy himself well, and be free from pain, death, or a relapse of the erythema is to be apprehended. It is much less hazardous when the swelling and redness are determined outwardly; but if determined to the lungs, they superinduce delirium, and frequently some of these cases terminate in empyema. It is very dangerous to cut off or scarify enlarged uvulæ while they are red and large, for inflammations and hemorrhages supervene; but one should try to reduce such swellings by some other means at this season. When the whole of it is converted into an abscess, which is called Uva, or when the extremity of the variety called Columella is larger and round, but the upper part thinner, at this time it will be safe to operate. But it will be better to open the bowels gently before proceeding to the operation, if time will permit, and the patient be not in danger of being suffocated.

24. When the fevers cease without any symptoms of resolution occurring, and not on the critical days, in such cases a relapse may be anticipated. When any of the fevers is protracted, although the man exhibits symptoms of recovery, and there is no longer pain from any inflammation, nor from any other visible cause, in such a case a deposit, with swelling and pain, may be expected in some one of the joints, and not improbably in those below. Such deposits occur more readily and in less time to persons under thirty years of age; and one should immediately suspect the formation of such a deposit, if the fever be protracted beyond twenty days; but to aged persons these less seldom happen, and not until the fever be much longer protracted. Such a deposit may be expected, when the fever is of a continual type, and that it will pass into a quartan, if it become intermittent, and its paroxysms come on in an irregular manner, and if in this form it approach autumn. As deposits form most readily in persons below thirty years of age, so quartans most commonly occur to persons beyond that age. It is proper to know that deposits occur most readily in winter, that then they are most protracted, but are less given to return. Whoever, in a fever that is not of a fatal character, says that he has pain in his head, and that something dark appears to be before his eyes, and that he has pain at the stomach, will be seized with vomiting of bile; but if rigor also attack him, and the inferior parts of the hypochondrium are cold, vomiting is still nearer at hand; and if he eat or drink anything at such a season, it will be quickly vomited. In these cases, when the pain commences on the first day, they are particularly oppressed on the fourth and the fifth; and they are relieved on the seventh, but the greater part of them begin to have pain on the third day, and are most especially tossed on the fifth, but are relieved on the ninth or eleventh; but in those who begin to have pains on the fifth day, and other matters proceed properly with them, the disease comes to a crisis on the fourteenth day. But when in such a fever persons affected with headache, instead of having a dark appearance before their eyes, have dimness of vision, or flashes of light appear before their eyes, and instead of pain at the pit of the stomach, they have in their hypochondrium a fullness stretching either to the right or left side, without either pain or inflammation, a hemorrhage from the nose is to be expected in such a case, rather than a vomiting. But it is in young persons particularly that the hemorrhage is to be expected, for in persons beyond the age of thirty-five, vomitings are rather to be anticipated. Convulsions occur to children if acute fever be present, and the belly be constipated, if they cannot sleep, are agitated, and moan, and change color, and become green, livid, or ruddy. These complaints occur most readily to children which are very young up to their seventh year; older children and adults are not equally liable to be seized with convulsions in fevers, unless some of the strongest and worst symptoms precede, such as those which occur in frenzy. One must judge of children as of others, which will die and which recover, from the whole of the symptoms, as they have been specially described. These things I say respecting acute diseases, and

the affections which spring from them.

25. He who would know correctly beforehand those that will recover, and those that will die, and in what cases the disease will be protracted for many days, and in what cases for a shorter time, must be able to form a judgment from having made himself acquainted with all the symptoms, and estimating their powers in comparison with one another, as has been described, with regard to the others, and the urine and sputa, as when the patient coughs up pus and bile together. One ought also to consider promptly the influx of epidemical diseases and the constitution of the season. One should likewise be well acquainted with the particular signs and the other symptoms, and not be ignorant how that, in every year, and at every season, bad symptoms prognosticate ill, and favorable symptoms good, since the aforesaid symptoms appear to have held true in Libya, in Delos, and in Scythia,[1] from which it may be known that, in the same regions, there is no difficulty in attaining a knowledge of many more things than these; if having learned them, one knows also how to judge and reason correctly of them. But you should not complain because the name of any disease may happen not to be described here, for you may know all such as come to a crisis in the afore-mentioned times, by the same symptoms.

[1] According to Galen, Hippocrates means here that good and bad symptoms tell the same in all places, in the hot regions of Libya, the cold of Scythia, and the temperate of Delos.

On Regimen in Acute Diseases

THOSE who composed what are called "The Cnidian Sentences"[2] have described accurately what symptoms the sick experience in every disease, and how certain of them terminate; and in so far a man, even who is not a physician, might describe them correctly, provided he put the proper inquiries to the sick themselves what their complaints are. But those symptoms which the physician ought to know beforehand without being informed of them by the patient, are, for the most part, omitted, some in one case and some in others, and certain symptoms of vital importance for a conjectural judgment. But when, in addition to the diagnosis, they describe how each complaint should be treated, in these cases I entertain a still greater difference of opinion with them respecting the rules they have laid down; and not only do I not agree with them on this account, but also because the remedies they use are few in number; for, with the exception of acute diseases, the only medicines which they give are drastic purgatives, with whey, and milk at certain times. If, indeed, these remedies had been good and suitable to the complaints in which they are recommended, they would have been still more deserving of recommendation, if, while few in number, they were sufficient; but this is by no means the case. Those, indeed, who have remodeled these "Sentences" have treated of the remedies applicable

[2] The Cnidian Sentences in all probability were the results of the observations and theories made in the Temple of Health at Cnidos, but they have not been preserved.

in each complaint more in a medical fashion. But neither have the ancients written anything worth mentioning respecting regimen, although this be a great omission. Some of them, indeed, were not ignorant of the many varieties of each complaint, and their manifold divisions, but when they wish to tell clearly the numbers (species?) of each disease they do not write correctly; for their species would be almost innumerable if every symptom experienced by the patients were held to constitute a disease, and receive a different name.

2. For my part, I approve of paying attention to everything relating to the art, and that those things which can be done well or properly should all be done properly; such as can be quickly done should be done quickly; such as can be neatly done should be done neatly; such operations as can be performed without pain should be done with the least possible pain; and that all other things of the like kind should be done better than they could be managed by the attendants. But I would more especially commend the physician who, in acute diseases, by which the bulk of mankind are cut off, conducts the treatment better than others. Acute diseases are those which the ancients named pleurisy, pneumonia, phrenitis, lethargy, causus, and the other diseases allied to these, including the continual fevers. For, unless when some general form of pestilential disease is epidemic, and diseases are sporadic and [not] of a similar character, there are more deaths from these diseases than from all the others taken together. The

vulgar, indeed, do not recognize the difference between such physicians and their common attendants, and are rather disposed to commend and censure extraordinary remedies. This, then, is a great proof that the common people are most incompetent, of themselves, to form a judgment how such diseases should be treated: since persons who are not physicians pass for physicians owing most especially to these diseases, for it is an easy matter to learn the names of those things which are applicable to persons laboring under such complaints. For, if one names the juice of ptisan, and such and such a wine, and hydromel, the vulgar fancy that he prescribes exactly the same things as the physicians do, both the good and the bad, but in these matters there is a great difference between them.

3. But it appears to me that those things are more especially deserving of being consigned to writing which are undetermined by physicians, notwithstanding that they are of vital importance, and either do much good or much harm. By undetermined I mean such as these, wherefore certain physicians, during their whole lives, are constantly administering unstrained ptisans, and fancy they thus accomplish the cure properly, whereas others take great pains that the patient should not swallow a particle of the barley (thinking it would do much harm), but strain the juice through a cloth before giving it; others, again, will neither give thick ptisan nor the juice, some until the seventh day of the disease, and some until after the crisis. Physicians are not in the practice of mooting such questions; nor, perhaps, if mooted, would a solution of them be found; although the whole art is thereby exposed to much censure from the vulgar, who fancy that there really is no such science as medicine, since, in acute diseases, practitioners differ so much among themselves, that those things which one administers as thinking it the best that can be given, another holds to be bad; and, in this respect, they might say that the art of medicine resembles augury, since augurs hold that the same bird (omen) if seen on the left hand is good, but if on the right bad: and in divination by the inspection of entrails you will find similar differences; but certain diviners hold the very opposite of these opinions. I say, then, that this question is a most excellent one, and allied to very many others, some of the most vital importance in the Art, for that it can contribute much to the recovery of the sick, and to the preservation of health in the case of those who are well; and that it promotes the strength of those who use gymnastic exercises, and is useful to whatever one may wish to apply it.

4. Ptisan, then, appears to me to be justly preferred before all the other preparations from grain in these diseases, and I commend those who made this choice,[1] for the mucilage of it is smooth, consistent, pleasant, lubricant, moderately diluent, quenches thirst if this be required, and has no astringency; gives no trouble nor swells up in the bowels, for in the boiling it swells up as much as it naturally can. Those, then, who make use of ptisan in such diseases, should never for a day allow their vessels to be empty of it, if I may say so, but should use it and not intermit, unless it be necessary to stop for a time, in order to administer medicine or a clyster. And to those who are accustomed to take two meals in the day it is to be given twice, and to those accustomed to live upon a single meal it is to be given once at first, and then, if the case permit, it is to be increased and given twice to them, if they appear to stand in need of it. At first it will be proper not to give a large quantity nor very thick, but in proportion to the quantity of food which one has been accustomed to take, and so as that the veins may not be much emptied. And, with regard to the augmentation of the dose, if the disease be of a drier nature than one had supposed, one must not give more of it, but should give before the draught of ptisan, either hydromel or wine, in as great quantity as may be proper; and what is proper in each case will be afterward stated by us. But if the mouth and the passages from the lungs be in a proper state as to moisture, the quantity of the draught is to be increased, as a general rule, for an early and abundant state of moisture indicates an early crisis, but a late and deficient moisture indicates a slower crisis. And these things are as I have stated for the most part; but many other things are omitted which are important to the prognosis, as will be explained afterwards. And the more that the patient is troubled with purging, in so much greater quantity is it to be given until the crisis, and moreover until two days beyond the crisis, in such cases as it appears to take place on the fifth, seventh, or ninth day, so as to have respect both for the odd and even day: after this the draught is to be given early in the day,

[1] Galen states that, on the principle that diseases are to be cured by their contraries, as the essence of a febrile disease is combined of heat and dryness, the indication of a cure is to use means of a cooling and moistening nature, and that the ptisan fulfils both these objects.

and the other food in place is to be given in the evening. These things are proper, for the most part, to be given to those who, from the first, have used ptisan containing its whole substance; for the pains in pleuritic affections immediately cease of their own accord whenever the patients begin to expectorate anything worth mentioning, and the purgings become much better, and empyema much more seldom takes place, than if the patients used a different regimen, and the crises are more simple, occur earlier, and the cases are less subject to relapses.

5. Ptisans are to be made of the very best barley, and are to be well boiled, more especially if you do not intend to use them strained. For, besides the other virtues of ptisan, its lubricant quality prevents the barley that is swallowed from proving injurious, for it does not stick nor remain in the region of the breast; for that which is well boiled is very lubricant, excellent for quenching thirst, of very easy digestion, and very weak, all which qualities are wanted. If, then, one do not pay proper attention to the mode of administering the ptisan, much harm may be done; for when the food is shut up in the bowels, unless one procure some evacuation speedily, before administering the draught, the pain, if present, will be exasperated; and, if not present, it will be immediately created, and the respiration will become more frequent, which does mischief, for it dries the lungs, fatigues the hypochondria, the hypogastrium, and diaphragm. And moreover if, while the pain of the side persists, and does not yield to warm fomentations, and the sputa are not brought up, but are viscid and unconcocted, unless one get the pain resolved, either by loosening the bowels, or opening a vein, whichever of these may be proper;—if to persons so circumstanced ptisan be administered, their speedy death will be the result. For these reasons, and for others of a similar kind still more, those who use unstrained ptisan die on the seventh day, or still earlier, some being seized with delirium, and others dying suffocated with orthopnœe and râles. Such persons the ancients thought *struck*, for this reason more especially, that when dead the affected side was livid, like that of a person who had been struck. The cause of this is that they die before the pain is resolved, being seized with difficulty of respiration, and by large and rapid breathing, as has been already explained, the spittle becoming thick, acid, and unconcocted, cannot be brought up, but, being retained in the bronchi of the lungs, produces râles; and, when it has come to this, death, for the most

part, is inevitable; for the sputa being retained prevent the breath from being drawn in, and force it speedily out, and thus the two conspire together to aggravate the mischief; for the sputa being retained renders the respiration frequent, while the respiration being frequent thickens the sputa, and prevents them from being evacuated. These symptoms supervene, not only if ptisan be administered unseasonably, but still more if any other food or drink worse than ptisan be given.

6. For the most part, then, the results are the same, whether the patient have used the unstrained ptisan or have used the juice alone; or even only drink; and sometimes it is necessary to proceed quite differently. In general, one should do thus: if fever commences shortly after taking food, and before the bowels have been evacuated, whether with or without pain, the physician ought to withhold the draught until he thinks that the food has descended to the lower part of the belly; and if any pain be present, the patient should use oxymel, hot if it is winter, and cold if it is summer; and, if there be much thirst, he should take hydromel and water. Then, if any pain be present, or any dangerous symptoms make their appearance, it will be proper to give the draught neither in large quantity nor thick, but after the seventh day, if the patient be strong. But if the earlier-taken food has not descended, in the case of a person who has recently swallowed food, and if he be strong and in the vigor of life, a clyster should be given, or if he be weaker, a suppository is to be administered, unless the bowels open properly of themselves. The time for administering the draught is to be particularly observed at the commencement and during the whole illness; when, then, the feet are cold, one should refrain from giving the ptisan, and more especially abstain from drink; but when the heat has descended to the feet, one may then give it; and one should look upon this season as of great consequence in all diseases, and not least in acute diseases, especially those of a febrile character, and those of a very dangerous nature. One may first use the juice, and then the ptisan, attending accurately to the rules formerly laid down.

7. When pain seizes the side, either at the commencement or at a later stage, it will not be improper to try to dissolve the pain by hot applications. Of hot applications the most powerful is hot water in a bottle, or bladder, or in a brazen vessel, or in an earthen one; but one must first apply something soft to the side, to prevent pain. A soft large sponge, squeezed out of

hot water and applied, forms a good application; but it should be covered up above, for thus the heat will remain the longer, and at the same time the vapor will be prevented from being carried up to the patient's breath, unless when this is thought of use, for sometimes it is the case. And further, barley or tares may be infused and boiled in diluted vinegar, stronger than that it could be drunk, and may then be sewed into bladders and applied; and one may use bran in like manner. Salts or toasted millet in woolen bags are excellent for forming a dry fomentation, for the millet is light and soothing. A soft fomentation like this soothes pains, even such as shoot to the clavicle. Venesection, however, does not alleviate the pain unless when it extends to the clavicle. But if the pain be not dissolved by the fomentations, one ought not to foment for a length of time, for this dries the lungs and promotes suppuration; but if the pain point to the clavicle, or if there be a heaviness in the arm, or about the breast, or above the diaphragm, one should open the inner vein at the elbow, and not hesitate to abstract a large quantity, until it become much redder, or instead of being pure red, it turns livid, for both these states occur. But if the pain be below the diaphragm, and do not point to the clavicle, we must open the belly either with black hellebore or peplium, mixing the black hellebore with carrot or seseli, or cumin, or anise, or any other of the fragrant herbs; and with the peplium the juice of sulphium (asafœtida), for these substances, when mixed up together, are of a similar nature. The black hellebore acts more pleasantly and effectually than the peplium, while, on the other hand, the peplium expels wind much more effectually than the black hellebore, and both these stop the pain, and many other of the laxatives also stop it, but these two are the most efficacious that I am acquainted with. And the laxatives given in draughts are beneficial, when not very unpalatable owing to bitterness, or any other disagreeable taste, or from quantity, color, or any apprehension. When the patient has drunk the medicine, one ought to give him to swallow but little less of the ptisan than what he had been accustomed to; but it is according to rule not to give any draughts while the medicine is under operation; but when the purging is stopped then he should take a smaller draught than what he had been accustomed to, and afterwards go on increasing it progressively, until the pain cease, provided nothing else contra-indicate. This is my rule, also, if one would use the juice of ptis-

an (for I hold that it is better, on the whole, to begin with taking the decoction at once, rather than by first emptying the veins before doing so, or on the third, fourth, fifth, sixth, or seventh day, provided the disease has not previously come to a crisis in the course of this time), and similar preparations to those formerly described are to be made in those cases.

8. Such are the opinions which I entertain respecting the administering of the ptisan; and, as regards drinks, whichsoever of those about to be described may be administered, the same directions are generally applicable. And here I know that physicians are in the practice of doing the very reverse of what is proper, for they all wish, at the commencement of diseases, to starve their patients for two, three, or more days, and then to administer the ptisans and drinks; and perhaps it appears to them reasonable that, as a great change has taken place in the body, it should be counteracted by another great change. Now, indeed, to produce a change is no small matter, but the change must be effected well and cautiously, and after the change the administration of food must be conducted still more so. Those persons, then, would be most injured if the change is not properly managed, who used unstrained ptisans; they also would suffer who made use of the juice alone; and so also they would suffer who took merely drink, but these least of all.

9. One may derive information from the regimen of persons in good health what things are proper; for if it appear that there is a great difference whether the diet be so and so, in other respects, but more especially in the changes, how can it be otherwise in diseases, and more especially in the most acute? But it is well ascertained that even a faulty diet of food and drink steadily persevered in, is safer in the main as regards health than if one suddenly change it to another. Wherefore, in the case of persons who take two meals in the day, or of those who take a single meal, sudden changes induce suffering and weakness; and thus persons who have not been accustomed to dine, if they shall take dinner, immediately become weak, have heaviness over their whole body, and become feeble and languid, and if, in addition, they take supper, they will have acid eructations, and some will have diarrhœa whose bowels were previously dry, and not having been accustomed to be twice swelled out with food and to digest it twice a day, have been loaded beyond their wont. It is beneficial, in such cases, to counterbalance this change, for

one should sleep after dinner, as if passing the night, and guard against cold in winter and heat in summer; or, if the person cannot sleep, he may stroll about slowly, but without making stops, for a good while, take no supper, or, at all events, eat little, and only things that are not unwholesome, and still more avoid drink, and especially water. Such a person will suffer still more if he take three full meals in the day, and more still if he take more meals; and yet there are many persons who readily bear to take three full meals in the day, provided they are so accustomed. And, moreover, those who have been in the habit of eating twice a day, if they omit dinner, become feeble and powerless, averse to all work, and have heartburn; their bowels seem, as it were, to hang loose, their urine is hot and green, and the excrement is parched; in some the mouth is bitter, the eyes are hollow, the temples throb, and the extremities are cold, and the most of those who have thus missed their dinner cannot eat supper; or, if they do sup, they load their stomach, and pass a much worse night than if they had previously taken dinner. Since, then, an unwonted change of diet for half a day produces such effects upon persons in health, it appears not to be a good thing either to add or take from. If, then, he who was restricted to a single meal, contrary to usage, having his veins thus left empty during a whole day, when he supped according to custom felt heavy, it is probable that if, because he was uneasy and weak from the want of dinner, he took a larger supper than wont, he would be still more oppressed; or if, wanting food for a still greater interval, he suddenly took a meal after supper, he will feel still greater oppression. He, then, who, contrary to usage, has had his veins kept empty by want of food, will find it beneficial to counteract the bad effects during that day as follows: let him avoid cold, heat, and exertion, for he could bear all these ill; let him make his supper considerably less than usual, and not of dry food, but rather liquid; and let him take some drink, not of a watery character, nor in smaller quantity than is proportionate to the food, and on the next day he should take a small dinner, so that, by degrees, he may return to his former practice. Persons who are bilious in the stomach bear these changes worst, while those who are pituitous, upon the whole, bear the want of food best, so that they suffer the least from being restricted to one meal in the day, contrary to usage. This, then, is a sufficient proof that the greatest changes as to those things which regard our constitutions and habits are most especially concerned in the production of diseases, for it is impossible to produce unseasonably a great emptying of the vessels by abstinence, or to administer food while diseases are at their acme, or when inflammation prevails; nor, on the whole, to make a great change either one way or another with impunity.

10. One might mention many things akin to these respecting the stomach and bowels, to show how people readily bear such food as they are accustomed to, even if it is not naturally good, and drink in like manner, and how they bear unpleasantly such food as they are not accustomed to, even although not bad, and so in like manner with drink; and as to the effects of eating much flesh, contrary to usage, or garlic, or asafœtida, or the stem of the plant which produces it, or things of a similar kind possessed of strong properties, one would be less surprised if such things produce pains in the bowels, but rather when one learned what trouble, swelling, flatulence, and tormina the cake (maza) will raise in the belly when eaten by a person not accustomed to it; and how much weight and distention of the bowels bread will create to a person accustomed to live upon the maza; and what thirst and sudden fullness will be occasioned by eating hot bread, owing to its desiccant and indigestible properties; and what different effects are produced by fine and coarse bread when eaten contrary to usage, or by the cake when usually dry, moist, or viscid; and what different effects polenta produces upon those who are accustomed and those who are unaccustomed to the use of it; or drinking of wine or drinking of water, when either custom is suddenly exchanged for the other; or when, contrary to usage, diluted wine or undiluted has been suddenly drunk, for the one will create water-brash in the upper part of the intestinal canal and flatulence in the lower, while the other will give rise to throbbing of the arteries, heaviness of the head, and thirst; and white and dark-colored wine, although both strong wines, if exchanged contrary to usage, will produce very different effects upon the body, so that one need the less wonder that a sweet and strong wine, if suddenly exchanged, should have by no means the same effect.

11. Let us here briefly advert to what may be said on the opposite side; namely, that a change of diet has occurred in these cases, without any change in their body, either as to strength, so as to require an increase of food, or as to weakness, so as to require a diminution. But the

strength of the patient is to be taken into consideration, and the manner of the disease, and of the constitution of the man, and the habitual regimen of the patient, not only as regards food but also drink. Yet one must much less resort to augmentation, since it is often beneficial to have recourse to abstraction, when the patient can bear it, until the disease having reached its acme and has become concocted. But in what cases this must be done will be afterwards described. One might write many other things akin to those which have been now said, but there is a better proof, for it is not akin to the matter on which my discourse has principally turned, but the subject-matter itself is a most seasonable proof. For some at the commencement of acute diseases have taken food on the same day, some on the next day; some have swallowed whatever has come in their way, and some have taken *cyceon*.[1] Now all these things are worse than if one had observed a different regimen; and yet these mistakes, committed at that time, do much less injury than if one were to abstain entirely from food for the first two or three days, and on the fourth or fifth day were to take such food; and it would be still worse, if one were to observe total abstinence for all these days, and on the following days were to take such a diet, before the disease is concocted; for in this way death would be the consequence to most people, unless the disease were of a very mild nature. But the mistakes committed at first were not so irremediable as these, but could be much more easily repaired. This, therefore, I think a strong proof that such or such a draught need not be prescribed on the first days to those who will use the same draughts afterwards. At the bottom, therefore, they do not know, neither those using unstrained ptisans, that they are hurt by them, when they begin to swallow them, if they abstain entirely from food for two, three, or more days; nor do those using the juice know that they are injured in swallowing them, when they do not commence with the draught seasonably. But this they guard against, and know that it does much mischief, if, before the disease be concocted, the patient swallow unstrained ptisan, when accustomed to use strained. All these things are strong proofs that physicians do not conduct the regimen of patients properly, but that in those diseases in which total abstinence from food should not be enforced on patients

[1] The *cyceon* was a mixture of various articles of food, but generally contained cheese, honey, and wine.

that will be put on the use of ptisans, they do enforce total abstinence; that in those cases in which there should be no change made from total abstinence to ptisans, they do make the change; and that, for the most part, they change from abstinence to ptisans, exactly at the time when it is often beneficial to proceed from ptisans almost to total abstinence, if the disease happen to be in the state of exacerbation. And sometimes crude matters are attracted from the head, and bilious from the region near the chest, and the patients are attacked with insomnolency, so that the disease is not concocted; they become sorrowful, peevish, and delirious; there are flashes of light in their eyes, and noises in their ears; their extremities are cold, their urine unconcocted; the sputa thin, saltish, tinged with an intense color and smell; sweats about the neck, and anxiety; respiration, interrupted in the expulsion of the air, frequent and very large; expression of the eyelids dreadful; dangerous *deliquia;* tossing of the bed-clothes from the breast; the hands trembling, and sometimes the lower lip agitated. These symptoms, appearing at the commencement, are indicative of strong delirium, and patients so affected generally die, or if they escape, it is with a deposit, hemorrhage from the nose, or the expectoration of thick matter, and not otherwise. Neither do I perceive that physicians are skilled in such things as these; how they ought to know such diseases as are connected with debility, and which are further weakened by abstinence from food, and those aggravated by some other irritation; those by pain, and from the acute nature of the disease, and what affections and various forms thereof our constitution and habit engender, although the knowledge or ignorance of such things brings safety or death to the patient. For it is a great mischief if to a patient debilitated by pain, and the acute nature of the disease, one administer drink, or more ptisan, or food, supposing that the debility proceeds from inanition. It is also disgraceful not to recognize a patient whose debility is connected with inanition, and to pinch him in his diet; this mistake, indeed, is attended with some danger, but much less than the other, and yet it is likely to expose one to much greater derision, for if another physician, or a private person, coming in and knowing what has happened, should give to eat or drink those things which the other had forbidden, the benefit thus done to the patient would be manifest. Such mistakes of practitioners are particularly ridiculed by mankind, for the physician or nonprofessional man thus coming in, seems as it were to resuscitate the dead. On this subject I will describe elsewhere the symptoms by which each of them may be recognized.

12. And the following observations are similar to those now made respecting the bowels. If the whole body rest long, contrary to usage, it does not immediately recover its strength; but if, after a protracted repose, it proceed to labor, it will clearly expose its weakness. So it is with every one part of the body, for the feet will make a similar display, and any other of the joints, if, being unaccustomed to labor, they be suddenly brought into action, after a time. The teeth and the eyes will suffer in like manner, and also every other part whatever. A couch, also, that is either softer or harder than one has been accustomed to will create uneasiness, and sleeping in the open air, contrary to usage, hardens the body. But it is sufficient merely to state examples of all these cases. If a person having received a wound in the leg, neither very serious nor very trifling, and he being neither in a condition very favorable to its healing nor the contrary, at first betakes himself to bed, in order to promote the cure, and never raises his leg, it will thus be much less disposed to inflammation, and be much sooner well, than it would have been if he had strolled about during the process of healing; but if upon the fifth or sixth day, or even earlier, he should get up and attempt to walk, he will suffer much more then than if he had walked about from the commencement of the cure, and if he should suddenly make many laborious exertions, he will suffer much more than if, when the treatment was conducted otherwise, he had made the same exertions on the same days. In fine, all these things concur in proving that all great changes, either one way or another, are hurtful. Wherefore much mischief takes place in the bowels, if from a state of great inanition more food than is moderate be administered (and also in the rest of the body, if from a state of great rest it be hastily brought to greater exertion, it will be much more injured), or if from the use of much food it be changed to complete abstinence, and therefore the body in such cases requires protracted repose, and if, from a state of laborious exertion, the body suddenly falls into a state of ease and indolence, in these cases also the bowels would require continued repose from abundance of food, for otherwise it will induce pain and heaviness in the whole body.

13. The greater part of my discourse has related to changes, this way or that. For all purposes it is profitable to know these things, and more especially respecting the subject under consideration,—that in acute diseases, in which a change is made to ptisans from a state of inanition, it should be made as I direct; and then that ptisans should not be used until the disease be concocted, or some other symptom, whether of evacuation or of irritation, appear in the intestines, or in the hypochondria, such as will be described. Obstinate insomnolency impairs the digestion of the food and drink, and in other respects changes and relaxes the body, and occasions a heated state, and heaviness of the head.[1]

14. One must determine by such marks as these, when sweet, strong, and dark wine, hydromel, water and oxymel, should be given in acute diseases. Wherefore the sweet affects the head less than the strong, attacks the brain less, evacuates the bowels more than the other, but induces swelling of the spleen and liver; it does not agree with bilious persons, for it causes them to thirst; it creates flatulence in the upper part of the intestinal canal, but does not disagree with the lower part, as far as regards flatulence; and yet flatulence engendered by sweet wine is not of a transient nature, but rests for a long time in the hypochondria. And therefore it in general is less diuretic than wine which is strong and thin; but sweet wine is more expectorant than the other. But when it creates thirst, it is less expectorant in such cases than the other wine, but if it do not create thirst, it promotes expectoration better than the other. The good and bad effects of a white, strong wine, have been already frequently and fully stated in the disquisition on sweet wine; it is determined to the bladder more than the other, is diuretic and laxative, and should be very useful in such complaints; for if in other respects it be less suitable than the other, the clearing out of the bladder effected by it is beneficial to the patient, if properly administered. There are excellent examples of the beneficial and injurious effects of wine, all which were left undetermined by my predecessors. In these diseases you may use a yellow wine, and a dark austere wine for the following purposes: if there be no heaviness of the head, nor delirium, nor stoppage of the expectoration, nor retention of the urine, and if the alvine discharges be more loose and like scrapings than usual,

[1] Galen finds the language in this last sentence so confused that he does not hesitate to declare that he is convinced the work must have been left by Hippocrates in an unfinished state.

in such cases a change from a white wine to such as I have mentioned, might be very proper. It deserves further to be known, that it will prove less injurious to all the parts above, and to the bladder, if it be of a more watery nature, but that the stronger it is, it will be the more beneficial to the bowels.

15. Hydromel, when drunk in any stage of acute disease, is less suitable to persons of a bilious temperament, and to those who have enlarged viscera, than to those of a different character; it increases thirst less than sweet wine; it softens the lungs, is moderately expectorant, and alleviates a cough; for it has some detergent quality in it, whence it lubricates the sputum. Hydromel is also moderately diuretic, unless prevented by the state of any of the viscera. And it also occasions bilious discharges downwards, sometimes of a proper character, and sometimes more intense and frothy than is suitable; but such rather occurs in persons who are bilious, and have enlarged viscera. Hydromel rather produces expectoration, and softening of the lungs, when given diluted with water. But unmixed hydromel, rather than the diluted, produces frothy evacuations, such as are unseasonably and intensely bilious, and too hot; but such an evacuation occasions other great mischiefs, for it neither extinguishes the heat in the hypochondria, but rouses it, induces inquietude, and jactitation of the limbs, and ulcerates the intestines and anus. The remedies for all these will be described afterwards. By using hydromel without ptisans, instead of any other drink, you will generally succeed in the treatment of such diseases, and fail in few cases; but in what instances it is to be given, and in what it is not to be given, and wherefore it is not to be given,—all this has been explained already, for the most part. Hydromel is generally condemned, as if it weakened the powers of those who drink it, and on that account it is supposed to accelerate death; and this opinion arose from persons who starve themselves to death, some of whom use hydromel alone for drink, as fancying that it really has this effect. But this is by no means always the case. For hydromel, if drunk alone, is much stronger than water, if it do not disorder the bowels; but in some respects it is stronger, and in some weaker, than wine that is thin, weak, and devoid of *bouquet*. There is a great difference between unmixed wine and unmixed honey, as to their nutritive powers, for if a man will drink double the quantity of pure wine, to a certain quantity of honey which is swallowed, he will

find himself much stronger from the honey, provided it do not disagree with his bowels, and that his alvine evacuations from it will be much more copious. But if he shall use ptisan for a draught, and drink afterward hydromel, he will feel full, flatulent, and uncomfortable in the viscera of the hypochondrium; but if the hydromel be taken before the draught, it will not have the same injurious effects as if taken after it, but will be rather beneficial. And boiled hydromel has a much more elegant appearance than the unboiled, being clear, thin, white, and transparent, but I am unable to mention any good quality which it possesses that the other wants. For it is not sweeter than the unboiled, provided the honey be fine, and it is weaker, and occasions less copious evacuations of the bowels, neither of which effects is required from the hydromel. But one should by all means use it boiled, provided the honey be bad, impure, black, and not fragrant, for the boiling will remove the most of its bad qualities and appearances.

16. You will find the drink, called oxymel, often very useful in these complaints, for it promotes expectoration and freedom of breathing. the following are the proper occasions for administering it. When strongly acid it has no mean operation in rendering the expectoration more easy, for by bringing up the sputa, which occasion troublesome hawking, and rendering them more slippery, and, as it were, clearing the windpipe with a feather, it relieves the lungs and proves emollient to them; and when it succeeds in producing these effects it must do much good. But there are cases in which hydromel, strongly acid, does not promote expectoration, but renders it more viscid and thus does harm, and it is most apt to produce these bad effects in cases which are otherwise of a fatal character, when the patient is unable to cough or bring up the sputa. On this account, then, one ought to consider beforehand the strength of the patient, and if there be any hope, then one may give it, but if given at all in such cases it should be quite tepid, and in by no means large doses. But if slightly acrid it moistens the mouth and throat, promotes expectoration, and quenches thirst; agrees with the viscera seated in the hypochondrium, and obviates the bad effects of the honey; for the bilious quality of the honey is thereby corrected. It also promotes flatulent discharges from the bowels, and is diuretic, but it occasions watery discharges and those resembling scrapings, from the lower part of the intestine, which is sometimes a bad thing

in acute diseases, more especially when the flat-ulence cannot be passed, but rolls backwards; and otherwise it diminishes the strength and makes the extremities cold, this is the only bad effect worth mentioning which I have known to arise from the oxymel. It may suit well to drink a little of this at night before the draught of ptisan, and when a considerable interval of time has passed after the draught there will be nothing to prevent its being taken. But to those who are restricted entirely to drinks without draughts of ptisan, it will therefore not be prop-er at all times to give it, more especially from the fretting and irritation of the intestine which it occasions, (and these bad effects it will be the more apt to produce provided there be no fæces in the intestines and the patient is laboring un-der inanition,) and then it will weaken the powers of the hydromel. But if it appears ad-vantageous to use a great deal of this drink dur-ing the whole course of the disease, one should add to it merely as much vinegar as can just be perceived by the taste, for thus what is prej-udicial in it will do the least possible harm, and what is beneficial will do the more good. In a word, the acidity of vinegar agrees rather with those who are troubled with bitter bile, than with those patients whose bile is black; for the bitter principle is dissolved in it and turned to phlegm, by being suspended in it; whereas black bile is fermented, swells up, and is mul-tiplied thereby: for vinegar is a melanogogue. Vinegar is more prejudicial to women than to men, for it creates pains in the uterus.

17. I have nothing further to add as to the effects of water when used as a drink in acute diseases; for it neither soothes the cough in pneumonia, nor promotes expectoration, but does less than the others in this respect, if used alone through the whole complaint. But if tak-en intermediate between oxymel and hydro-mel, in small quantity, it promotes expectora-tion from the change which it occasions in the qualities of these drinks, for it produces, as it were, a certain overflow. Otherwise it does not quench the thirst, for it creates bile in a bilious temperament, and is injurious to the hypochon-drium; and it does the most harm, engenders most bile, and does the least good when the bowels are empty; and it increases the swelling of the spleen and liver when they are in an in-flamed state; it produces a gurgling noise in the intestines and swims on the stomach; for it passes slowly downwards, as being of a coldish and indigestible nature, and neither proves lax-ative nor diuretic; and in this respect, too, it

proves prejudicial, that it does not naturally form fæces in the intestines: and, if it be drunk while the feet are cold, its injurious effects will be greatly aggravated, in all those parts to which it may be determined. When you suspect in these diseases either strong heaviness of the head, or mental alienation, you must abstain entirely from wine, and in this case use water, or give weak, straw-colored wine, entirely de-void of *bouquet,* after which a little water is to be given in addition; for thus the strength of the wine will less affect the head and the under-standing: but in which cases water is mostly to be given for drink, when in large quantity, when in moderate, when cold, and when hot; all these things have either been discussed al-ready or will be treated of at the proper time. In like manner, with respect to all the others, such as barley-water, the drinks made from green shoots, those from raisins, and the skins of grapes and wheat, and bastard saffron, and myrtles, pomegranates, and the others, when the proper time for using them is come, they will be treated of along with the disease in ques-tion, in like manner as the other compound medicines.

18. The bath is useful in many diseases, in some of them when used steadily, and in others when not so. Sometimes it must be less used than it would be otherwise, from the want of accommodation; for in few families are all the conveniences prepared, and persons who can manage them as they ought to be. And if the patient be not bathed properly, he may be there-by hurt in no inconsiderable degree, for there is required a place to cover him that is free of smoke, abundance of water, materials for fre-quent baths, but not very large, unless this should be required. It is better that no friction should be applied, but if so, a hot soap (*smeg-ma*) must be used in greater abundance than is common, and an affusion of a considerable quantity of water is to be made at the same time and afterwards repeated. There must also be a short passage to the basin, and it should be of easy ingress and egress. But the person who takes the bath should be orderly and reserved in his manner, should do nothing for himself, but others should pour the water upon him and rub him, and plenty of waters, of various tem-peratures, should be in readiness for the *douche,* and the affusions quickly made; and sponges should be used instead of the comb (*strigil*), and the body should be anointed when not quite dry. But the head should be rubbed by the sponge until it is quite dry; the extremities

should be protected from cold, as also the head and the rest of the body; and a man should not be washed immediately after he has taken a draught of ptisan or a drink; neither should he take ptisan as a drink immediately after the bath. Much will depend upon whether the patient, when in good health, was very fond of the bath, and in the custom of taking it: for such persons, especially, feel the want of it, and are benefited if they are bathed, and injured if they are not. In general it suits better with cases of pneumonia than in ardent fevers; for the bath soothes the pain in the side, chest, and back; concocts the sputa, promotes expectoration, improves the respiration, and allays lassitude; for it soothes the joints and outer skin, and is diuretic, removes heaviness of the head, and moistens the nose. Such are the benefits to be derived from the bath, if all the proper requisites be present; but if one or more of these be wanting, the bath, instead of doing good, may rather prove injurious; for every one of them may do harm if not prepared by the attendants in the proper manner. It is by no means a suitable thing in these diseases to persons whose bowels are too loose, or when they are unusually confined, and there has been no previous evacuation; neither must we bathe those who are debilitated, nor such as have nausea or vomiting, or bilious eructations; nor such as have hemorrhage from the nose, unless it be less than required at that stage of the disease (with those stages you are acquainted), but if the discharge be less than proper, one should use the bath, whether in order to benefit the whole body or the head alone. If then the proper requisites be at hand, and the patient be well disposed to the bath, it may be administered once every day, or if the patient be fond of the bath there will be no harm, though he should take it twice in the day. The use of the bath is much more appropriate to those who take unstrained ptisan, than to those who take only the juice of it, although even in their case it may be proper; but least of all does it suit with those who use only plain drink, although, in their case too it may be suitable; but one must form a judgment from the rules laid down before, in which of these modes of regimen the bath will be beneficial, and in which not. Such as want some of the requisites for a proper bath, but have those symptoms which would be benefited by it, should be bathed; whereas those who want none of the proper requisites, but have certain symptoms which contraindicate the bath, are not to be bathed.

APPENDIX

Ardent fever (causus) takes place when the veins, being dried up in the summer season, attract acrid and bilious humors to themselves; and strong fever seizes the whole body, which experiences aches of the bones, and is in a state of lassitude and pain. It takes place most commonly from a long walk and protracted thirst, when the veins being dried up attract acrid and hot defluxions to themselves. The tongue becomes rough, dry, and very black; there are gnawing pains about the bowels; the alvine discharges are watery and yellow; there is intense thirst, insomnolency, and sometimes wandering of the mind. To a person in such a state give to drink water and as much boiled hydromel of a watery consistence as he will take; and if the mouth be bitter, it may be advantageous to administer an emetic and clyster; and if these things do not loosen the bowels, purge with the boiled milk of asses. Give nothing saltish nor acrid, for they will not be borne; and give no draughts of ptisan until the crisis be past. And the affection is resolved if there be an epistaxis, or if true critical sweats supervene with urine having white, thick, and smooth sediments, or if a deposit take place anywhere; but if it be resolved without these, there will be a relapse of the complaint, or pain in the hips and legs will ensue, with thick sputa, provided the patient be convalescent. Another species of ardent fever: belly loose, much thirst, tongue rough, dry, and saltish, retention of urine, insomnolency, extremities cold. In such a case, unless there be a flow of blood from the nose, or an abscess form about the neck, or pain in the limbs, or the patient expectorate thick sputa (these occur when the belly is constipated), or pain of the hips, or lividity of the genital organs, there is no crisis; tension of the testicle is also a critical symptom. Give attractive draughts.

2. Bleed in the acute affections, if the disease appear strong, and the patients be in the vigor of life, and if they have strength. If it be quinsy or any other of the pleuritic affections, purge with electuaries; but if the patient be weaker, or if you abstract more blood, you may administer a clyster every third day, until he be out of danger, and enjoin total abstinence if necessary.

3. Hypochondria inflamed not from retention of flatus, tension of the diaphragm, checked respiration, with dry orthopnœa, when no pus is formed, but when these complaints are connected with obstructed respiration; but more especially strong pains of the liver, heaviness of

the spleen, and other phlegmasiæ and intense pains above the diaphragm, diseases connected with collections of humors,—all these diseases do not admit of resolution, if treated at first by medicine, but venesection holds the first place in conducting the treatment; then we may have recourse to a clyster, unless the disease be great and strong; but if so, purging also may be necessary; but bleeding and purging together require caution and moderation. Those who attempt to resolve inflammatory diseases at the commencement by the administration of purgative medicines, remove none of the morbific humors which produce the inflammation and tension; for the diseases while unconcocted could not yield, but they melt down those parts which are healthy and resist the disease; so when the body is debilitated the malady obtains the mastery; and when the disease has the upper hand of the body, it does not admit of a cure.

4. When a person suddenly loses his speech, in connection with obstruction of the veins,— if this happen without warning or any other strong cause, one ought to open the internal vein of the right arm, and abstract blood more or less according to the habit and age of the patient. Such cases are mostly attended with the following symptoms: redness of the face, eyes fixed, hands distended, grinding of the teeth, palpitations, jaws fixed, coldness of the extremities, retention of airs in the veins.

5. When pains precede, and there are influxes of black bile and of acrid humors, and when by their pungency the internal parts are pained, and the veins being pinched and dried become distended, and getting inflamed attract the humors running into the parts, whence the blood being vitiated, and the airs collected there not being able to find their natural passages, coldness comes on in consequence of this stasis, with vertigo, loss of speech, heaviness of the head, and convulsion, if the disease fix on the liver, the heart, or the great vein (vena cava?); whence they are seized with epilepsy or apoplexy, if the defluxions fall upon the containing parts, and if they are dried up by airs which cannot make their escape; such persons having been first fomented are to be immediately bled at the commencement, while all the peccant vapors and humors are buoyant, for then the cases more easily admit of a cure; and then supporting the strength and attending to the crisis, we may give emetics, unless the disease be alleviated; or if the bowels be not moved, we may administer a clyster and give the boiled milk

of asses, to the amount of not less than twelve heminæ, or if the strength permit, to more than sixteen.

6. Quinsy takes place when a copious and viscid defluxion from the head, in the season of winter or spring, flows into the jugular veins, and when from their large size they attract a greater defluxion; and when owing to the defluxion being of a cold and viscid nature it becomes enfarcted, obstructing the passages of the respiration and of the blood, coagulates the surrounding blood, and renders it motionless and stationary, it being naturally cold and disposed to obstructions. Hence they are seized with convulsive suffocation, the tongue turning livid, assuming a rounded shape, and being vent owing to the veins which are seated below the tongue (for when an enlarged uvula, which is called *uva,* is cut, a large vein may be observed on each side). These veins, then, becoming filled, and their roots extending into the tongue, which is of a loose and spongy texture, it, owing to its dryness receiving forcibly the juice from the veins, changes from broad and becomes round, its natural color turns to livid, from a soft consistence it grows hard, instead of being flexible it becomes inflexible, so that the patient would soon be suffocated unless speedily relieved. Bleeding, then, in the arm, and opening the sublingual veins, and purging with the electuaries, and giving warm gargles, and shaving the head, we must apply to it and the neck a cerate, and wrap them round with wool, and foment with soft sponges squeezed out of hot water; give to drink water and hydromel, not cold; and administer the juice of ptisan when, having passed the crisis, the patient is out of danger. When, in the season of summer or autumn, there is a hot and nitrous defluxion from the head (it is rendered hot and acrid by the season), being of such a nature it corrodes and ulcerates, and fills with air, and orthopnœa attended with great dryness supervenes; the fauces, when examined, do not seem swollen; the tendons on the back part of the neck are contracted, and have the appearance as if it were tetanus; the voice is lost, the breathing is small, and inspiration becomes frequent and laborious. In such persons the trachea becomes ulcerated, and the lungs engorged, from the patient's not being able to draw in the external air. In such cases, unless there be a spontaneous determination to the external parts of the neck, the symptoms become still more dreadful, and the danger more imminent, partly owing to the season, and the hot

and acrid humors which cause the disease.

7. When fever seizes a person who has lately taken food, and whose bowels are loaded with fæces which have been long retained, whether it be attended with pain of the side or not, he ought to lie quiet until the food descend to the lower region of the bowels, and use oxymel for drink; but when the load descends to the loins, a clyster should be administered, or he should be purged by medicine; and when purged, he should take ptisan for food and hydromel for drink; then he may take the cerealia, and boiled fishes, and a watery wine in small quantity, at night, but during the day, a watery hydromel. When the flatus is offensive, either a suppository or clyster is to be administered; but otherwise the oxymel is to be discontinued, until the matters descend to the lower part of the bowels, and then they are to be evacuated by a clyster. But if the ardent fever (*causus*) supervene when the bowels are empty, should you still judge it proper to administer purgative medicine, it ought not be done during the first three days, nor earlier than the fourth. When you give the medicine, use the ptisan, observing the paroxysms of the fevers, so as not to give it when the fever is setting in, but when it is ceasing, or on the decline, and as far as possible from the commencement. When the feet are cold, give neither drink nor ptisan, nor anything else of the kind, but reckon it an important rule to refrain until they become warm, and then you may administer them with advantage. For the most part, coldness of the feet is a symptom of a paroxysm of the fever coming on; and if at such a season you apply those things, you will commit the greatest possible mistake, for you will augment the disease in no small degree. But when the fever ceases, the feet, on the contrary, become hotter than the rest of the body; for when the heat leaves the feet, it is kindled up in the breast, and sends its flame up to the head. And when all the heat rushes upwards, and is exhaled at the head, it is not to be wondered at that the feet become cold, being devoid of flesh, and tendinous; and besides, they contract cold, owing to their distance from the hotter parts of the body, an accumulation of heat having taken place in the chest: and again, in like manner, when the fever is resolved and dissipated, the heat descends to the feet, and, at the same time, the head and chest become cold. Wherefore one should attend to this; that when the feet are cold, the bowels are necessarily hot, and filled with nauseous matters; the hypochondrium distended:

there is jactitation of the body, owing to the internal disturbance; and aberration of the intellect, and pains; the patient is agitated, and wishes to vomit, and if he vomits bad matters he is pained; but when the heat descends to the feet, and the urine passes freely, he is every way lightened, even although he does not sweat; at this season, then, the ptisan ought to be given; it would be death to give it before.

8. When the bowels are loose during the whole course of fevers, in this case we are most especially to warm the feet, and see that they are properly treated with cerates, and wrapped in shawls, so that they may not become colder than the rest of the body; but when they are hot, no fomentation must be made to them, but care is to be taken that they do not become cold; and very little drink is to be used, either cold water or hydromel. In those cases of fever where the bowels are loose, and the mind is disordered, the greater number of patients pick the wool from their blankets, scratch their noses, answer briefly when questions are put to them, but, when left to themselves, utter nothing that is rational. Such attacks appear to me to be connected with black bile. When in these cases there is a colliquative diarrhœa, I am of opinion that we ought to give the colder and thicker ptisans, and that the drinks ought to be binding, of a vinous nature, and rather astringent. In cases of fever attended from the first with vertigo, throbbing of the head, and thin urine, you may expect the fever to be exacerbated at the crisis; neither need it excite wonder, although there be delirium. When, at the commencement, the urine is cloudy or thick, it is proper to purge gently, provided this be otherwise proper; but when the urine at first is thin, do not purge such patients, but, if thought necessary, give a clyster; such patients should be thus treated; they should be kept in a quiet state, have unguents applied to them, and be covered up properly with clothes, and they should use for drink a watery hydromel, and the juice of ptisan as a draught in the evening; clear out the bowels at first with a clyster, but give no purgative medicines to them, for, if you move the bowels strongly, the urine is not concocted, but the fever remains long, without sweats and without a crisis. Do not give draughts when the time of the crisis is at hand, if there be agitation, but only when the fever abates and is alleviated. It is proper to be guarded at the crises of other fevers, and to withhold the draughts at that season. Fevers of this description are apt to be protracted, and to have determinations,

if the inferior extremities be cold, about the ears and neck, or, if these parts are not cold, to have other changes; they have epistaxis, and disorder of the bowels. But in cases of fever attended with nausea, or distention of the hypochondria, when the patients cannot lie reclined in the same position, and the extremities are cold, the greatest care and precaution are necessary; nothing should be given to them, except oxymel diluted with water; no draught should be administered, until the fever abate and the urine be concocted; the patient should be laid in a dark apartment, and recline upon the softest couch, and he should be kept as long as possible in the same position, so as not to toss about, for this is particularly beneficial to him. Apply to the hypochondrium linseed by inunctions, taking care that he do not catch cold when the application is made; let it be in a tepid state, and boiled in water and oil. One may judge from the urine what is to take place, for if the urine be thicker, and more yellowish, so much the better; but if it be thinner, and blacker, so much the worse; but if it undergo changes, it indicates a prolongation of the disease, and the patient, in like manner, must experience a change to the worse and the better. Irregular fevers should be let alone until they become settled, and, when they do settle, they are to be treated by a suitable diet and medicine, attending to the constitution of the patient.

9. The aspects of the sick are various; wherefore the physician should pay attention, that he may not miss observing the exciting causes, as far as they can be ascertained by reasoning, nor such symptoms as should appear on an even or odd day, but he ought to be particularly guarded in observing the odd days, as it is in them, more especially, that changes take place in patients. He should mark, particularly, the first day on which the patient became ill, considering when and whence the disease commenced, for this is of primary importance to know. When you examine the patient, inquire into all particulars; first how the head is, and if there be no headache, nor heaviness in it; then examine if the hypochondria and sides be free of pain; for if the hypochondrium be painful, swelled, and unequal, with a sense of satiety, or if there be pain in the side, and, along with the pain, either cough, tormina, or belly-ache, if any of these symptoms be present in the hypochondrium, the bowels should be opened with clysters, and the patient should drink boiled hydromel in a hot state. The physician should ascertain whether the patient be apt to faint when he is

raised up, and whether his breathing be free; and examine the discharges from the bowels, whether they be very black, or of a proper color, like those of persons in good health, and ascertain whether the fever has a paroxysm every third day, and look well to such persons on those days. And should the fourth day prove like the third, the patient is in a dangerous state. With regard to the symptoms, black stools prognosticate death; but if they resemble the discharges of a healthy person, and if such is their appearance every day, it is a favorable symptom; but when the bowels do not yield to a suppository, and when, though the respiration be natural, the patient when raised to the nighttable, or even in bed, be seized with deliquium, you may expect that the patient, man or woman, who experiences these symptoms, is about to fall into a state of delirium. Attention also should be paid to the hands, for if they tremble, you may expect epistaxis; and observe the nostrils, whether the breath be drawn in equally by both; and if expiration by the nostrils be large, a convulsion is apt to take place; and should a convulsion occur to such a person, death may be anticipated, and it is well to announce it beforehand.

10. If, in a winter fever, the tongue be rough, and if there be swoonings, it is likely to be the remission of the fever. Nevertheless such a person is to be kept upon a restricted diet, with water for drink, and hydromel, and the strained juices, not trusting to the remission of the fevers, as persons having these symptoms are in danger of dying; when, therefore, you perceive these symptoms, announce this prognostic, if you shall judge proper, after making the suitable observations. When, in fevers, any dangerous symptom appears on the fifth day, when watery discharges suddenly take place from the bowels, when deliquium animi occurs, or the patient is attacked with loss of speech, convulsions, or hiccup, under such circumstances he is likely to be affected with nausea, and sweats break out under the nose and forehead, or on the back part of the neck and head, and patients with such symptoms shortly die, from stoppage of the respiration. When, in fevers, abscesses form about the legs, and, getting into a chronic state, are not concocted while the fever persists, and if one is seized with a sense of suffocation in the throat, while the fauces are not swelled, and if it do not come to maturation, but is repressed, in such a case there is apt to be a flow of blood from the nose; if this, then, be copious, it indicates a resolution of the disease, but if not,

a prolongation of the complaint; and the less the discharge, so much worse the symptoms, and the more protracted the disease; but if the other symptoms are very favorable, expect in such a case that pains will fall upon the feet; if then they attack the feet, and if these continue long in a very painful, and inflamed state, and if there be no resolution, the pains will extend by degrees to the neck, to the clavicle, shoulder, breast, or to some articulation, in which an inflammatory tumor will necessarily form. When these are reduced, if the hands are contracted, and become trembling, convulsion and delirium seize such a person; but blisters break out on the eyebrow, erythema takes place, the one eyelid being tumefied overtops the other, a hard inflammation sets in, the eye become strongly swelled, and the delirium increases much, but makes its attacks rather at night than by day. These symptoms more frequently occur on odd than on even days, but, whether on the one or the other, they are of a fatal character. Should you determine to give purgative medicines in such cases, at the commencement, you should do so before the fifth day, if there be borborygmi in the bowels, or, if not, you should omit the medicines altogether. If there be borborygmi, with bilious stools, purge moderately with scammony; but with regard to the treatment otherwise, administer as few drinks and draughts as possible, until there be some amendment, and the disease is past the fourteenth day. When loss of speech seizes a person, on the fourteenth day of a fever, there is not usually a speedy resolution, nor any removal of the disease, for this symptom indicates a protracted disease; and when it appears on that day, it will be still more prolonged. When, on the fourth day of a fever, the tongue articulates confusedly, and when there are watery and bilious discharges from the bowels, such a patient is apt to fall into a state of delirium; the physician ought, therefore, to watch him, and attend to whatever symptoms may turn up. In the season of summer and autumn an epistaxis, suddenly occurring in acute diseases, indicates vehemence of the attack, and inflammation in the course of the veins, and on the day following, the discharge of thin urine; and if the patient be in the prime of life, and if his body be strong from exercise, and brawny, or of a melancholic temperament, or if from drinking he has trembling hands, it may be well to announce beforehand either delirium or convulsion; and if these symptoms occur on even days, so much the better; but on critical days, they are of a deadly character. If, then, a copious discharge of blood procure an issue to the fullness thereof about the nose, or what is collected about the anus, there will be an abscess, or pains in the hypochondrium, or testicles, or in the limbs; and when these are resolved, there will be a discharge of thick sputa, and of smooth, thin urine. In fever attended with singultus, give asafœtida, oxymel, and carrot, triturated together, in a draught; or galbanum in honey, and cumin in a linctus, or the juice of ptisan. Such a person cannot escape, unless critical sweats and gentle sleep supervene, and thick and acrid urine be passed, or the disease terminate in an abscess: give pine-fruit and myrrh in a linctus, and further give a very little oxymel to drink; but if they are very thirsty, some barley-water.

11. Peripneumonia, and pleuritic affections, are to be thus observed: If the fever be acute, and if there be pains on either side, or in both, and if expiration be attended with pain, if cough be present, and the sputa expectorated be of a blond or livid color, or likewise thin, frothy, and florid, or having any other character different from the common, in such a case, the physician should proceed thus: if the pain pass upward to the clavicle, or the breast, or the arm, the inner vein in the arm should be opened on the side affected, and blood abstracted according to the habit, age, and color of the patient, and the season of the year, and that largely and boldly, if the pain be acute, so as to bring on deliquium animi, and afterwards a clyster is to be given. But if the pain be below the chest, and if very intense, purge the bowels gently in such an attack of pleurisy, and during the act of purging give nothing; but after the purging give oxymel. The medicine is to be administered on the fourth day; on the first three days after the commencement, a clyster should be given, and if it does not relieve the patient, he should then be gently purged, but he is to be watched until the fever goes off, and till the seventh day; then if he appear to be free from danger, give him some unstrained ptisan, in small quantity, and thin at first, mixing it with honey. If the expectoration be easy, and the breathing free, if his sides be free of pain, and if the fever be gone, he may take the ptisan thicker, and in larger quantity, twice a day. But if he do not progress favorably, he must get less of the drink, and of the draught, which should be thin, and only given once a day, at whatever is judged to be the most favorable hour; this you will ascertain from the urine. The draught is not to be given to persons after fever, until you see that the

urine and sputa are concocted (if, indeed, after the administration of the medicine he be purged frequently, it may be necessary to give it, but it should be given in smaller quantities and thinner than usual, for from inanition he will be unable to sleep, or digest properly, or wait the crisis); but when the melting down of crude matters has taken place, and his system has cast off what is offensive, there will then be no objection. The sputa are concocted when they resemble pus, and the urine when it has reddish sediments like tares. But there is nothing to prevent fomentations and cerates being applied for the other pains of the sides; and the legs and loins may be rubbed with hot oil, or anointed with fat; linseed, too, in the form of a cataplasm, may be applied to the hypochondrium and as far up as the breasts. When pneumonia is at its height, the case is beyond remedy if he is not purged, and it is bad if he has dyspnœa, and urine that is thin and acrid, and if sweats come out about the neck and head, for such sweats are bad, as proceeding from the suffocation, *râles,* and the violence of the disease which is obtaining the upper hand, unless there be a copious evacuation of thick urine, and the sputa be concocted; when either of these come on spontaneously, that will carry off the disease. A linctus for pneumonia: Galbanum and pine-fruit in Attic honey; and southernwood in oxymel; make a decoction of pepper and black hellebore, and give it in cases of pleurisy attended with violent pain at the commencement. It is also a good thing to boil opoponax in oxymel, and, having strained it, to give it to drink; it answers well, also, in diseases of the liver, and in severe pains proceeding from the diaphragm, and in all cases in which it is beneficial to determine to the bowels or urinary organs, when given in wine and honey; when given to act upon the bowels, it should be drunk in larger quantity, along with a watery hydromel.

12. A dysentery, when stopped, will give rise to an aposteme, or tumor, if it do not terminate in fevers with sweats, or with thick and white urine, or in a tertian fever, or the pain fix upon a varix, or the testicles, or on the hip-joints.

13. In a bilious fever, jaundice coming on with rigor before the seventh day carries off the fever, but if it occur without the fever, and not at the proper time, it is a fatal symptom.

14. When the loins are in a tetanic state, and the spirits in the veins are obstructed by melancholic humors, venesection will afford relief. But when, on the other hand, the anterior tendons are strongly contracted, and if there be

sweats about the neck and face, extorted by the violent pain of the parched and dried tendons of the sacral extremity (these are very thick, sustaining the spine, and giving rise to very great ligaments, which terminate in the feet,) in such a case, unless fever and sleep come on, followed by concocted urine and critical sweats, give to drink a strong Cretan wine, and boiled barley-meal for food; anoint and rub with ointments containing wax; bathe the legs and feet in hot water, and then cover them up; and so in like manner the arms, as far as the hands, and the spine, from the neck to the sacrum, are to be wrapped in a skin smeared with wax; this must extend to the parts beyond, and intervals are to be left for applying fomentations, by means of leather bottles filled with hot water, then, wrapping him up in a linen cloth, lay him down in bed. Do not open the bowels, unless by means of a suppository, when they have been long of being moved. If there be any remission of the disease, so far well, but otherwise, pound of the root of bryonia in fragrant wine, and that of the carrot, and give to the patient fasting early in the morning, before using the affusion, and immediately afterwards let him eat boiled barley-meal in a tepid state, and as much as he can take, and in addition let him drink, if he will, wine well diluted. If the disease yield to these means, so much the better, but, if otherwise, you must prognosticate accordingly.

15. All diseases are resolved either by the mouth, the bowels, the bladder, or some other such organ. Sweat is a common form of resolution in all these cases.

16. You should put persons on a course of hellebore who are troubled with a defluxion from the head. But do not administer hellebore to such persons as are laboring under empyema connected with abscesses, hæmoptysis, and intemperament, or any other strong cause, for it will do no good; and if any thing unpleasant occur the hellebore will get the blame of it. But if the body have suddenly lost its powers, or if there be pain in the head, or obstruction of the ears and nose, or ptyalism, or heaviness of the limbs, or an extraordinary swelling of the body, you may administer the hellebore, provided these symptoms be not connected with drinking, nor with immoderate venery; nor with sorrow, vexation, nor insomnolency, for, if any of these causes exist, the treatment must have respect to it.

17. From walking arise pains of the sides, of the back, of the loins, and of the hip-joint, and disorder of the respiration has often been from

the same cause, for, after excesses of wine and flatulent food, pains shoot to the loins and hips, accompanied with dysuria. Walking is the cause of such complaints, and also of coryza and hoarseness.

18. Disorders connected with regimen, for the most part, make their attack accordingly as any one has changed his habitual mode of diet. For persons who dine contrary to custom experience much swelling of the stomach, drowsiness, and fullness; and if they take supper over and above, their belly is disordered; such persons will be benefited by sleeping after taking the bath, and by walking slowly for a considerable time after sleep; if, then, the bowels be moved, he may dine and drink a small quantity of wine not much diluted; but if the bowels are not opened, he should get his body rubbed with hot oil, and, if thirsty, drink of some weak and white wine, or a sweet wine, and take repose; if he does not sleep he should repose the longer. In other respects he should observe the regimen laid down for those who have taken a debauch. With regard to the bad effects of drinks, such as are of a watery nature pass more slowly through the body, they regurgitate, as it were, and float about the hypochondria, and do not flow readily by urine; when filled up with such a drink, he should not attempt any violent exertion, requiring either strength or swiftness, but should rest as much as possible until the drink has been digested along with the food; but such drinks as are stronger or more austere, occasion palpitation in the body and throbbing in the head, and in this case the person affected will do well to sleep, and take some hot draught for which he feels disposed; for abstinence is bad in headache and the effects of a surfeit. Those who, contrary to usage, restrict themselves to one meal, feel empty and feeble, and pass hot urine in consequence of the emptiness of their vessels; they have a salt and bitter taste in the mouth; they tremble at any work they attempt; their temples throb; and they cannot digest their supper so well as if they had previously taken their dinner. Such persons should take less supper than they are wont, and a pudding of barley-meal more moist than usual instead of bread, and of potherbs the dock, or mallow, and ptisan, or beets, and along with the food they should take wine in moderation, and diluted with water; after supper they should take a short walk, until the urine descend and be passed; and they may use boiled fish.

Articles of food have generally such effects as the following: Garlic occasions flatulence and heat about the chest, heaviness of the head, and nausea, and any other habitual pain is apt to be exasperated by it; it is diuretic, which, in so far, is a good property which it possesses; but it is best to eat it when one means to drink to excess, or when intoxicated. Cheese produces flatulence and constipation, and heats the other articles of food; and it gives rise to crudities and indigestion, but it is worst of all to eat it along with drink after a full meal. Pulse of all kinds are flatulent, whether raw, boiled, or fried; least so when macerated in water, or in a green state; they should not be used except along with food prepared from the cerealia. Each of these articles, however, has bad effects peculiar to itself. The vetch, whether raw or boiled, creates flatulence and pain. The lentil is astringent, and disorders the stomach if taken with its hull. The lupine has the fewest bad effects of all these things. The stalk and the juice of silphium (asafœtida), pass through some people's bowels very readily, but in others, not accustomed to them, they engender what is called dry cholera; this complaint is more especially produced by it if mixed with much cheese, or eaten along with beef. Melancholic diseases are most particularly exacerbated by beef, for it is of an unmanageable nature, and requires no ordinary powers of stomach to digest it; it will agree best with those who use it well boiled and pretty long kept. Goat's flesh has all the bad properties of beef; it is an indigestible, more flatulent and engenders acid eructations and cholera; such as has a fragrant smell, is firm, and sweet to the taste, is the best, when well baked and cooled; but those kinds which are disagreeable to the taste, have a bad smell, and are hard, such are particularly bad, and especially if very fresh; it is best in summer and worst in autumn. The flesh of young pigs is bad, either when it is too raw or when it is over-roasted, for it engenders bile and disorders the bowels. Of all kinds of flesh, pork is the best; it is best when neither very fat, nor, on the other hand, very lean, and the animal had not attained the age of what is reckoned an old victim; it should be eaten without the skin, and in a coldish state.

19. In dry cholera the belly is distended with wind, there is rumbling in the bowels, pain in the sides and loins, no dejections, but, on the contrary, the bowels are constipated. In such a case you should guard against vomiting, but endeavor to get the bowels opened. As quickly as possible give a clyster of hot water with plenty of oil in it, and having rubbed the patient freely with unguents, put him into hot water,

laying him down in the basin, and pouring the hot water upon him by degrees; and if, when heated in the bath, the bowels be moved, he will be freed from the complaint. To a person in such a complaint it will do good if he sleep, and drink a thin, old, and strong wine; and you should give him oil, so that he may settle, and have his bowels moved, when he will be relieved. He must abstain from all other kinds of food; but when the pain remits, give him asses' milk to drink until he is purged. But if the bowels are loose, with bilious discharges, tormina, vomitings, a feeling of suffocation, and gnawing pains, it is best to enjoin repose, and to drink hydromel, and avoid vomiting.

20. There are two kinds of dropsy, the one anasarca, which, when formed, is incurable; the other is accompanied with emphysema (tympanites?) and requires much good fortune to enable one to triumph over it. Laborious exertion, fomentation, and abstinence (are to be enjoined). The patient should eat dry and acrid things, for thus will he pass the more water, and his strength be kept up. If he labors under difficulty of breathing, if it is the summer season, and if he is in the prime of life, and is strong, blood should be abstracted from the arm, and then he should eat hot pieces of bread, dipped in dark wine and oil, drink very little, and labor much, and live on well-fed pork, boiled with vinegar, so that he may be able to endure hard exercises.

21. Those who have the inferior intestines hot, and who pass acrid and irregular stools of a colliquative nature, if they can bear it, should procure revulsion by vomiting with hellebore; but if not, should get a thick decoction of summer wheat in a cold state, lentil soup, bread cooked with cinders, and fish, which should be taken boiled if they have fever, but roasted if not feverish; and also dark-colored wine if free of fever; but otherwise they should take the water from medlars, myrtles, apples, services, dates, or wild vine. If there be no fever, and if there be tormina, the patient should drink hot asses' milk in small quantity at first, and gradually increase it, and linseed, and wheaten flour, and having removed the bitter part of Egyptian beans, and ground them, sprinkle on the milk and drink; and let him eat eggs half-roasted, and fine flour, and millet, and perl-spelt (chondrus) boiled in milk;—all these things should be eaten cold, and similar articles of food and drink should be administered.

22. The most important point of regimen to observe and be guarded about in protracted diseases, is to pay attention to the exacerbations and remissions of fevers, so as to avoid the times when food should not be given, and to know when it may be administered without danger; this last season is at the greatest possible distance from the exacerbation.

23. One should be able to recognize those who have headache from gymnastic exercises, or running, or walking or hunting, or any other unseasonable labor, or from immoderate venery; also those who are of a pale color, or troubled with hoarseness; those who have enlarged spleen, those who are in a state of anæmia, those who are suffering from tympanites, those having dry cough and thirst, those who are flatulent, and have the course of the blood in their veins intercepted; those persons whose hypochondria, sides, and back are distended: those having torpor; those laboring under amaurosis, or having noises in their ears; those suffering from incontinence of urine or jaundice, or whose food is passed undigested; those who have discharges of blood from the nose or anus, or who have flatulence and intense pain, and who cannot retain the wind. In these cases you may do mischief, but cannot possibly do any good by purging, but may interrupt the spontaneous remissions and crises of the complaints.

24. If you think it expedient to let blood, see that the bowels be previously settled, and then bleed; enjoin abstinence, and forbid the use of wine; and complete the cure by means of a suitable regimen, and wet fomentations. But if the bowels appear to be constipated, administer a soothing clyster.

25. If you think it necessary to give medicines, you may safely purge upwards by hellebore, but none of those should be purged downwards. The most effectual mode of treatment is by the urine, sweats, and exercise; and use gentle friction so as not to harden the constitution; and if he be confined to bed let others rub him. When the pain is seated above the diaphragm, place him erect for the most part, and let him be as little reclined as possible; and when he is raised up let him be rubbed for a considerable time with plenty of hot oil. But if the pains be in the lower belly below the diaphragm, it will be useful to lie reclined and make no motion, and to such a person nothing should be administered except the friction. Those pains which are dissolved by discharges from the bowels, by urine, or moderate sweats, cease spontaneously, if they are slight, but if strong they prove troublesome; for persons so affected either die, or at least do not recover

without further mischief, for they terminate in abscesses.

26. *A draught for a dropsical person.* Take three cantharides, and removing their head, feet, and wings, triturate their bodies in three cupfuls (cyathi) of water, and when the person who has drunk the draught complains of pain, let him have hot fomentations applied. The patient should be first anointed with oil, should take the draught fasting, and eat hot bread with oil.

27. *A styptic.* Apply the juice of the fig inwardly to the vein; or having moulded biestings into a tent, introduce up the nostril, or push up some chalcitis with the finger, and press the cartilages of the nostrils together; and open the bowels with the boiled milk of asses: or having shaved the head apply cold things to it if in the summer season.

28. The sesamoides purges upwards when pounded in oxymel to the amount of a drachm and a half, and drunk; it is combined with the hellebores, to the amount of the third part, and thus it is less apt to produce suffocation.

29. *Trichiasis.* Having introduced a thread into the eye of a needle push it through the upper part of the distended eyelid, and do the same at the base of it; having stretched the threads tie a knot on them, and bind up until they drop out: and, if this be sufficient, so far well; but if otherwise, you must do the same thing again. And hemorrhoids, in like manner, you may treat by transfixing them with a needle and tying them with a very thick and large woolen thread; for thus the cure will be more certain. When you have secured them, use a septic application, and do not foment until they drop off, and always leave one behind; and when the patient recovers, let him be put upon a course of hellebore. Then let him be exercised and sweated; the friction of the gymnasium and wrestling in the morning will be proper; but he must abstain from running, drinking, and all acrid substances, except marjoram; let him take an emetic every seven days, or three times in a month; for thus will he enjoy the best bodily health. Let him take straw-colored, austere, and watery wine, and use little drink.

30. *For persons affected with empyema.* Having cut some bulbs or squill, boil in water, and when well boiled, throw this away, and having poured in more water, boil until it appear to the touch soft and well-boiled; then triturate finely and mix roasted cumin, and white sesames, and young almonds pounded in honey, form into an electuary and give; and afterwards

sweet wine. In draughts, having pounded about a small acetabulum of the white poppy, moisten it with water in which summer wheat has been washed, add honey, and boil. Let him take this frequently during the day. And then taking into account what is to happen, give him supper.

31. *For dysentery.* A fourth part of a pound of cleaned beans, and twelve shoots of madder having been triturated, are to be mixed together and boiled, and given as a linctus with some fatty substance.

32. *For diseases of the eyes.* Washed spodium (tutty?) mixed with grease, and not of a thinner consistence than dough, is to be carefully triturated, and moistened with the juice of unripe raisins; and having dried in the sun, moisten until it is of the consistence of an ointment. When it becomes again dry, let it be finely levigated, anoint the eyes with it, and dust it upon the angles of the eyes.

33. *For watery eyes.* Take one drachm of ebeny and nine oboli of burnt copper, rub them upon a whetstone, add three oboli of saffron; triturate all these things reduced to a fine powder, pour in an Attic hemina of sweet wine, and then place in the sun and cover up; when sufficiently digested, use it.

34. *For violent pains of the eyes.* Take of chalcitis, and of raisin, of each 1 dr., when digested for two days, strain; and pounding myrrh and saffron, and having mixed must, with these things, digest in the sun; and with this anoint the eyes when in a state of severe pain. Let it be kept in a copper vessel.

35. *Mode of distinguishing persons in an hysterical fit.* Pinch them with your fingers, and if they feel, it is hysterical; but if not, it is a convulsion.

36. *To persons in coma,* (dropsy?) give to drink meconium (*euphorbia peplus?*) to the amount of a round Attic *leciskion* (small acetabulum).

37. Of squama æris, as much as three specilla can contain, with the gluten of summer wheat: levigate, pound, form into pills, and give; it purges water downwards.

38. *A medicine for opening the bowels.* Pour upon figs the juice of spurge, in the proportion of seven to one: then put into a new vessel and lay past when properly mixed. Give before food.

39. Pounding meconium, pouring on it water, and straining, and mixing flour, and baking into a cake, with the addition of boiled honey, give in affections of the anus and in

dropsy; and after eating of it, let the patient drink of a sweet watery wine, and diluted hydromel prepared from wax: or collecting meconium, lay it up for medicinal purposes.

Of the Epidemics

BOOK I. Sect. I. First Constitution

1. IN THASUS, about the autumn equinox, and under the Pleiades, the rains were abundant, constant, and soft, with southerly winds; the winter southerly, the northerly winds faint, droughts; on the whole, the winter having the character of spring. The spring was southerly, cool, rains small in quantity. Summer, for the most part, cloudy, no rain, the Etesian winds, rare and small, blew in an irregular manner. The whole constitution of the season being thus inclined to the southerly, and with droughts early in the spring, from the preceding opposite and northerly state, ardent fevers occurred in a few instances, and these very mild, being rarely attended with hemorrhage, and never proving fatal. Swellings appeared about the ears, in many on either side, and in the greatest number on both sides, being unaccompanied by fever so as not to confine the patient to bed; in all cases they disappeared without giving trouble, neither did any of them come to suppuration, as is common in swellings from other causes. They were of a lax, large, diffused character, without inflammation or pain, and they went away without any critical sign. They seized children, adults, and mostly those who were engaged in the exercises of the palestra and gymnasium, but seldom attacked women. Many had dry coughs without expectoration, and accompanied with hoarseness of voice. In some instances earlier, and in others later, inflammations with pain seized sometimes one of the testicles, and sometimes both; some of these cases were accompanied with fever and some not; the greater part of these were attended with much suffering. In other respects they were free of disease, so as not to require medical assistance.

2. Early in the beginning of spring, and through the summer, and towards winter, many of those who had been long gradually declining, took to bed with symptoms of phthisis; in many cases formerly of a doubtful character the disease then became confirmed; in these the constitution inclined to the phthisical. Many, and, in fact, the most of them, died; and of those confined to bed, I do not know if a single individual survived for any considerable time; they died more suddenly than is common in such cases. But other diseases, of a protracted character, and attended with fever, were well supported, and did not prove fatal: of these we will give a description afterwards. Consumption was the most considerable of the diseases which then prevailed, and the only one which proved fatal to many persons. Most of them were affected by these diseases in the following manner: fevers accompanied with rigors, of the continual type, acute, having no complete intermissions, but of the form of the semi-tertians, being milder the one day, and the next having an exacerbation, and increasing in violence; constant sweats, but not diffused over the whole body; extremities very cold, and warmed with difficulty; bowels disordered, with bilious, scanty, unmixed, thin, pungent, and frequent dejections. The urine was thin, colorless, unconcocted, or thick, with a deficient sediment, not settling favorably, but casting down a crude and unseasonable sediment. Sputa small, dense, concocted, but brought up rarely and with difficulty; and in those who encountered the most violent symptoms there was no concoction at all, but they continued throughout spitting crude matters. Their fauces, in most of them, were painful from first to last, having redness with inflammation; defluxions thin, small and acrid; they were soon wasted and became worse, having no appetite for any kind of food throughout; no thirst; most persons delirious when near death. So much concerning the phthisical affections.

3. In the course of the summer and autumn many fevers of the continual type, but not violent; they attacked persons who had been long indisposed, but who were otherwise not in an uncomfortable state. In most cases the bowels were disordered in a very moderate degree, and they did not suffer thereby in any manner worth mentioning; the urine was generally well colored, clear, thin, and after a time becoming concocted near the crisis. They had not much cough, nor was it troublesome; they were not deficient in appetite, for it was necessary to give them food (on the whole, persons laboring under phthisis were not affected in the usual manner). They were affected with fevers, rigors,

and deficient sweats, with varied and irregular paroxysms, in general not intermitting, but having exacerbations in the tertian form. The earliest crisis which occurred was about the twentieth day, in most about the fortieth, and in many about the eightieth. But there were cases in which it did not leave them thus at all, but in an irregular manner, and without any crisis; in most of these the fevers, after a brief interval, relapsed again; and from these relapses they came to a crisis in the same periods; but in many they were prolonged so that the disease was not gone at the approach of winter. Of all those which are described under this constitution, the phthisical diseases alone were of a fatal character; for in all the others the patients bore up well, and did not die of the other fevers.

Sect. II. Second Constitution

1. In Thasus, early in autumn, the winter suddenly set in rainy before the usual time, with much northerly and southerly winds. These things all continued so during the season of the Pleiades, and until their setting. The winter was northerly, the rains frequent, in torrents, and large, with snow, but with a frequent mixture of fair weather. These things were all so, but the setting in of the cold was not much out of season. After the winter solstice, and at the time when the zephyr usually begins to blow, severe winterly storms out of season, with much northerly wind, snow, continued and copious rains; the sky tempestuous and clouded; these things were protracted, and did not remit until the equinox. The spring was cold, northerly, rainy, and clouded; the summer was not very sultry, the Etesian winds blew constant, but quickly afterwards, about the rising of Arcturus, there were again many rains with north winds. The whole season being wet, cold, and northerly, people were, for the most part, healthy during winter; but early in the spring very many, indeed, the greater part, were valetudinary. At first ophthalmies set in, with rheums, pains, unconcocted discharges, small concretions, generally breaking with difficulty, in most instances they relapsed, and they did not cease until late in autumn. During summer and autumn there were dysenteric affections, attacks of tenesmus and lientery, bilious diarrhœa, with thin, copious, undigested, and acrid dejections, and sometimes with watery stools; many had copious defluxions, with pain, of a bilious, watery, slimy, purulent nature, attended with strangury, not connected with disease of the kidneys, but one complaint succeeding the other; vomitings of bile, phlegm, and undigested food, sweats, in all cases a redundance of humors. In many instances these complaints were unattended with fever, and did not prevent the patients from walking about, but some cases were febrile, as will be described. In some all those described below occurred with pain. During autumn, and at the commencement of winter, there were phthisical complaints, continual fevers; and, in a few cases, ardent; some diurnal, others nocturnal, semi-tertians, true tertians, quartans, irregular fevers.

2. All these fevers described attacked great numbers. The ardent fevers attacked the smallest numbers, and the patients suffered the least from them, for there were no hemorrhages, except a few and to a small amount, nor was there delirium; all the other complaints were slight; in these the crises were regular, in most instances, with the intermittents, in seventeen days; and I know no instance of a person dying of causus, nor becoming phrenitic. The tertians were more numerous than the ardent fevers, and attended with more pain; but these all had four periods in regular succession from the first attack, and they had a complete crisis in seven, without a relapse in any instance. The quartans attacked many at first, in the form of regular quartans, but in no few cases a transition from other fevers and diseases into quartans took place; they were protracted, as is wont with them, indeed, more so than usual. Quotidian, nocturnal, and wandering fevers attacked many persons, some of whom continued to keep up, and others were confined to bed. In most instances these fevers were prolonged under the Pleiades and till winter. Many persons, and more especially children, had convulsions from the commencement; and they had fever, and the convulsions supervened upon the fevers; in most cases they were protracted, but free from danger, unless in those who were in a deadly state from other complaints. Those fevers which were continual in the main, and with no intermissions, but having exacerbations in the tertian form, there being remissions the one day and exacerbations the next, were the most violent of all those which occurred at that time, and the most protracted, and occurring with the greatest pains, beginning mildly, always on the whole increasing, and being exacerbated, and always turning worse, having small remissions, and after an abatement having more violent paroxysms, and growing worse, for the most part, on the critical days. Rigors, in all cases, took place in an irregular and uncertain manner, very rare and

weak in them, but greater in all other fevers; frequent sweats, but most seldom in them, bringing no alleviation, but, on the contrary, doing mischief. Much cold of the extremities in them, and these were warmed with difficulty. Insomnolency, for the most part, especially in these fevers, and again a disposition to coma. The bowels, in all diseases, were disordered, and in a bad state, but worst of all in these. The urine, in most of them, was either thin and crude, yellow, and after a time with slight symptoms of concoction in a critical form, or having the proper thickness, but muddy, and neither settling nor subsiding; or having small and bad, and crude sediments; these being the worst of all. Coughs attended these fevers, but I cannot state that any harm or good ever resulted from the cough.

3. The most of these were protracted and troublesome, went on in a very disorderly and irregular form, and, for the most part, did not end in a crisis, either in the fatal cases or in the others; for if it left some of them for a season it soon returned again. In a few instances the fever terminated with a crisis; in the earliest of these about the eightieth day, and some of these relapsed, so that most of them were not free from the fever during the winter; but the fever left most of them without a crisis, and these things happened alike to those who recovered and to those who did not. There being much want of crisis and much variety as to these diseases, the greatest and worst symptom attended the most of them, namely, a loathing of all articles of food, more especially with those who had otherwise fatal symptoms; but they were not unseasonably thirsty in such fevers. After a length of time, with much suffering and great wasting, abscesses were formed in these cases, either unusually large, so that the patients could not support them, or unusually small, so that they did no good, but soon relapsed and speedily got worse. The diseases which attacked them were in the form of dysenteries, tenesmus, lientery, and fluxes; but, in some cases, there were dropsies, with or without these complaints. Whatever attacked them violently speedily cut them off, or again, did them no good. Small rashes, and not corresponding to the violence of the disease, and quickly disappearing, or swellings occurred about the ears, which were not resolved, and brought on no crisis. In some they were determined to the joints, and especially to the hip-joint, terminating critically with a few, and quickly again increasing to its original habit.

4. People died of all these diseases, but mostly of these fevers, and notably infants just weaned, and older children, until eight or ten years of age, and those before puberty. These things occurred to those affected with the complaints described above, and to many persons at first without them. The only favorable symptom, and the greatest of those which occurred, and what saved most of those who were in the greatest dangers, was the conversion of it to a strangury, and when, in addition to this, abscesses were formed. The strangury attacked, most especially, persons of the ages I have mentioned, but it also occurred in many others, both of those who were not confined to bed and those who were. There was a speedy and great change in all these cases. For the bowels, if they happened previously to have watery discharges of a bad character, became regular, they got an appetite for food, and the fevers were mild afterwards. But, with regard to the strangury itself, the symptoms were protracted and painful. Their urine was copious, thick, of various characters, red, mixed with pus, and was passed with pain. These all recovered, and I did not see a single instance of death among them.

5. With regard to the dangers of these cases, one must always attend to the seasonable concoction of all the evacuations, and to the favorable and critical abscesses. The concoctions indicate a speedy crisis and recovery of health; crude and undigested evacuations, and those which are converted into bad abscesses, indicate either want of crisis, or pains, or prolongation of the disease, or death, or relapses; which of these it is to be must be determined from other circumstances. *The physician must be able to tell the antecedents, know the present, and foretell the future—must meditate these things, and have two special objects in view with regard to diseases, namely, to do good or to do no harm. The art consists in three things—the disease, the patient, and the physician. The physician is the servant of the art, and the patient must combat the disease along with the physician.* [1]

6. Pains about the head and neck, and heaviness of the same along with pain, occur either

---

[1] Galen, in his Commentary, remarks that the first time he read this passage he thought it unworthy of Hippocrates to lay it down as a rule of practice, that "the physician should do good to his patient, or at least no harm"; but that, after having seen a good deal of the practice of other physicians, and observed how often they were justly exposed to censure for having bled, or applied the bath, or given medicines, or wine unseasonably, he came to recognize the propriety and importance of the

without fevers or in fevers. Convulsions occurring in persons attacked with frenzy, and having vomitings of verdigris-green bile, in some cases quickly prove fatal. In ardent fevers, and in those other fevers in which there is pain of the neck, heaviness of the temples, mistiness about the eyes, and distention about the hypochondriac region, not unattended with pain, hemorrhage from the nose takes place, but those who have heaviness of the whole head, cardialgia and nausea, vomit bilious and pituitous matters; children, in such affections, are generally attacked with convulsions, and women have these and also pains of the uterus; whereas, in elder persons, and those in whom the heat is already more subdued, these cases end in paralysis, mania, and loss of sight.

Third Constitution

7. In Thasus, a little before and during the season of Arcturus, there were frequent and great rains, with northerly winds. About the equinox, and till the setting of the Pleiades, there were a few southerly rains: the winter northerly and parched, cold, with great winds and snow. Great storms about the equinox, the spring northerly, dryness, rains few and cold. About the summer solstice, scanty rains, and great cold until near the season of the Dog-star. After the Dog-days, until the season of Arcturus, the summer hot, great droughts, not in intervals, but continued and severe: no rain; the Etesian winds blew; about the season of Arcturus southerly rains until the equinox.

8. In this state of things, during winter, paraplegia set in, and attacked many, and some died speedily; and otherwise the disease prevailed much in an epidemical form, but persons remained free from all other diseases. Early in the spring, ardent fevers commenced and continued through the summer until the equinox. Those then that were attacked immediately after the commencement of the spring and summer, for the most part recovered, and but few of them died. But when the autumn and the rains had set in, they were of a fatal character, and the greater part then died. When in these attacks of ardent fevers there was a proper and copious hemorrhage from the nose, they

were generally saved by it, and I do not know a single person who had a proper hemorrhage who died in this constitution. Philiscus, Epaminon, and Silenus, indeed, who had a trifling epistaxis on the fourth and fifth day, died. Most of those taken with the disease had a rigor about the time of the crisis, and notably those who had no hemorrhage; these had also rigor associated.

9. Some were attacked with jaundice on the sixth day, but these were benefited either by an urinary purgation, or a disorder of the bowels, or a copious hemorrhage, as in the case of Heraclides, who was lodged with Aristocydes: this person, though he had the hemorrhage from the nose, the purgation by the bladder, and disorder of the bowels, experienced a favorable crisis on the twentieth day, not like the servant of Phanagoras, who had none of these symptoms, and died. The hemorrhages attacked most persons, but especially young persons and those in the prime of life, and the greater part of those who had not the hemorrhage died: elderly persons had jaundice or disorder of the bowels, such as Bion, who was lodged with Silenus. Dysenteries were epidemical during the summer, and some of those cases in which the hemorrhage occurred, terminated in dysentery, as happened to the slave of Eraton, and to Mullus, who had a copious hemorrhage, which settled down into dysentery, and they recovered. This humor was redundant in many cases, since in those who had not the hemorrhage about the crisis, but the risings about the ears disappeared, after their disappearance there was a sense of weight in the left flank extending to the extremity of the hip, and pain setting in after the crisis, with a discharge of thin urine; they began to have small hemorrhages about the twenty-fourth day, and the swelling was converted into the hemorrhage. In the case of Antiphon, the son of Critobulus' son, the fever ceased and came to a crisis about the fortieth day.

10. Many women were seized, but fewer than of the men, and there were fewer deaths among them. But most of them had difficult parturition, and after labor they were taken ill, and these most especially died, as, for example, the daughter of Telebolus died on the sixth day after delivery. Most females had the menstrual discharge during the fever, and many girls had it then for the first time: in certain individuals both the hemorrhage from the nose and the menses appeared; thus, in the case of the virgin daughter of Dætharses, the menses then took place for the first time, and she had also a copi-

rule laid down by Hippocrates. The practice of certain physicians, Galen remarks, is like playing at the dice, when what turns up may occasion the greatest mischief to their patients. Galen, however, informs us that in some of the MSS. instead of "art" he found "nature"; that is to say, that the physician is "the minister (or servant) of nature."

ous hemorrhage from the the nose, and I knew no instance of any one dying when one or other of these took place properly. But all those in the pregnant state that were attacked had abortions, as far as I observed. The urine in most cases was of the proper color, but thin, and having scanty sediments: in most the bowels were disordered with thin and bilious dejections; and many, after passing through the other crises, terminated in dysenteries, as happened to Xenophanes and Critias. The urine was watery, copious, clear, and thin; and even after the crises, when the sediment was natural, and all the other critical symptoms were favorable, as I recollect having happened to Bion, who was lodged in the house of Silenus, and Critias, who lived with Xenophanes, the slave of Areton, and the wife of Mnesistratus. But afterwards all these were attacked with dysentery. It would be worth while to inquire whether the watery urine was the cause of this. About the season of Arcturus many had the crisis on the eleventh day, and in them the regular relapses did not take place, but they became comatose about this time, especially children; but there were fewest deaths of all among them.

11. About the equinox, and until the season of the Pleiades, and at the approach of winter, many ardent fevers set in; but great numbers at that season were seized with phrenitis, and many died; a few cases also occurred during the summer. These then made their attack at the commencement of ardent fevers, which were attended with fatal symptoms; for immediately upon their setting in, there were acute fever and small rigors, insomnolency, aberration, thirst, nausea, insignificant sweats about the forehead and clavicles, but no general perspiration; they had much delirious talking, fears, despondency, great coldness of the extremities, in the feet, but more especially in their hands: the paroxysms were on the even days; and in most cases, on the fourth day, the most violent pains set in, with sweats, generally coldish, and the extremities could not be warmed, but were livid and rather cold, and they had then no thirst; in them the urine was black, scanty, thin, and the bowels were constipated; there was an hemorrhage from the nose in no case in which these symptoms occurred, but merely a trifling epistaxis; and none of them had a relapse, but they died on the sixth day with sweats. In the phrenitic cases, all the symptoms which have been described did not occur, but in them the disease mostly came to a crisis on the eleventh day, and in some on the twen-

tieth. In those cases in which the phrenitis did not begin immediately, but about the third or fourth day, the disease was moderate at the commencement, but assumed a violent character about the seventh day. There was a great number of diseases, and of those affected, they who died were principally infants, young persons, adults having smooth bodies, white skins, straight and black hair, dark eyes, those living recklessly and luxuriously; persons with shrill, or rough voices, who stammered and were passionate, and women more especially died from this form. In this constitution, four symptoms in particular proved salutary; either a hemorrhage from the nose, or a copious discharge by the bladder of urine, having an abundant and proper sediment, or a bilious disorder of the bowels at the proper time, or an attack of dysentery. And in many cases it happened, that the crisis did not take place by any one of the symptoms which have been mentioned, but the patient passed through most of them, and appeared to be in an uncomfortable way, and yet all who were attacked with these symptoms recovered. All the symptoms which I have described occurred also to women and girls; and whoever of them had any of these symptoms in a favorable manner, or the menses appeared abundantly, were saved thereby, and had a crisis, so that I do not know a single female who had any of these favorably that died. But the daughter of Philo, who had a copious hemorrhage from the nose, and took supper unseasonably on the seventh day, died. In those cases of acute, and more especially of ardent fevers, in which there is an involuntary discharge of tears, you may expect a nasal hemorrhage unless the other symptoms be of a fatal type, for in those of a bad description, they do not indicate a hemorrhage, but death.

12. Swellings about the ears, with pain in fevers, sometimes when the fever went off critically, neither subsided nor were converted into pus; in these cases a bilious diarrhœa, or dysentery, or thick urine having a sediment, carried off the disease, as happened to Hermippus of Clazomenæ. The circumstances relating to crises, as far as we can recognize them, were so far similar and so far dissimilar. Thus two brothers became ill at the same hour (they were brothers of Epigenes, and lodged near the theatre), of these the elder had a crisis on the sixth day, and the younger on the seventh, and both had a relapse at the same hour; it then left them for five days, and from the return of the fever both had a crisis together on the seven-

teenth day. Most had a crisis on the sixth day; it then left them for six days, and from the relapse there was a crisis on the fifth day. But those who had a crisis on the seventh day, had an intermission for seven days; and the crisis took place on the third day after the relapse. Those who had a crisis on the sixth day, after an interval of six days were seized again on the third, and having left them for one day, the fever attacked them again on the next and came to a crisis, as happened to Evagon the son of Dætharses. Those in whom the crisis happened on the sixth day, had an intermission of seven days, and from the relapse there was a crisis on the fourth, as happened to the daughter of Aglaïdas. The greater part of those who were taken ill under this constitution of things, were affected in this manner, and I did not know a single case of recovery, in which there was not a relapse agreeably to the stated order of relapses; and all those recovered in which the relapses took place according to this form: nor did I know a single instance of those who then passed through the disease in this manner who had another relapse.

13. In these diseases death generally happened on the sixth day, as with Epaminondas, Silenus, and Philiscus the son of Antagoras. Those who had parotid swellings experienced a crisis on the twentieth day, but in all these cases the disease went off without coming to a suppuration, and was turned upon the bladder. But in Cratistonax, who lived by the temple of Hercules, and in the maid servant of Scymnus the fuller, it turned to a suppuration, and they died. Those who had a crisis on the seventh day, had an intermission of nine days, and a relapse which came to a crisis on the fourth day from the return of the fever, as was the case with Pantacles, who resided close by the temple of Bacchus. Those who had a crisis on the seventh day, after an interval of six days had a relapse, from which they had a crisis on the seventh day, as happened to Phanocritus, who was lodged with Gnathon the fuller. During the winter, about the winter solstices, and until the equinox, the ardent fevers and frenzies prevailed, and many died. The crisis, however, changed, and happened to the greater number on the fifth day from the commencement, left them for four days and relapsed; and after the return, there was a crisis on the fifth day, making in all fourteen days. The crisis took place thus in the case of most children, also in elder persons. Some had a crisis on the eleventh day, a relapse on the fourteenth, a complete crisis on the twentieth; but certain persons, who had a rigor about the twentieth, had a crisis on the fortieth. The greater part had a rigor along with the original crisis, and these had also a rigor about the crisis in the relapse. There were fewest cases of rigor in the spring, more in summer, still more in autumn, but by far the most in winter; then hemorrhages ceased.

Sect. III

1. With regard to diseases, the circumstances from which we form a judgment of them are, —by attending to the general nature of all, and the peculiar nature of each individual,—to the disease, the patient, and the applications,—to the person who applies them, as that makes a difference for better or for worse,—to the whole constitution of the season, and particularly to the state of the heavens, and the nature of each country;—to the patient's habits, regimen, and pursuits;—to his conversation, manners, taciturnity, thoughts, sleep, or absence of sleep, and sometimes his dreams, what and when they occur;—to his picking and scratching;—to his tears;—to the alvine discharges, urine, sputa, and vomitings; and to the changes of diseases from the one into the other;—to the deposits, whether of a deadly or critical character;—to the sweat, coldness, rigor, cough, sneezing, hiccup, respiration, eructation, flatulence, whether passed silently or with a noise;—to hemorrhages and hemorrhoids;—from these, and their consequences, we must form our judgment.

2. Fevers are,—the continual, some of which hold during the day and have a remission at night, and others hold during the night and have a remission during the day; semi-tertians, tertians, quartans, quintans, septans, nonans. The most acute, strongest, most dangerous, and fatal diseases, occur in the continual fever. The least dangerous of all, and the mildest and most protracted, is the quartan, for it is not only such from itself, but it also carries off other great diseases. In what is called the semi-tertian, other acute diseases are apt to occur, and it is the most fatal of all others, and moreover phthisical persons, and those laboring under other protracted diseases, are apt to be attacked by it. The nocturnal fever is not very fatal, but protracted; the diurnal is still more protracted, and in some cases passes into phthisis. The septan is protracted, but not fatal; the nonan more protracted, and not fatal. The true tertian comes quickly to a crisis, and is not fatal; but the quintan is the worst of all, for it proves fatal when it precedes an attack of phthisis, and when it supervenes on persons who are already consumptive. There

are peculiar modes, and constitutions, and paroxysms, in every one of these fevers; for example,—the continual, in some cases at the very commencement, grows, as it were, and attains its full strength, and rises to its most dangerous pitch, but is diminished about and at the crisis; in others it begins gentle and suppressed, but gains ground and is exacerbated every day, and bursts forth with all its heat about and at the crisis; while in others, again, it commences mildly, increases, and is exacerbated until it reaches its acmé, and then remits until at and about the crisis. These varieties occur in every fever, and in every disease. From these observations one must regulate the regimen accordingly. There are many other important symptoms allied to these, part of which have been already noticed, and part will be described afterwards, from a consideration of which one may judge, and decided in each case, whether the disease be acute, and whether it will end in death or recovery; or whether it will be protracted, and will end in death or recovery; and in what cases food is to be given, and in what not; and when and to what amount, and what particular kind of food is to be administered.

3. Those diseases which have their paroxysms on even days have their crises on even days; and those which have their paroxysms on uneven days have their crises on uneven days. The first period of those which have the crisis on even days, is the 4th, 6th, 8th, 10th, 14th, 20th, 30th, 40th, 60th, 80th, 100th; and the first period of those which have their crises on uneven days, is the 1st, 3d, 5th, 7th, 9th, 11th, 17th, 21st, 27th, 31st. It should be known, that if the crisis take place on any other day than on those described, it indicates that there will be a relapse, which may prove fatal. But one ought to pay attention, and know in these seasons what crises will lead to recovery and what to death, or to changes for the better or the worse. Irregular fevers, quartans, quintans, septans, and nonans should be studied, in order to find out in what periods their crises take place.

Fourteen Cases of Disease

Case I. Philiscus, who lived by the Wall, took to bed on the first day of acute fever; he sweated; towards night was uneasy. On the second day all the symptoms were exacerbated; late in the evening had a proper stool from a small clyster; the night quiet. On the third day, early in the morning and until noon, he appeared to be free from fever; towards evening, acute fever, with sweating, thirst, tongue parched; passed black urine; night uncomfortable, no sleep; he was delirious on all subjects. On the fourth, all the symptoms exacerbated, urine black; night more comfortable, urine of a better color. On the fifth, about mid-day, had a slight trickling of pure blood from the nose; urine varied in character, having floating in it round bodies, resembling semen, and scattered, but which did not fall to the bottom; a suppository having been applied, some scanty flatulent matters were passed; night uncomfortable, little sleep, talking incoherently; extremities altogether cold, and could not be warmed; urine black; slept a little towards day; loss of speech, cold sweats; extremities livid; about the middle of the sixth day he died. The respiration throughout, like that of a person recollecting himself, was rare, and large, and spleen was swelled upon in a round tumor, the sweats cold throughout, the paroxysms on the even days.

Case II. Silenus lived on the Broad-way, near the house of Evalcidas. From fatigue, drinking, and unseasonable exercises, he was seized with fever. He began with having pain in the loins; he had heaviness of the head, and there was stiffness of the neck. On the first day the alvine discharges were bilious, unmixed, frothy, high colored, and copious; urine black, having a black sediment; he was thirsty, tongue dry; no sleep at night. On the second, acute fever, stools more copious, thinner, frothy; urine black, an uncomfortable night, slight delirium. On the third, all the symptoms exacerbated; an oblong distention, of a softish nature, from both sides of the hypochondrium to the navel; stools thin, and darkish; urine muddy, and darkish; no sleep at night; much talking, laughter, singing, he could not restrain himself. On the fourth, in the same state. On the fifth, stools bilious, unmixed, smooth, greasy; urine thin, and transparent; slight absence of delirium. On the sixth, slight perspiration about the head; extremities cold and livid; much tossing about; no passage from the bowels, urine suppressed, acute fever. On the seventh, loss of speech; extremities could no longer be kept warm; no discharge of urine. On the eighth, a cold sweat all over; red rashes with sweat, of a round figure, small, like *vari,* persistent, not subsiding; by means of a slight stimulus, a copious discharge from the bowels, of a thin and undigested character, with pain; urine acrid, and passed with pain; extremities slightly heated; sleep slight, and comatose; speechless; urine thin, and transparent. On the ninth, in the same state. On the tenth, no drink taken; comatose, sleep slight; alvine discharges the same; urine abundant, and thickish; when allowed to stand, the sediment farinaceous and white; extremities again cold. On the eleventh, he died. At the commencement, and throughout, the respiration was slow and large; there was a constant throbbing in the hypochondrium; his age was about twenty.

CASE III. Herophon was seized with an acute fever; alvine discharges at first were scanty, and attended with tenesmus; but afterwards they were passed of a thin, bilious character, and frequent; there was no sleep; urine black, and thin. On the fifth, in the morning, deafness; all the symptoms exacerbated; spleen swollen; distention of the hypochondrium; alvine discharges scanty, and black; he became delirious. On the sixth, delirious; at night, sweating, coldness; the delirium continued. On the seventh, he became cold, thirsty, was disordered in mind; at night recovered his senses; slept. On the eighth, was feverish; the spleen diminished in size; quite collected; had pain at first about the groin, on the same side as the spleen; had pains in both legs; night comfortable; urine better colored, had a scanty sediment. On the ninth, sweated; the crisis took place; fever remitted. On the fifth day afterwards, fever relapsed, spleen immediately became swollen; acute fever; deafness again. On the third day after the relapse, the spleen diminished; deafness less; legs painful; sweated during the night; crisis took place on the seventeenth day; had no disorder of the senses during the relapse.

CASE IV. In Thasus, the wife of Philinus, having been delivered of a daughter, the lochial discharge being natural, and other matters going on mildly, on the fourteenth day after delivery was seized with fever, attended with rigor; was pained at first in the cardiac region of the stomach and right hypochondrium; pain in the genital organs; lochial discharge ceased. Upon the application of a pessary all these symptoms were alleviated; pains of the head, neck, and loins remained; no sleep; extremities cold; thirst; bowels in a hot state; stools scanty; urine thin, and colorless at first. On the sixth, towards night, senses much disordered, but again were restored. On the seventh, thirsty; the evacuations bilious, and high colored. On the eighth, had a rigor; acute fever; much spasm, with pain; talked much, incoherently; upon the application of a suppository, rose to stool, and passed copious dejections, with a bilious flux; no sleep. On the ninth, spasms. On the tenth, slightly recollected. On the eleventh, slept; had perfect recollection, but again immediately wandered;

passed a large quantity of urine with spasms, (the attendants seldom putting her in mind), it was thick, white, like urine which has been shaken after it has stood for a considerable time until it has subsided, but it had no sediment; in color and consistence, the urine resembled that of cattle, as far as I observed. About the fourteenth day, startings over the whole body; talked much; slightly collected, but presently became again delirious. About the seventeenth day became speechless, on the twentieth died.

CASE V. The wife of Epicrates, who was lodged at the house of Archigetes, being near the term of delivery, was seized with a violent rigor, and, as was said, she did not become heated; next day the same. On the third, she was delivered of a daughter, and everything went on properly. On the day following her delivery, she was seized with acute fever, pain in the cardiac region of the stomach, and in the genital parts. Having had a suppository, was in so far relieved; pain in the head, neck, and loins; no sleep; alvine discharges scanty, bilious, thin, and unmixed; urine thin, and blackish. Towards the night of the sixth day from the time she was seized with the fever, became delirious. On the seventh, all the symptoms exacerbated; insomnolency, delirium, thirst; stools bilious, and high colored. On the eighth, had a rigor; slept more. On the ninth, the same. On the tenth, her limbs painfully affected; pain again of the cardiac region of the stomach; heaviness of the head; no delirium; slept more; bowels constipated. On the eleventh, passed urine of a better color, and having an abundant sediment; felt lighter. On the fourteenth had a rigor; acute fever. On the fifteenth, had a copious vomiting of bilious and yellow matters; sweated; fever gone; at night acute fever; urine thick, sediment white. On the seventeenth, an exacerbation; night uncomfortable; no sleep; delirium. On the eighteenth, thirsty; tongue parched; no sleep; much delirium; legs painfully affected. About the twentieth, in the morning, had a slight rigor; was comatose; slept tranquilly; had slight vomiting of bilious and black matters; towards night deafness. About the twenty-first, weight generally in the left side, with pain; slight cough; urine thick, muddy, and reddish; when allowed to stand, had no sediment; in other respects felt lighter; fever not gone; fauces painful from the commencement, and red; uvula retracted; defluxion remained acrid, pungent, and saltish throughout. About the twenty-seventh, free of fever; sediment in the urine; pain in the side. About the thirty-first, was attacked with fever, bilious diarrhea; slight bilious vomiting on the fortieth. Had a complete crisis, and was freed from the fever on the eightieth day.

CASE VI. Cleonactides, who was lodged above the Temple of Hercules, was seized with a fever in an irregular form; was pained in the head and left side from the commencement, and had other pains resembling those produced by fatigue; paroxysms of the fevers inconstant and irregular; occasional sweats; the paroxysms generally attacked on the critical days. About the twenty-fourth was cold in the extremities of the hands, vomitings bilious, yellow, and frequent, soon turning to a verdigris-green color; general relief. About the thirtieth, began to have hemorrhage from both nostrils, and this continued in an irregular manner until near the crisis; did not loathe food, and had no thirst throughout, nor was troubled with insomnolency; urine thin, and not devoid of color. When about the thirtieth day, passed reddish urine, having a copious red sediment; was relieved, but afterwards the characters of the urine varied, sometimes having sediment, and sometimes not. On the sixtieth, the sediment in the urine copious, white, and smooth; all the symptoms ameliorated; intermission of the fever; urine thin, and well colored. On the seventieth, fever gone for ten days. On the eightieth had a rigor, was seized with acute fever, sweated much; a red, smooth sediment in the urine; and a perfect crisis.

CASE VII. Meton was seized with fever; there was a painful weight in the loins. Next day, after drinking water pretty copiously, had proper evacuations from the bowels. On the third, heaviness of the head, stools thin, bilious, and reddish. On the fourth, all the symptoms exacerbated; had twice a scanty trickling of blood from the right nostril; passed an uncomfortable night; alvine discharges like those on the third day; urine darkish, had a darkish cloud floating in it, of a scattered form, which did not subside. On the fifth, a copious hemorrhage of pure blood from the left nostril; he sweated, and had a crisis. After the fever restless, and had some delirium; urine thin, and darkish; had an affusion of warm water on the head; slept and recovered his senses. In this case there was no relapse, but there were frequent hemorrhages after the crisis.

CASE VIII. Erasinus, who lived near the Canal of Bootes, was seized with fever after supper; passed the night in an agitated state. During the first day quiet, but in pain at night. On the second, symptoms all exacerbated; at night delirious. On the third, was in a painful condition; great incoherence. On the fourth, in a most uncomfortable state; had no sound sleep at night, but dreaming and talking; then all the appearances worse, of a formidable and alarming character; fear, impatience. On the morning of the fifth, was composed, and quite coherent, but long before noon was furiously mad, so that he could not constrain himself; extremities cold, and somewhat livid; urine without sediment; died about sunset. The fever in this case was accompanied by sweats throughout; the hypochondria were in a state of meteorism, with distention and pain; the urine was black, had round substances floating in it, which did not subside; the alvine evacuations were not stopped; thirst throughout not great; much spasms with sweats about the time of death.

CASE IX. Criton, in Thasus, while still on foot, and going about, was seized with a violent pain in the great toe; he took to bed the same day, had rigors and nausea, recovered his heat slightly, at night was delirious. On the second, swelling of the whole foot, and about the ankle erythema, with distention, and small bullæ (phlyctænæ); acute fever; he became furiously deranged; alvine discharges bilious, unmixed, and rather frequent. He died on the second day from the commencement.

CASE X. The Clazomenian who was lodged by the Well of Phrynichides was seized with fever. He had pain in the head, neck, and loins from the beginning, and immediately afterwards deafness; no sleep, acute fever, hypochondria elevated with a swelling, but not much distention; tongue dry. On the fourth, towards night, he became delirious. On the fifth, in an uneasy state. On the sixth, all the symptoms exacerbated. About the eleventh a slight remission; from the commencement to the fourteenth day the alvine discharges thin, copious, and of the color of water, but were well supported; the bowels then became constipated. Urine throughout thin, and well colored, and had many substances scattered through it, but no sediment. About the sixteenth, urine somewhat thicker, which had a slight sediment; somewhat better, and more collected. On the seventeenth, urine again thin; swellings about both his ears, with pain; no sleep, some incoherence; legs painfully affected. On the twentieth, free of fever, had a crisis, no sweat, perfectly collected. About the twenty-seventh, violent pain of the right hip; it speedily went off. The swellings about the ears subsided, and did not suppurate, but were painful. About the thirty-first, a diarrhœa, attended with a copious discharge of watery matter, and symptoms of dysentery; passed thick urine; swellings about the ears gone. About the fortieth day, had pain in the right eye, sight dull. It went away.

CASE XI. The wife of Dromeades having been delivered of a female child, and all other matters going on properly, on the second day after was seized with rigor and acute fever. Began to have pain about the hypochondrium on the first day; had nausea and incoherence, and for some hours afterwards had no sleep; respiration rare, large, and suddenly interrupted. On the day following that on which she had the rigor, alvine discharges proper; urine thick, white, muddy, like urine which has been shaken after standing for some time, until the sediment had fallen to the bottom; it had no sediment; she did not sleep during the night. On the third day, about noon, had a rigor, acute fever; urine the same; pain of the hypochondria, nausea, an uncomfortable night, no sleep; a coldish sweat all over, but heat quickly restored. On the fourth, slight alleviation of the symptoms about the hypochondria; heaviness of the head, with pain; somewhat comatose; slight epistaxis, tongue dry, thirst, urine thin and oily; slept a little, upon awaking was somewhat comatose; slight coldness, slept during the night, was delirious. On the morning of the sixth had a rigor, but soon recovered her heat, sweated all over; extremities cold, was delirious, respiration rare and large. Shortly afterwards spasms from the head began, and she immediately expired.

CASE XII. A man, in a heated state, took supper, and drank more than enough; he vomited the whole during the night; acute fever, pain of the right hypochondrium, a softish inflammation from the inner part; passed an uncomfortable night; urine at the commencement thick, red, but when allowed to stand, had no sediment, tongue dry, and not very thirsty. On the fourth, acute fever, pains all over. On the fifth, urine smooth, oily, and copious; acute fever. On the sixth, in the evening, very incoherent, no sleep during the night. On the seventh, all the symptoms exacerbated; urine of the same characters; much talking, and he could not contain himself; the bowels being stimulated, passed a watery discharge with lumbrici: night equally painful. In the morning had a rigor; acute fever, hot sweat, appeared to be free of fever; did not sleep long; after the sleep a chill, ptyalism; in the evening, great incoherence; after a little, vomited a small quantity of dark bilious matters. On the ninth, coldness, much delirium, did not sleep. On the tenth, pains in the limbs, all the symptoms exacerbated; he was delirious. On the eleventh, he died.

CASE XIII. A woman, who lodged on the Quay, being three months gone with child, was seized with fever, and immediately began to have pains in the loins. On the third day, pain of the head and neck, extending to the clavicle, and right hand; she immediately lost the power of speech; was paralyzed in the right hand, with spasms, after the manner of paraplegia; was quite incoherent; passed an uncomfortable night; did not sleep; disorder of the bowels, attended with bilious, unmixed, and scanty stools. On the fourth, recovered the use of her tongue; spasms of the same parts, and general pains remained; swelling in the hypochondrium, accompanied with pain; did not sleep, was quite incoherent; bowels disordered, urine thin, and not of a good color. On the fifth, acute fever; pain of the hypochondrium, quite incoherent; alvine evacuations bilious; towards night had a sweat, and was freed from the fever. On the sixth, recovered her reason; was every way relieved; the pain remained about the left clavicle; was thirsty, urine thin, had no sleep. On the seventh trembling, slight coma, some incoherence, pains about the clavicle and left arm remained; in all other respects was alleviated; quite coherent. For three days remained free from fever. On the eleventh, had a relapse, with rigor and fever. About the fourteenth day, vomited pretty abundantly bilious and yellow matters, had a sweat, the fever went off, by coming to a crisis.

CASE XIV. Melidia, who lodged near the Temple of Juno, began to feel a violent pain of the head, neck, and chest. She was straightway seized with acute fever; a slight appearance of the menses; continued pains of all these parts. On the sixth, was affected with coma, nausea, and rigor; redness about the cheeks; slight delirium. On the seventh, had a sweat; the fever intermitted, the pains remained. A relapse; little sleep; urine throughout of a good color, but thin; the alvine evacuations were thin, bilious, acrid, very scanty, black, and fetid; a white, smooth sediment in the urine; had a sweat, and experienced a perfect crisis on the eleventh day.

BOOK III. SECT. I

CASE I. Pythion, who lived by the Temple of the Earth, on the first day, trembling commencing from his hands; acute fever, delirium. On the second, all the symptoms were exacerbated. On the third, the same. On the fourth alvine discharges scanty, unmixed, and bilious. On the fifth, all the symptoms were exacerbated, the tremors remained; little sleep, the bowels constipated. On the sixth sputa mixed, reddish. On the seventh, mouth drawn aside. On the eighth, all the symptoms were exacerbated; the tremblings were again constant; urine, from the beginning to the eighth day, thin, and devoid of color; substances floating in it, cloudy. On the tenth he sweated; sputa somewhat digested, had a crisis; urine thinnish about the crisis; but after the crisis, on the fortieth day, an abscess about the anus, which passed off by a strangury.

Explanation of the characters. It is probably that the great discharge of urine brought about the resolution of the disease, and the cure of the patient on the fortieth day.

Case II. Hermocrates, who lived by the New Wall, was seized with fever. He began to have pain in the head and loins; an empty distention of the hypochondrium; the tongue at first was parched; deafness at the commencement; there was no sleep; not very thirsty; urine thick and red, when allowed to stand it did not subside; alvine discharge very dry, and not scanty. On the fifth, urine thin, had substances floating in it which did not fall to the bottom; at night he was delirious. On the sixth, had jaundice; all the symptoms were exacerbated; had no recollection. On the seventh, in an uncomfortable state; urine thin, as formerly; on the following days the same. About the eleventh day, all the symptoms appeared to be lightened. Coma set in; urine thicker, reddish, thin substances below, had no sediment; by degrees he became collected. On the fourteenth, fever gone; had no sweat; slept, quite collected; urine of the same characters. About the seventeenth, had a relapse, became hot. On the following days, acute fever, urine thin, was delirious. Again, on the twentieth, had a crisis; free of fever; had no sweat; no appetite through the whole time; was perfectly collected; could not speak, tongue dry, without thirst; deep sleep. About the twenty-fourth day he became heated; bowels loose, with a thin, watery discharge; on the following days acute fever, tongue parched. On the twenty-seventh he died. In this patient deafness continued throughout; the urine either thick and red, without sediment, or thin, devoid of color, and, having substances floating in it: he could taste nothing.

Explanation of the characters. It is probably that it was the suppression of the discharges from the bowels which occasioned death on the twenty-seventh day.

Case III. The man who was lodged in the Garden of Dealces: had heaviness of the head and pain in the right temple for a considerable time, from some accidental cause, was seized with fever, and took to bed. On the second, there was a trickling of pure blood from the left nostril, but the alvine discharges were proper, urine thin, mixed, having small substances floating in it, like coarse barley meal, or semen. On the third, acute fever; stools black, thin, frothy, a livid sediment in the dejections; slight coma; uneasiness at the times he had to get up; sediment in the urine livid, and somewhat viscid. On the fourth, slight vomiting of bilious, yellow matters, and, after a short interval, of the color of verdigris; a few drops of pure blood ran from the left nostril; stools the same; urine the same; sweated about the head and clavicles; spleen enlarged, pain of the thigh on the same side; loose swelling of the right hypochondrium; at night had no sleep, slight delirium. On the sixth, stools black, fatty, viscid, fetid; slept, more collected. On the seventh, tongue dry, thirsty, did not sleep; was somewhat delirious; urine thin, not of a good color. On the eighth, stools black, scanty, and compact; slept, became collected; not very thirsty. On the ninth had a rigor, acute fever, sweated, a chill, was delirious, strabismus of the right eye, tongue dry, thirsty, without sleep. On the tenth, much the same. On the eleventh, became quite collected; free from fever, slept, urine thin about the crisis. The two following days without fever; it returned on the fourteenth, then immediately insomnolency and complete delirium. On the fifteenth, urine muddy, like that which has been shaken after the sediment has fallen to the bottom; acute fever, quite delirious, did not sleep; knees and legs painful; after a suppository, had alvine dejections of a black color. On the sixteenth, urine thin, had a cloudy eneorema, was delirious. On the seventeenth, in the morning, extremities cold, was covered up with the bedclothes, acute fever, general sweat, felt relieved, more collected; not free of fever, thirsty, vomited yellow bile, in small quantities; formed fæces passed from the bowels, but soon afterwards black, scanty, and thin; urine thin, not well colored. On the eighteenth, not collected, comatose. On the nineteenth, in the same state. On the twentieth, slept; quite collected, sweated, free from fever, not thirsty, but the urine thin. On the twenty-first, slight delirium; somewhat thirsty, pain of the hypochondrium, and throbbing about the navel throughout. On the twenty-fourth, sediment in the urine, quite collected. Twenty-seventh, pain of the right hip joint;

urine thin and bad, a sediment; all the other symptoms milder. About the twenty-ninth, pain of the right eye; urine thin. Fortieth, dejections pituitous, white, rather frequent; sweated abundantly all over; had a complete crisis.

Explanation of the characters. It is probable that, by means of the stools, the urine, and the sweat, this patient was cured in forty days.

Sect. II

Case I. In Thasus, Philistes had headache of long continuance, and sometimes was confined to bed, with a tendency to deep sleep; having been seized with continual fevers from drinking, the pain was exacerbated; during the night he, at first, became hot. On the first day, he vomited some bilious matters, at first yellow, but afterwards of a verdigris-green color, and in greater quantity; formed fæces passed from the bowels; passed the night uncomfortably. On the second, deafness, acute fever; retraction of the right hypochondrium; urine thin, transparent, had some small substances like semen floating in it; delirium ferox about mid-day. On the third, in an uncomfortable state. On the fourth, convulsions; all the symptoms exacerbated. On the fifth, early in the morning, died.

Explanation of the characters. It is probable that the death of the patient on the fifth day is to be attributed to a phrenitis, with unfavorable evacuations.

Case II. Charion, who was lodged at the house of Demænetus, contracted a fever from drinking. Immediately he had a painful heaviness of the head; did not sleep; bowels disordered, with thin and somewhat bilious discharges. On the third day, acute fever; trembling of the head, but especially of the lower lip; after a little time a rigor, convulsions; he was quite delirious; passed the night uncomfortably. On the fourth, quiet, slept little, talked incoherently. On the fifth, in pain; all the symptoms exacerbated; delirium; passed the night uncomfortably; did not sleep. On the sixth, in the same state. On the seventh had a rigor, acute fever, sweated all over his body; had a crisis. Throughout the alvine discharges were bilious, scanty, and unmixed; urine thin, well colored, having cloudy substances floating in it. About the eighth day, passed urine of a better color, having a white scanty sediment; was collected, free from fever for a season. On the ninth it relapsed. About the fourteenth, acute fever. On the sixteenth, vomited pretty frequently yellow, bilious matters. On the seventeenth had a rigor, acute fever, sweat-

ed, free of fever; had a crisis; urine, after the relapse and the crisis, well colored, having a sediment; neither was he delirious in the relapse. On the eighteenth, became a little heated; some thirst, urine thin, with cloudy substances floating in it; slight wandering in his mind. About the nineteenth, free of fever, had a pain in his neck; a sediment in the urine. Had a complete crisis on the twentieth.

Explanation of the characters. It is probable that the patient was cured in twenty days, by the abundance of bilious stools and urine.

Case III. The daughter of Euryanax, a maid, was taken ill of fever. She was free of thirst throughout, but had no relish for food. Alvine discharges small, urine thin, scanty, not well colored. In the beginning of the fever, had a pain about the nates. On the sixth day, was free of fever, did not sweat, had a crisis; the complaint about the nates came to a small suppuration, and burst at the crisis. After the crisis, on the seventh day, had a rigor, became slightly heated, sweated. On the eighth day after the rigor, had an inconsiderable rigor; the extremities cold ever after. About the tenth day, after a sweat which came on, she became delirious, and again immediately afterwards was collected; these symptoms were said to have been brought on by eating grapes. After an intermission of the twelfth day, she again talked much incoherently; her bowels disordered with bilious, scanty, unmixed, thin, acrid discharges; she required to get frequently up. She died on the seventh day after the return of the delirium. At the commencement of the disease she had pain in the throat, and it was red throughout, uvula retracted, defluxions abundant, thin, acrid; coughed, but had no concocted sputa; during the whole time loathed all kinds of food, nor had the least desire of anything; had no thirst, nor drank anything worth mentioning; was silent, and never spoke a word; despondency; had no hopes of herself. She had a congenital tendency to phthisis.

Case IV. The woman affected with quinsy, who lodged in the house of Aristion: her complaint began in the tongue; speech inarticulate; tongue red and parched. On the first day, felt chilly, and afterwards became heated. On the third day, a rigor, acute fever; a reddish and hard swelling on both sides of the neck and chest, extremities cold and livid; respiration elevated; the drink returned by the nose; she could not swallow; alvine and urinary discharges suppressed. On the fourth, all of the symptoms were exacerbated. On the fifth she died of the quinsy.

Explanation of the characters. It is probable that the cause of death on the sixth day was the suppression of the discharges.

Case V. The young man who was lodged by the Liars' Market was seized with fever from fatigue, labor, and running out of season. On the first day, the bowels disordered, with bilious, thin, and copious dejections; urine thin and blackish; had no sleep; was thirsty. On the second all the symptoms were exacerbated; dejections more copious and unseasonable; he had no sleep; disorder of the intellect; slight sweat. On the third day, restless, thirst, nausea, much tossing about, bewilderment, delirium; extremities livid and cold; softish distention of the hypochondrium on both sides. On the fourth, did not sleep; still worse. On the seventh he died. He was about twenty years of age.

Explanation of the characters. It is probable that the cause of his death on the seventh day was the unseasonable practices mentioned above. An acute affection.

Case VI. The woman who lodged at the house of Tisamenas had a troublesome attack of iliac passion, much vomiting; could not keep her drink; pains about the hypochondria, and pains also in the lower part of the belly; constant tormina; not thirsty; became hot; extremities cold throughout, with nausea and insomnolency; urine scanty and thin; dejections undigested, thin, scanty. Nothing could do her any good. She died.

Case VII. A woman of those who lodged with Pantimides, from a miscarriage, was taken ill of fever. On the first day, tongue dry, thirst, nausea, insomnolency, belly disordered, with thin, copious, undigested dejections. On the second day, had a rigor, acute fever; alvine discharges copious; had no sleep. On the third, pains greater. On the fourth, delirious. On the seventh she died. Belly throughout loose, with copious, thin, undigested evacuations; urine scanty, thin. An ardent fever.

Case VIII. Another woman, after a miscarriage about the fifth month, the wife of Ocetes, was seized with fever. At first had sometimes coma and sometimes insomnolency; pain of the loins; heaviness of the head. On the second, the bowels were disordered, with scanty, thin, and at first unmixed dejections. On the third, more copious, and worse; at night did not sleep. On the fourth was delirious; frights, despondency; strabismus of the right eye; a faint cold sweat about the head; extremities cold. On the fifth day, all the symptoms were exacerbated; talked much incoherently, and again immediately became collected; had no thirst; labored under insomnolency; alvine dejections copious, and unseasonable throughout; urine scanty, thin, darkish; extremities cold, somewhat livid. On the sixth day, in the same state. On the seventh she died. Phrenitis.

Case IX. A woman who lodged near the Liars' Market, having then brought forth a son in a first and difficult labor, was seized with fever. Immediately on the commencement had thirst, nausea, and cardialgia; tongue dry; bowels disordered, with thin and scanty dejections; had no sleep. On the second, had slight rigor, acute fever; a faint cold sweat about the head. On the third, painfully affected; evacuations from the bowels undigested, thin, and copious. On the fourth, had a rigor; all the symptoms exacerbated; insomnolency. On the fifth, in a painful state. On the sixth, in the same state; discharges from the bowels liquid and copious. On the seventh, had a rigor, fever acute; much thirst; much tossing about; towards evening a cold sweat over all; extremities cold, could no longer be kept warm; and again at night had a rigor; extremities could not be warmed; she did not sleep; was slightly delirious, and again speedily collected. On the eighth, about mid-day, she became warm, was thirsty, comatose, had nausea; vomited small quantities of yellowish bile; restless at night, did not sleep; passed frequently large quantities of urine without consciousness. On the ninth, all the symptoms gave way; comatose, towards evening slight rigors; small vomitings of bile. On the tenth, rigor; exacerbation of the fever, did not sleep at all; in the morning passed much urine having a sediment; extremities recovered their heat. On the eleventh, vomited bile of a verdigris-green color; not long after had a rigor, and again the extremities cold; towards evening a rigor, a cold sweat, much vomiting; passed a painful night. On the twelfth, had copious black and fetid vomitings; much hiccup, painful thirst. On the thirteenth, vomitings black, fetid, and copious; rigor about mid-day, loss of speech. On the fourteenth, some blood ran from her nose, she died. In this case the bowels were loose throughout; with rigors: her age about seventeen. An ardent fever.

Sect. III

1. The year was southerly, rainy; no winds throughout. Droughts having prevailed during the previous seasons of the year, the south winds towards the rising of Arcturus were attended with much rain. Autumn gloomy and cloudy, with copious rains. Winter southerly, damp,

and soft. But long after the solstice, and near the equinox, much wintery weather out of season; and when now close to the equinox, northerly, and winterly weather for no long time. The spring again southerly, calm, much rain until the dog-days. Summer fine and hot; great suffocating heats. The Etesian winds blew small and irregular; again, about the season of Arcturus, much rains with north winds.

2. The year being southerly, damp, and soft towards winter, all were healthy, except those affected with phthisis, of whom we shall write afterwards.

3. Early in spring, along with the prevailing cold, there were many cases of erysipelas, some from a manifest cause, and some not. They were of a malignant nature, and proved fatal to many; many had sore-throat and loss of speech. There were many cases of ardent fever, phrensy, aphthous affections of the mouth, tumors on the genital organs; of ophthalmia, anthrax, disorder of the bowels, anorexia, with thirst and without it; of disordered urine, large in quantity, and bad in quality; of persons affected with coma for a long time, and then falling into a state of insomnolency. There were many cases of failure of crisis, and many of unfavorable crisis; many of dropsy and of phthisis. Such were the diseases then epidemic. There were patients affected with every one of the species which have been mentioned, and many died. The symptoms in each of these cases were as follows:

4. In many cases erysipelas, from some obvious cause, such as an accident, and sometimes from even a very small wound, broke out all over the body, especially, in persons about sixty years of age, about the head, if such an accident was neglected in the slightest degree; and this happened in some who were under treatment; great inflammation took place, and the erysipelas quickly spread all over. In the most of them the abscesses ended in suppurations, and there were great fallings off (sloughing) of the flesh, tendons, and bones; and the defluxion which seated in the part was not like pus, but a sort of putrefaction, and the running was large and of various characters. Those cases in which any of these things happened about the head were accompanied with falling off of the hairs of the head and chin, the bones were laid bare and separated, and there were excessive runnings; and these symptoms happened in fevers and without fevers. But these things were more formidable in appearance than dangerous; for when the concoction in these cases turned to a suppuration, most of them recovered; but when

the inflammation and erysipelas disappeared, and when no abscess was formed, a great number of these died. In like manner, the same things happened to whatever part of the body the disease wandered, for in many cases both forearm and arm dropped off; and in those cases in which it fell upon the sides, the parts there, either before or behind, got into a bad state; and in some cases the whole femur and bones of the leg and whole foot were laid bare. But of all such cases, the most formidable were those which took place about the pubes and genital organs.[1] Such was the nature of these cases when attended with sores, and proceeding from an external cause; but the same things occurred in fevers, before fevers, and after fevers. But those cases in which an abscess was formed, and turned to a suppuration, or a seasonable diarrhea or discharge of good urine took place, were relieved thereby: but those cases in which none of these symptoms occurred, but they disappeared without a crisis, proved fatal. The greater number of these erysipelatous cases took place in the spring, but were prolonged through the summer and during autumn.

5. In certain cases there was much disorder, and tumors about the fauces, and inflammations of the tongue, and abscesses about the teeth. And many were attacked with impairment or loss of speech; at first, those in the commencement of phthisis, but also persons in ardent fever and in phrenitis.

6. The cases of ardent fever and phrenitis occurred early in spring after the cold set in, and great numbers were taken ill at that time, and these cases were attended with acute and fatal symptoms. The constitution of the ardent fevers which then occurred was as follows: at the commencement they were affected with coma, nausea, and rigors; fever not acute, not much thirst, nor delirium, slight epistaxis, the paroxysms for the most part on even days; and, about the time of the paroxysms, forgetfulness, loss of strength and of speech, the extremities, that is to say, the hands and feet, at all times, but more especially about the time of the paroxysms, were colder than natural; they slowly and imperfectly became warmed, and again recovered their recollection and speech. They were constantly affected either with coma, in which they got no sleep, or with insomnolency, attended with pains; most had disorders of the bowels, attended with undigested, thin, and copious evacuations; urine copious, thin, having noth-

[1] Compare Thucydides' description of the plague of Athens.

ing critical nor favorable about it; neither was there any other critical appearance in persons affected thus; for neither was there any proper hemorrhage, nor any other of the accustomed evacuations, to prove a crisis. They died, as it happened, in an irregular manner, mostly about the crisis, but in some instances after having lost their speech for a long time, and having had copious sweats. These were the symptoms which marked the fatal cases of ardent fever; similar symptoms occurred in the phrenitic cases; but these were particularly free from thirst, and none of these had wild delirium as in other cases, but they died oppressed by a bad tendency to sleep, and stupor.

7. But there were also other fevers, as will be described. Many had their mouths affected with aphthous ulcerations. There were also many defluxions about the genital parts, and ulcerations, boils (phymata), externally and internally, about the groins. Watery ophthalmies of a chronic character, with pains; fungous excrescences of the eyelids, externally and internally, called fici, which destroyed the sight of many persons. There were fungous growths, in many other instances, on ulcers, especially on those seated on the genital organs. There were many attacks of carbuncle (anthrax) through the summer, and other affections, which are called "the putrefaction" (*seps*); also large ecthymata, and large tetters (*herpetes*) in many instances.

8. And many and serious complaints attacked many persons in the region of the belly. In the first place, tenesmus, accompanied with pain, attacked many, but more especially children, and all who had not attained to puberty; and the most of these died. There were many cases of lientery and of dysentery; but these were not attended with much pain. The evacuations were bilious, and fatty, and thin, and watery; in many instances the disease terminated in this way, with and without fever; there were painful tormina and volvuli of a malignant kind; copious evacuations of the contents of the guts, and yet much remained behind; and the passages did not carry off the pains, but yielded with difficulty to the means administered; for in most cases purgings were hurtful to those affected in this manner; many died speedily, but in many others they held out longer. In a word, all died, both those who had acute attacks and those who had chronic, most especially from affections of the belly, for it was the belly which carried them all off.

9. All persons had an aversion to food in all the afore-mentioned complaints to a degree such as I never met with before, and persons in these complaints most especially, and those recovering from them, and in all other diseases of a mortal nature. Some were troubled with thirst, and some not; and both in febrile complaints and in others no one drank unseasonably or disobeyed injunctions.

10. The urine in many cases was not in proportion to the drink administered, but greatly in excess; and the badness of the urine voided was great, for it had not the proper thickness, nor concoction, nor purged properly; for in many cases purgings by the bladder indicate favorably, but in the greatest number they indicated a melting of the body, disorder of the bowels, pains, and a want of crisis.

11. Persons laboring under phrenitis and causus were particularly disposed to coma; but also in all other great diseases which occurred along with fever. In the main, most cases were attended either by heavy coma, or by short and light sleep.

12. And many other forms of fevers were then epidemic, of tertian, of quartan, of nocturnal, of continual, of chronic, of erratic, of fevers attended with nausea, and of irregular fevers. All these were attended with much disorder, for the bowels in most cases were disordered, accompanied with rigors, sweats not of a critical character, and with the state of the urine as described. In most instances the disease was protracted, for neither did the deposits which took place prove critical as in other cases; for in all complaints and in all cases there was difficulty of crisis, want of crisis, and protraction of the disease, but most especially in these. A few had the crisis about the eightieth day, but in most instances it (the disease?) left them irregularly. A few of them died of dropsy without being confined to bed. And in many other diseases people were troubled with swelling, but more especially in phthisical cases.

13. The greatest and most dangerous disease, and the one that proved fatal to the greatest number, was the consumption. With many persons it commenced during the winter, and of these some were confined to bed, and others bore up on foot; the most of those died early in spring who were confined to bed; of the others, the cough left not a single person, but it became milder through the summer; during the autumn, all these were confined to bed, and many of them died, but in the greater number of cases the disease was long protracted. Most of these were suddenly attacked with these diseases, having frequent rigors, often continual and acute

fevers; unseasonable, copious, and cold sweats throughout; great coldness, from which they had great difficulty in being restored to heat; the bowels variously constipated, and again immediately in a loose state, but towards the termination in all cases with violent looseness of the bowels; a determination downwards of all matters collected about the lungs; urine excessive, and not good; troublesome melting. The coughs throughout were frequent, and sputa copious, digested, and liquid, but not brought up with much pain; and even when they had some slight pain, in all cases the purging of the matters about the lungs went on mildly. The fauces were not very irritable, nor were they troubled with any saltish humors; but there were viscid, white, liquid, frothy, and copious defluxions from the head. But by far the greatest mischief attending these and the other complaints, was the aversion to food, as has been described. For neither had they any relish for drink along with their food, but continued without thirst. There was heaviness of the body, disposition to coma, in most cases swelling, which ended in dropsy; they had rigors, and were delirious towards death.

14. The form of body peculiarly subject to phthisical complaints was the smooth, the whitish, that resembling the lentil; the reddish, the blue-eyed, the leucophlegmatic, and that with the scapulæ having the appearance of wings: and women in like manner, with regard to the melancholic and subsanguineous, phrenitic and dysenteric affections principally attacked them. Tenesmus troubled young persons of a phlegmatic temperament. Chronic diarrhœa, acrid and viscid discharges from the bowels, attacked those who were troubled with bitter bile.

15. To all those which have been described, the season of spring was most inimical, and proved fatal to the greatest numbers: the summer was the most favorable to them, and the fewest died then; in autumn, and under the Pleiades, again there died great numbers. It appears to me, according to the reason of things, that the coming on of summer should have done good in these cases; for winter coming on cures the diseases of summer, and summer coming on removes the diseases of winter. And yet the summer in question was not of itself well constituted, for it became suddenly hot, southerly, and calm; but, notwithstanding, it proved beneficial by producing a change on the other constitution.

16. I look upon it as being a great part of the art to be able to judge properly of that which has been written. For he that knows and makes a proper use of these things, would appear to me not likely to commit any great mistake in the art. He ought to learn accurately the constitution of every one of the seasons, and of the diseases; whatever that is common in each constitution and disease is good, and whatever is bad; whatever disease will be protracted and end in death, and whatever will be protracted and end in recovery; which disease of an acute nature will end in death, and which in recovery. From these it is easy to know the order of the critical days, and prognosticate from them accordingly. And to a person who is skilled in these things, it is easy to know to whom, when, and how aliment ought to be administered.

Sixteen Cases of Disease

CASE I. In Thasus, the Parian who lodged above the Temple of Diana was seized with an acute fever, at first of a continual and ardent type; thirsty, inclined to be comatose at first, and afterwards troubled with insomnolency; bowels disordered at the beginning, urine thin. On the sixth day, passed oily urine, was delirious. On the seventh, all the symptoms were exacerbated; had no sleep, but the urine of the same characters, and the understanding disordered; alvine dejections bilious and fatty. On the eighth, a slight epistaxis; small vomiting of verdigris-green matters; slept a little. On the ninth, in the same state. On the tenth, all the symptoms gave way. On the eleventh, he sweated, but not over the whole body; he became cold, but immediately recovered his heat again. On the fourteenth, acute fever; discharges bilious, thin, and copious; substances floating in the urine; he became incoherent. On the seventeenth, in a painful state, for he had no sleep, and the fever was more intense. On the twentieth, sweated all over; apyrexia, dejections bilious; aversion to food, comatose. On the twenty-fourth, had a relapse. On the thirty-fourth, apyrexia; bowels not confined; and he again recovered his heat. Fortieth, apyrexia, bowels confined for no long time, aversion to food; had again slight symptoms of fever, and throughout in an irregular form; apyrexia at times, and at others not; for if the fever intermitted, and was alleviated for a little, it immediately relapsed again; he used much and improper food; sleep bad; about the time of the relapse he was delirious; passed thick urine at that time, but troubled, and of bad characters; bowels at first confined, and again loose; slight fevers of a continual type; discharges copious and thin. On the hundred and twentieth day he died. In this patient the bowels were constantly from the first either loose, with bilious, liquid, and copious dejections, or constipated with hot and undigested fæces; the urine throughout bad; for the most part coma, or insomnolency with pain; continued aversion to food. Ardent fever.

Explanation of the characters. It is probable that the weakness produced by the fever, the phrenitis, and affection of the hypochondrium caused death on the hundred and twentieth day.

CASE II. In Thasus, the woman who lodged near the Cold Water, on the third day after delivery of a daughter, the lochial discharge not taking place, was seized with acute fever, accompanied with rigors. But a considerable time before delivery she was feverish, confined to bed, and loathed her food. After the rigor which took place, continual and acute fevers, with rigors. On the eighth and following days, was very incoherent, and immediately afterwards became collected; bowels disordered, with copious, thin, watery, and bilious stools; no thirst. On the eleventh was collected, but disposed to coma; urine copious, thin, and black; no sleep. On the twentieth, slight chills, and immediately afterwards was warm; slight incoherence; no sleep; with regard to the bowels, in the same condition; urine watery, and copious. On the twenty-seventh, free from fever; bowels constipated; not long afterwards violent pain of the right hip-joint for a considerable time; fevers afterwards supervened; urine watery. On the fortieth, complaints about the hip-joint better; continued coughs, with copious, watery sputa; bowels constipated; aversion to food; urine the same; fever not leaving her entirely, but having paroxysms in an irregular form, sometimes present, sometimes not. On the sixtieth, the coughs left her without a crisis, for no concoction of the sputa took place, nor any of the usual abscesses; jaw on the right side convulsively retracted; comatose, was again incoherent, and immediately became collected; utter aversion to food; the jaw became relaxed; alvine discharges small, and bilious; fever more acute, affected with rigors; on the following days lost her speech, and again became collected, and talked. On the eightieth she died. In this case the urine throughout was black, thin, and watery; coma supervened; there was aversion to food, despondency, and insomnolency; irritability, restlessness; she was of a melancholic turn of mind.

Explanation of the characters. It is probable that the suppression of the lochial discharge caused death on the eightieth day.

CASE III. In Thasus, Pythion, who was lodged above the Temple of Hercules, from labor, fatigue, and neglected diet, was seized with strong rigor and acute fever; tongue dry, thirsty, and bilious; had no sleep; urine darkish, eneorema floating on the top of the urine, did not subside. On the second day, about noon, coldness of the extremities, especially about the hands and head; loss of speech and of articulation; breathing short for a considerable time; recovered his heat; thirst; passed the night quietly; slight sweats about the head. On the third, passed the day in a composed state; in the evening, about sunset, slight chills; nausea, agitation; passed the night in a painful state; had no sleep; small stools of compact fæces passed from the bowels. On the fourth, in the morning, composed; about noon all the symptoms became exacerbated; coldness, loss of speech, and of articulation; became worse; recovered his heat after a time; passed black urine, having substances floating in it; the night quiet; slept. On the fifth, seemed to be lightened, but a painful weight about the belly; thirsty, passed the night in a painful state. On the sixth, in the morning, in a quiet state; in the evening the pains greater; had a paroxysm; in the evening the bowels properly opened by a small clyster; slept at night. On the seventh, during the day, in a state of nausea, somewhat disturbed; passed urine of the appearance of oil; at night, much agitation, was incoherent, did not sleep. On the eighth, in the morning, slept a little; but immediately coldness, loss of speech, respiration small and weak; but in the evening recovered his heat again; was delirious, but towards day was somewhat lightened; stools small, bilious, and unmixed. On the ninth, affected with coma, and with nausea when roused; not very thirsty; about sunset he became restless and incoherent; passed a bad night. On the tenth, in the morning, had become speechless; great coldness; acute fever; much perspiration; he died. His sufferings were on the even days.

Explanation of the characters. It is probable that the excessive sweats caused death on the tenth day.

CASE IV. The patient affected with phrenitis, having taken to bed on the first day, vomited largely of verdigris-green and thin matters; fever, accompanied with rigors, copious and continued sweats all over; heaviness of the head and neck, with pain; urine thin, substances floating in the urine small, scattered, did not subside; had copious dejections from the bowels; very delirious; no sleep. On the second, in the morning, loss of speech; acute fever; he sweated, fever did not leave him; palpitations over the whole body, at night, convulsions. On the third, all the symptoms exacerbated; he died.

Explanation of the characters. It is probable that the sweats and convulsions caused death.

CASE V. In Larissa, a man, who was bald, suddenly was seized with pain in the right thigh; none of the things which were administered did him any good. On the first day, fever acute, of the ardent type, not agitated, but the pains persisted. On the second, the pains in the thigh abated, but the fever increased; somewhat tossed about; did not sleep; extremities cold; passed a large quantity of urine, not of a good character. On the third, the pain of the thigh ceased; derangement of the intellect, confusion, and much tossing about. On the fourth, about noon, he died. An acute disease.

CASE VI. In Abdera, Pericles was seized with a fever of the acute, continual type, with pain; much thirst, nausea, could not retain his drink; somewhat swelled about the spleen, with heaviness of the head. On the first day, had hemorrhage from the left nostril, but still the fever became more violent; passed much muddy, white urine, which when allowed to stand did not subside. On the second day, all the symptoms were exacerbated, yet the urine was thick, and more inclined to have a sediment; the nausea less; he slept. On the third, fever was milder; abundance of urine, which was concocted, and had a copious sediment; passed a quiet night. On the fourth, had a copious and warm sweat all over about noon; was free of fever, had a crisis, no relapse. An acute affection.

CASE VII. In Abdera, the young woman who was lodged in the Sacred Walk was seized with an ardent fever. She was thirsty, and could not sleep; had menstruation for the first time. On the sixth, much nausea, flushing, was chilly, and tossed about. On the seventh, in the same state; urine thin, but of a good color; no disturbance about the bowels. On the eighth, deafness, acute fever, insomnolency, nausea, rigors, became collected; urine the same. On the ninth, in the same state, and also on the following days; thus the deafness persisted. On the fourteenth, disorder of the intellect; the fever abated. On the seventeenth, a copious hemorrhage from the nose; the deafness slightly better; and on the following days, nausea, deafness, and incoherence. On the twentieth, pain of the feet; deafness and delirium left her; a small hemorrhage from the nose; sweat, apyrexia. On the twenty-fourth, the fever returned, deafness again; pain of the feet remained; incoherence. On the twen-ty-seventh, had a copious sweat, apyrexia; the deafness left her; the pain of her feet partly remained; in other respects had a complete crisis.

Explanation of the characters. It is probable that the restoration of health on the twentieth day was the result of the evacuation of urine.

CASE VIII. In Abdera, Anaxion, who was lodged near the Thracian Gates, was seized with an acute fever; continued pain of the right side; dry cough, without expectoration during the first days, thirst, insomnolency; urine well colored, copious, and thin. On the sixth, delirious; no relief from the warm applications. On the seventh, in a painful state, for the fever increased, while the pains did not abate, and the cough was troublesome, and attended with dyspnœa. On the eighth, I opened a vein at the elbow, and much blood, of a proper character, flowed; the pains were abated, but the dry coughs continued. On the eleventh, the fever diminished; slight sweats about the head; coughs, with more liquid sputa; he was relieved. On the twentieth, sweat, apyrexia; but after the crisis he was thirsty, and the expectorations were not good. On the twenty-seventh the fever relapsed; he coughed, and brought up much concocted sputa: sediment in the urine copious and white; he became free of thirst, and the respiration was good. On the thirty-fourth, sweated all over, apyrexia, general crisis.

Explanation of the characters. It is probable that the evacuation of the sputa brought about the recovery on the thirty-fourth day.

CASE IX. In Abdera, Heropythus, while still on foot, had pain in the head, and not long afterwards he took to bed; he lived near the High Street. Was seized with acute fever of the ardent type; vomitings at first of much bilious matter; thirst; great restlessness; urine thin, black, substances sometimes floating high in it, and sometimes not; passed the night in a painful state; paroxysms of the fever diversified, and for the most part irregular. About the fourteenth day, deafness; the fever increased; urine the same. On the twentieth and following days, much delirium. On the thirtieth, copious hemorrhage from the nose, and became more collected; deafness continued, but less; the fever diminished; on the following days, frequent hemorrhages, at short intervals. About the sixtieth, the hemorrhages ceased, but violent pain of the hip-joint, and increase of fever. Not long afterwards, pains of all the inferior parts; it then became a rule, that either the fever and deafness increased, or, if these abated and were lightened, the pains of the inferior parts were increased. About the eightieth day, all the complaints gave way, without leaving any behind; for the urine was of a good color, and had a copious sediment, while the delirium became less. About the hundredth day, disorder of the bowels, with copious and bilious evacuations, and these continued for a considerable time, and again assumed the dysenteric form with pain; but relief of all the other complaints. On the whole, the fevers went off, and the deafness ceased. On the hundred and twentieth day, had a complete crisis. Ardent fever.

Explanation of the characters. It is probable that the bilious discharge brought about the recovery on the hundred and twentieth day.

Case X. In Abdera, Nicodemus was seized with fever from venery and drinking. At the commencement he was troubled with nausea and cardialgia; thirsty, tongue was parched; urine thin and dark. On the second day, the fever exacerbated; he was troubled with rigors and nausea; had no sleep; vomited yellow bile; urine the same; passed a quiet night, and slept. On the third, a general remission; amelioration; but about sunset felt again somewhat uncomfortable; passed an uneasy night. On the fourth, rigor, much fever, general pains; urine thin, with substances floating in it; again a quiet night. On the fifth, all the symptoms remained, but there was an amelioration. On the sixth, some general pains; substances floating in the urine; very incoherent. On the seventh, better. On the eighth, all the other symptoms abated. On the tenth, and following days, there were pains, but all less; in this case throughout, the paroxysms and pains were greater on the even days. On the twentieth, the urine white and thick, but when allowed to stand had no sediment; much sweat; seemed to be free from fever; but again in the evening he became hot, with the same pains, rigor, thirst, slightly incoherent. On the twenty-fourth, urine copious, white, with an abundant sediment; a copious and warm sweat all over; apyrexia; the fever came to its crisis.

Explanation of the characters. It is probable that the cure was owing to the bilious evacuations and the sweats.

Case XI. In Thasus, a woman, of a melancholic turn of mind, from some accidental cause of sorrow, while still going about, became affected with loss of sleep, aversion to food, and had thirst and nausea. She lived near the Pylates, upon the Plain. On the first, at the commencement of night, frights, much talking, despondency, slight fever; in the morning, frequent spasms, and when they ceased, she was incoherent and talked obscurely; pains frequent, great, and continued. On the second, in the same state; had no sleep; fever more acute. On the third, the spasms left her; but coma, and disposition to sleep, and again awaked, started up, and could not contain herself; much incoherence; acute fever; on that night a copious sweat all over; apyrexia, slept, quite collected; had a crisis. About the third day, the urine black, thin, substances floating in it generally round, did not fall to the bottom; about the crisis a copious menstruation.

Case XII. In Larissa, a young unmarried woman was seized with a fever of the acute and ardent type; insomnolency, thirst; tongue sooty and dry; urine of a good color, but thin. On the second, in an uneasy state, did not sleep. On the third, alvine discharges copious, watery, and greenish, and on the following days passed such with relief. On the fourth, passed a small quantity of thin urine, having substances floating towards its surface, which did not subside; was delirious towards night. On the sixth, a great hemorrhage from the nose; a chill, with a copious and hot sweat all over; apyrexia, had a crisis. In the fever, and when it had passed the crisis, the menses took place for the first time, for she was a young woman. Throughout she was oppressed with nausea, and rigors; redness of the face; pain of the eyes; heaviness of the head; she had no relapse, but the fever came to a crisis. The pains were on the even days.

Case XIII. Apollonius, in Abdera, bore up (under the fever?) for some time, without betaking himself to bed. His viscera were enlarged, and for a considerable time there was a constant pain about the liver, and then he became affected with jaundice; he was flatulent, and of a whitish complexion. Having eaten beef, and drunk unseasonably, he became a little heated at first, and betook himself to bed, and having used large quantities of milk, that of goats and sheep, and both boiled and raw, with a bad diet otherwise, great mischief was occasioned by all these things; for the fever was exacerbated, and of the food taken scarcely any portion worth mentioning was passed from the bowels; the urine was thin and scanty; no sleep; troublesome meteorism; much thirst; disposition to coma; painful swelling of the right hypochondrium; extremities altogether coldish; slight incoherence, forgetfulness of everything he said; he was beside himself. About the fourteenth day after he betook himself to bed, had a rigor, became heated, and was seized with furious delirium; loud cries, much talking, again composed, and then coma came on; afterwards the bowels disordered, with copious, bilious, unmixed, and undigested stools; urine black, scanty, and thin; much restlessness; alvine evacuations of varied characters, either black, scanty, and verdigrisgreen, or fatty, undigested, and acrid; and at times the dejections resembled milk. About the twenty-fourth, enjoyed a calm; other matters in the same state; became somewhat collected; remembered nothing that had happened since he was confined to bed; immediately afterwards became delirious; every symptom rapidly getting worse. About the thirtieth, acute fever; stools copious and thin; was delirious; extremities cold; loss of speech. On the thirty-fourth he died. In this case, as far as I saw, the bowels were disordered; urine thin and black; disposition to coma; insomnolency; extremities cold; delirious throughout. Phrenitis.

CASE XIV. In Cyzicus, a woman who had brought forth twin daughters, after a difficult labor, and in whom the lochial discharge was insufficient, at first was seized with an acute fever, attended with chills; heaviness of the head and neck, with pain; insomnolency from the commencement; she was silent, sullen, and disobedient; urine thin, and devoid of color; thirst, nausea for the most part; bowels irregularly disordered, and again constipated. On the sixth, towards night, talked much incoherently; had no sleep. About the eleventh day was seized with wild delirium, and again became collected; urine black, thin, and again deficient, and of an oily appearance; copious, thin, and disordered evacuations from the bowels. On the fourteenth, frequent convulsions; extremities cold; not in anywise collected; suppression of urine. On the sixteenth loss of speech. On the seventeenth, she died. Phrenitis.

Explanation of the characters. It is probable that death was caused, on the seventeenth day, by the affection of the brain consequent upon her accouchement.

CASE XV. In Thasus, the wife of Dealces, who was lodged upon the Plain, from sorrow was seized with an acute fever, attended with chills. From first to last she wrapped herself up in her bedclothes; still silent, she fumbled, picked, bored, and gathered hairs (from them); tears, and again laughter; no sleep; bowels irritable, but passed nothing; when directed, drank a little; urine thin and scanty; to the touch of the hand the fever was slight; coldness of the extremities. On the ninth, talked much incoherently, and again became composed and silent. On the fourteenth, breathing rare, large, at intervals; and again hurried respiration. On the sixteenth, looseness of the bowels from a stimulant clyster; afterwards she passed her drink, nor could retain anything, for she was completely insensible; skin parched and tense. On the twentieth, much talk, and again became composed; loss of speech; respiration hurried. On the twenty-first she died. Her respiration throughout was rare and large; she was totally insensible; always wrapped up in her bedclothes; either much talk, or completely silent throughout. Phrenitis.

CASE XVI. In Meliboea, a young man having become heated by drinking and much venery, was confined to bed; he was affected with rigors and nausea; insomnolency and absence of thirst. On the first day much fæces passed from the bowels along with a copious flux; and on the following days he passed many watery stools of a green color; urine thin, scanty, and deficient in color; respiration rare, large, at long intervals; softish distention of the hypochondrium, of an oblong form, on both sides; continued palpitation in the epigastric region throughout; passed urine of an oily appearance. On the tenth, he had calm delirium, for he was naturally of an orderly and quiet disposition; skin parched and tense; dejections either copious and thin, or bilious and fatty. On the fourteenth, all the symptoms were exacerbated; he became delirious, and talked much incoherently. On the twentieth, wild delirium, jactitation, passed no urine; small drinks were retained. On the twenty-fourth he died. Phrenitis.

On Injuries of the Head

MEN'S heads are by no means all like to one another, nor are the sutures of the head of all men constructed in the same form. Thus, whoever has a prominence in the anterior part of the head (by prominence is meant the round protuberant part of the bone which projects beyond the rest of it), in him the sutures of the head take the form of the Greek letter *tau*, T; for the head has the shorter line running transverse before the prominence, while the other line runs through the middle of the head, all the way to the neck. But whoever has the prominence in the back part of the head, in him the sutures are constructed in quite the opposite form to the former; for in this case the shorter line runs in front of the prominence, while the longer runs through the middle all along to the forehead. But whoever has a prominence of the head both before and behind, in him the sutures resemble the Greek letter *éta* H; for the long lines of the letter run transverse before each prominence while the short one runs through the middle and terminates in the long lines. But whoever has no prominence on either part he has the sutures of the head resembling the Greek letter χ; for the one line comes transverse to the temple while the other passes along the middle of the head. The bone at the middle of the head is double, the hardest and most compact part being the upper portion, where it is connected with the skin, and the lowest, where it is connected with the meninx (dura mater); and from the uppermost and lowermost parts the bone gradually becomes softer and less compact, till you come to the *diploe*. The diploe is the most porous, the softest, and most cavernous part. But the whole bone of the head, with the exception of a small portion of the uppermost and lowermost portions of it, is like a sponge; and the bone has in it many juicy substances, like caruncles; and if one will rub them with the fingers, some blood will issue from them. There are also in the bone certain very slender and hollow vessels full of blood. So it is with regard to hardness, softness, and porosity.

2. In respect to thickness and thinness; the thinnest and weakest part of the whole head is the part about the bregma; and the bone there has the smallest and thinnest covering of flesh upon it, and the largest proportion of brain is situated in that region of the head. And hence it happens that from similar or even smaller wounds and instruments, when a person is wounded to the same or a less degree, the bone of the head there is more contused, fractured, and depressed; and that injuries there are more deadly and more difficult to cure; and it is more difficult to save one's life in injuries there than in any other part of the head; that from having sustained a similar or even a less wound a man will die, and that, too, in a shorter space of time than from a wound in any other part of the head. For the brain about the bregma feels more quickly and strongly any mischief that may occur to the flesh or the bone; for the brain about the bregma is in largest quantity, and is covered by the thinnest bone and the least flesh. Of the other portions, the weakest is that about

the temples; for it is the conjunction of the lower jaw with the cranium, and there is motion there up and down as at a joint; and the organ of hearing is near it; and further, a hollow and important vein runs along the temple. But the whole bone of the head behind the vertex and the ear is stronger than the whole anterior part, and the bone itself has a larger and deeper covering of flesh upon it. And hence it follows, that when exposed to the same or even greater injuries from instruments of the same or greater size, the bone is less liable to be fractured and depressed than elsewhere; and that in a fatal accident the patient will live longer when the wound is in the posterior part of the head than when elsewhere; and that pus takes longer time to form and penetrate through the bone to the brain, owing to the thickness of the bone; and moreover, as there is less brain in that part of the head, more persons who are wounded in the back part of the head escape than of those who are wounded in the anterior part. And in fatal cases, a man will survive longer in winter than in summer, whatever be the part of the head in which the wound is situated.

3. As to the *hædræ* (dints *or* marks?) of sharp and light weapons, when they take place in the bone without fissure, contusion, or depression inwards (and these take place equally in the anterior and posterior part of the head), death, when it does occur, does not properly result from them. A suture appearing in a wound, when the bone is laid bare, on whatever part of the head the wound may have been inflicted, is the weakest point of the head to resist a blow or a weapon, when the weapon happens to be impinged into the suture itself; but more especially when this occurs in the bregma at the weakest part of the head, and the sutures happen to be situated near the wound, and the weapon has hit the sutures themselves.

4. The bone in the head is liable to be wounded in the following modes, and there are many varieties in each of these modes of fracture: When a wounded bone breaks, in the bone comprehending the fissure, contusion necessarily takes place where the bone is broken; for an instrument that breaks the bone occasions a contusion thereof more or less, both at the fracture and in the parts of the bone surrounding the fracture. This is the first mode. But there are all possible varieties of fissures; for some of them are fine, and so very fine that they cannot be discovered, either immediately after the injury, or during the period in which it would

be of use to the patient if this could be ascertained. And some of these fissures are thicker and wider, certain of them being very wide. And some of them extend to a greater, and some to a smaller, distance. And some are more straight, nay, completely straight; and some are more curved, and that in a remarkable degree. And some are deep, so as to extend downwards and through the whole bone; and some are less so, and do not penetrate through the whole bone.

5. But a bone may be contused, and yet remain in its natural condition without any fracture in it; this is the second mode. And there are many varieties of contusion; for they occur to a greater or less degree, and to a greater depth, so as sometimes to extend through the whole bone; or to a less depth, so as not to extend through the whole bone; and to a greater and smaller length and breadth. But it is not possible to recognize any of these varieties by the sight, so as to determine their form and extent; neither, indeed, is it visible to the eyes when any mischief of this kind takes place, and immediately after the injury, whether or not the bone has been actually bruised, as is likewise the case with certain fractures at a distance from the seat of injury.

6. And the bone being fractured, is sometimes depressed inwards from its natural level along with the fractures, otherwise there would be no depression; for the depressed portion being fractured and broken off, is pushed inwards, while the rest of the bone remains in its natural position; and in this manner a fracture is combined with the depression. This is the third mode. There are many varieties of depression, for it may comprehend a greater and a small extent of bone, and may either be to a greater depth, or less so, and more superficial.

7. When a *hedra,* or dint of a weapon, takes place in a bone, there may be a fracture combined with it; and provided there be a fracture, contusion must necessarily be joined, to a greater or less extent, in the seat of the dint and fracture, and in the bone which comprehends them. This is the fourth mode. And there may be a *hedra,* or indentation of the bone, along with contusion of the surrounding bone, but without any fracture either in the *hedra* or in the contusion inflicted by the weapon. But the indentation of a weapon takes place in a bone, and is called *hedra,* when the bone remaining in its natural state, the weapon which struck against the bone leaves its impression on the part which it struck. In each of these modes there are many

varieties, with regard to the contusion and fracture, if both these be combined with the *hedra,* or if contusion alone, as it has been already stated that there are many varieties of contusion and fracture. And the *hedra, or* dint, of itself may be longer and shorter, crooked, straight, and circular; and there are many varieties of this mode, according to the shape of the weapon; and they may be more or less deep, and narrower or broader, and extremely broad. When a part is cleft, the cleft or notch which occurs in the bone, to whatever length or breadth, is a *hedra,* if the other bones comprehending the cleft remain in their natural position, and be not driven inwards; for in this case it would be a depression, and no longer a *hedra.*

8. A bone may be injured in a different part of the head from that on which the person has received the wound, and the bone has been laid bare. This is the fifth mode. And for this misfortune, when it occurs, there is no remedy; for when this mischief takes place, there is no means of ascertaining by any examination whether or not it has occurred, or on what part of the head.

9. Of these modes of fracture, the following require trepanning: the contusion, whether the bone be laid bare or not; and the fissure, whether apparent or not. And if, when an indentation (*hedra*) by a weapon takes place in a bone it be attended with fracture and contusion, and even if contusion alone, without fracture, be combined with the indentation, it requires trepanning. A bone depressed from its natural position rarely requires trepanning; and those which are most pressed and broken require trepanning the least; neither does an indentation (*hedra*) without fracture and contusion require trepanning; nor does a notch, provided it is large and wide; for a notch and a *hedra* are the same.

10. In the first place, one must examine the wounded person, in what part of the head the wound is situated, whether in the stronger or weaker parts; and ascertain respecting the hairs about the wound, whether they have been cut off by the instrument, and have gone into the wound; and if so, one should declare that the bone runs the risk of being denuded of flesh, and of having sustained some injury from the weapon. These things one should say from a distant inspection, and before laying a hand on the man; but on a close examination one should endeavor to ascertain clearly whether the bone be denuded of flesh or not; and if the denuded bone be visible to the eyes, this will be enough; but otherwise an examination must be made with the sound. And if you find the bone denuded of the

flesh, and not safe from the wound, you must first ascertain the state of the bone, and the extent of the mischief, and of what assistance it stands in need. One should also inquire of the wounded person how and in what way he sustained the injury; and if it be not apparent whether the bone has sustained an injury or not, it will be still more necessary, provided the bone be denuded, to make inquiry how the wound occurred, and in what manner; for when contusions and fractures exist in the bone, but are not apparent, we must ascertain, in the first place from the patient's answers, whether or not the bone has sustained any such injuries, and then find out the nature of the case by word and deed, with the exception of sounding. For sounding does not discover to us whether the bone has sustained any of these injuries or not; but sounding discovers to us an indentation inflicted by a weapon, and whether a bone be depressed from its natural position, and whether the bone be strongly fractured; all which may also be ascertained visibly with the eyes.

11. And a bone sustains fractures, either so fine as to escape the sight, or such as are apparent, and contusions which are not apparent, and depression from its natural position, especially when one person is intentionally wounded by another, or when, whether intentionally or not, a blow or stroke is received from an elevated place, and if the instrument in the hand, whether used in throwing or striking, be of a powerful nature, and if a stronger person wound a weaker. Of those who are wounded in the parts about the bone, or in the bone itself, by a fall, he who falls from a very high place upon a very hard and blunt object is in most danger of sustaining a fracture and contusion of the bone, and of having it depressed from its natural position; whereas he that falls upon more level ground, and upon a softer object, is likely to suffer less injury in the bone, or it may not be injured at all. Of those instruments which, falling upon the head, wound the parts about the bone, or the bone itself, that which falls from a very high place, and the least on a level with the person struck, and which is at the same time very hard, very blunt, and very heavy, and which is the least light, sharp, and soft, such an instrument would occasion a fracture and contusion of the bone. And there is most danger that the bone may sustain these injuries, under such circumstances, when the wound is direct and perpendicular to the bone, whether struck from the hand or from a throw, or when any object falls upon the person, or when he is wounded by falling, or in whatever way the bone sustains a direct wound from this instrument. Those weapons which graze the bone obliquely are less apt to fracture, contuse, or depress the bone, even when the bone is denuded of flesh; for in some of those wounds thus inflicted the bone is not laid bare of the flesh. Those instruments more especially produce fractures in the bone, whether apparent or not, and contusions, and inward depression of the bone, which are rounded, globular, smooth on all sides, blunt, heavy, and hard; and such weapons bruise, compress, and pound the flesh; and the wounds inflicted by such instruments, whether obliquely or circularly, are round, and are more disposed to suppurate, and to have a discharge, and take longer time to become clean; for the flesh which has been bruised and pounded must necessarily suppurate and slough away. But weapons of an oblong form, being, for the most part, slender, sharp, and light, penetrate the flesh rather than bruise it, and the bone in like manner; and such an instrument may occasion a *hedra* and a cut (for a *hedra* and a cut are same thing); but weapons of this description do not produce contusions, nor fractures, nor depressions inwardly. And in addition to the appearances in the bone, which you can detect by the sight, you should make inquiry as to all these particulars (for they are symptoms of a greater or less injury), whether the wounded person was stunned, and whether darkness was diffused over his eyes, and whether he had vertigo, and fell to the ground.

12. When the bone happens to be denuded of flesh by the weapon, and when the wound occurs upon the sutures, it is difficult to distinguish the indentation (*hedra*) of a weapon which is clearly recognized in other parts of the bone, whether it exist or not, and especially if the *hedra* be seated in the sutures themselves. For the suture being rougher than the rest of the bone occasions confusion, and it is not clear which is the suture, and which the mark inflicted by the instrument, unless the latter (*hedra*) be large. Fracture also for the most part is combined with the indentation when it occurs in the sutures; and this fracture is more difficult to discern when the bone is broken, on this account, that if there be a fracture, it is situated for the most part in the suture. For the bone is liable to be broken and slackened there, owing to the natural weakness of the bone there, and to its porosity, and from the suture being readily ruptured and slackened: but the other bones which surround the suture remain unbroken,

because they are stronger than the suture. For the fracture which occurs at the suture is also a slackening of the suture, and it is not easy to detect whether the bone be broken and slackened by the indentation of a weapon occurring in the suture, or from a contusion of the bone at the sutures; but it is still more difficult to detect a fracture connected with contusion. For the sutures, having the appearance of fissures, elude the discernment and sight of the physician, as being rougher than the rest of the bone, unless the bone be strongly cut and slackened (for a cut and a *hedra* are the same thing). But it is necessary, if the wound has occurred at the sutures, and the weapon has impinged on the bone or the parts about it, to pay attention and find out what injury the bone has sustained. For a person wounded to the same, or a much smaller, extent, and by weapons of the same size and quality, and even much less, will sustain a much greater injury, provided he has received the blow at the sutures, than if it was elsewhere. And many of these require trepanning, but you must not apply the trepan to the sutures themselves, but on the adjoining bone.

13. And with regard to the cure of wounds in the head, and the mode of detecting injuries in the bone which are not apparent, the following is my opinion:—In a wound of the head, you must not apply anything liquid, not even wine, but as little as possible, nor a cataplasm, nor conduct the treatment with tents, nor apply a bandage to an ulcer on the head, unless it be situated on the forehead, in the part which is bare of hairs, or about the eyebrow and eye, for wounds occurring there require cataplasms and bandages more than upon any other part of the head. For the rest of the head surrounds the whole forehead, and the wounds wherever situated become inflamed and swelled, owing to an influx of blood from the surrounding parts. And neither must you apply cataplasms and bandages to the forehead at all times; but when the inflammation is stopped and the swelling has subsided, you must give up the cataplasms and bandages. A wound in any other part of the head must not be treated with tents, bandages, or cataplasms, unless it also requires incision. You must perform incision on wounds situated on the head and forehead, whenever the bone is denuded of flesh, and appears to have sustained some injury from the blow, but the wound has not sufficient length and breadth for the inspection of the bone, so that it may be seen whether it has received any mischief from the blow, and of what nature the injury is, and

to what extent the flesh has been contused, and whether the bone has sustained any injury, or whether it be uninjured by the blow, and has suffered no mischief; and with regard to the treatment, what the wound, and the flesh, and the injury of the bone stand in need of. Ulcers of this description stand in need of incision; and, if the bone be denuded of the flesh, and if it be hollow, and extend far obliquely, we cut up the cavity wherever the medicine cannot penetrate readily, whatever medicine it may be; and wounds which are more inclined to be circular and hollow, and for the most part others of the like shape, are cut up by making a double incision in the circle lengthways, according to the figure of the man, so as to make the wound of a long form. Incisions may be practiced with impunity on other parts of the head, with the exception of the temple and the parts above it, where there is a vein that runs across the temple, in which region an incision is not to be made. For convulsions seize on a person who has been thus treated; and if the incision be on the left temple, the convulsions seize on the right side; and if the incision be on the right side, the convulsions take place on the left side.

14. When, then, you lay open a wound in the head on account of the bones having been denuded of the flesh, as wishing to ascertain whether or not the bone has received an injury from the blow, you must make an incision proportionate to the size of the wound, and as much as shall be judged necessary. And in making the incision you must separate the flesh from the bone where it is united to the membrane (*pericranium?*) and to the bone, and then fill the whole wound with a tent, which will expand the wound very wide next day with as little pain as possible; and along with the tents apply a cataplasm, consisting of a mass (*maza*) of fine flour pounded in vinegar, or boiled so as to render it as glutinous as possible. On the next day, when you remove the tent, having examined the bone to see what injury it has sustained, if the wound in the bone be not right seen by you, nor can you discover what mischief the bone itself has sustained, but the instrument seems to have penetrated to the bone so as to have injured it, you must scrape the bone with a raspatory to a depth and length proportionate to the suture of the patient, and again in a transverse direction, for the sake of the fractures which are not seen, and of the contusions which are not discovered, as not being accompanied with depression of the bone from its natural position. For the scraping discovers the mis-

chief, if the injuries in the bone be not otherwise manifest. And if you perceive an indentation (*hedra*) left in the bone by the blow, you must scrape the dint itself and the surrounding bones, lest, as often happens, there should be a fracture and contusion, or a contusion alone, combined with the dint, and escape observation. And when you scrape the bone with the raspatory, and it appears that the wound in the bone requires the operation, you must not postpone it for three days, but do it during this period, more especially if the weather be hot, and you have had the management of the treatment from the commencement. If you suspect that the bone is broken or contused, or has sustained both these injuries, having formed your judgement from the severity of the wound, and from the information of the patient, as that the person who inflicted the wound, provided it was done by another person, was remarkably strong, and that the weapon by which he was wounded was of a dangerous description, and then that the man had been seized with vertigo, dimness of vision, and stupor, and fell to the ground,— under these circumstances, if you cannot discover whether the bone be broken, contused, or both the one and the other, nor can see the truth of the matter, you must dissolve the jet-black ointment, and fill the wound with it when this dissolved, and apply a linen rag smeared with oil, and then a cataplasm of the maza with a bandage; and on the next day, having cleaned out the wound, scrape the bone with the raspatory. And if the bone is not sound, but fractured and contused, the rest of it which is scraped will be white; but the fracture and contusion, having imbibed the preparation, will appear black, while the rest of the bone is white. And you must again scrape more deeply the fracture where it appears black; and, if you thus remove the fissure, and cause it to disappear, you may conclude that there has been a contusion of the bone to a greater or less extent, which has occasioned the fracture that has disappeared under the raspatory; but it is less dangerous, and a matter of less consequence, when the fissure has been effaced. But if the fracture extend deep, and do not seem likely to disappear when scraped, such an accident requires trepanning. But having performed this operation, you must apply the other treatment to the wound.

15. You must be upon your guard lest the bone sustain any injury from the fleshy parts if not properly treated. When the bone has been sawed and otherwise denuded, whether it be actually sound, or only appears to be so, but has sustained some injury from the blow, there may be danger of its suppurating (although it would not otherwise have done so), if the flesh which surrounds the bone be ill cured, and become inflamed and strangled; for it gets into a febrile state, and becomes much inflamed. For the bone acquires heat and inflammation from the surrounding flesh, along with irritation and throbbing, and the other mischiefs which are in the flesh itself, and from these it gets into a state of suppuration. It is a bad thing for the flesh (*granulations?*) in an ulcer to be moist and mouldy, and to require a long time to become clean. But the wound should be made to suppurate as quickly as possible; for, thus the parts surrounding the wound would be the least disposed to inflammation, and would become the soonest clean; for the flesh which has been chopped and bruised by the blow, must necessarily suppurate and slough away. But when cleaned the wound must be dried, for thus the wound will most speedily become whole, when flesh devoid of humors grows up, and thus there will be no fungous flesh in the sore. The same thing applies to the membrane which surrounds the brain: for when, by sawing the bone, and removing it from the meninx, you lay the latter bare, you must make it clean and dry as quickly as possible, lest being in a moist state for a considerable time, it become soaked therewith and swelled; for when these things occur, there is danger of its mortifying.

16. A piece of bone that must separate from the rest of the bone, in consequence of a wound in the head, either from the indentation (*hedra*) of a blow in the bone, or from the bone being otherwise denuded for a long time, separates mostly by becoming exsanguous. For the bone becomes dried up and loses its blood by time and a multiplicity of medicines which are used; and the separation will take place most quickly, if one having cleaned the wound as quickly as possible will next dry it, and the piece of bone, whether larger or smaller. For a piece of bone which is quickly dried and converted, as it were, into a shell, is most readily separated from the rest of the bone which retains its blood and vitality; for, the part having become exsanguous and dry, more readily drops off from that which retains its blood and is alive.

17. Such pieces of bone as are depressed from their natural position, either being broken off or chopped off to a considerable extent, are attended with less danger, provided the membrane be safe; and bones which are broken by

numerous and broader fractures are still less dangerous and more easily extracted. And you must not trepan any of them, nor run any risks in attempting to extract the pieces of bone, until they rise up of their own accord, upon the subsidence of the swelling. They rise up when the flesh (*granulations*) grows below, and it grows from the diploe of the bone, and from the sound portion, provided the upper table alone be in a state of necrosis. And the flesh will shoot up and grow below the more quickly, and the pieces of bone ascend, if one will get the wound to suppurate and make it clean as quickly as possible. And when both the tables of the bone are driven in upon the membrane, I mean the upper and lower, the wound, if treated in the same way, will very soon get well, and the depressed bones will quickly rise up.

18. The bones of children are thinner and softer, for this reason, that they contain more blood [than those of adults]; and they are porous and spongy, and neither dense nor hard. And when wounded to a similar or inferior degree by weapons of the same or even of an inferior power, the bone of a young person more readily and quickly suppurates, and that in less time than the bone of an older person; and in accidents, which are to prove fatal, the younger person will die sooner than the elder. But if the bone is laid bare of flesh, one must attend and try to find out, what even is not obvious to the sight, and discover whether the bone be broken and contused, or only contused; and if, when there is an indentation in the bone, whether contusion, or fracture, or both be joined to it; and if the bone has sustained any of these injuries, we must give issue to the blood by perforating the bone with a small trepan, observing the greatest precautions, for the bone of young persons is thinner and more superficial than that of elder persons.

19. When a person has sustained a mortal wound on the head, which cannot be cured, nor his life preserved, you may form an opinion of his approaching dissolution, and foretell what is to happen from the following symptoms which such a person experiences. When a bone is broken, or cleft, or contused, or otherwise injured, and when by mistake it has not been discovered, and neither the raspatory nor trepan has been applied as required, but the case has been neglected as if the bone were sound, fever will generally come on before the fourteenth day if in winter, and in summer the fever usually seizes after seven days. And when this happens, the wound loses its color, and the inflammation

dies in it; and it becomes glutinous, and appears like a pickle, being of a tawny and somewhat livid color; and the bone then begins to sphacelate, and turns black where it was white before, and at last becomes pale and blanched. But when suppuration is fairly established in it, small blisters form on the tongue and he dies delirious. And, for the most part, convulsions seize the other side of the body; for, if the wound be situated on the left side, the convulsions will seize the right side of the body; or if the wound be on the right side of the head, the convulsion attacks the left side of the body. And some become apoplectic. And thus they die before the end of seven days, if in summer; and before fourteen, if in winter. And these symptoms indicate, in the same manner, whether the wound be older or more recent. But if you perceive that fever is coming on, and that any of these symptoms accompany it, you must not put off, but having sawed the bone to the membrane (*meninx*), or scraped it with a raspatory (and it is then easily sawed or scraped), you must apply the other treatment as may seem proper, attention being paid to circumstances.

20. When in any wound of the head, whether the man has been trepanned or not, but the bone has been laid bare, a red and erysipelatous swelling supervenes in the face, and in both eyes, or in either of them, and if the swelling be painful to the touch, and if fever and rigor come on, and if the wound look well, whether as regards the flesh or the bone, and if the parts surrounding the wound be well, except the swelling in the face, and if the swelling be not connected with any error in the regimen, you must purge the bowels in such a case with a medicine which will evacuate bile; and when thus purged the fever goes off, the swelling subsides, and the patient gets well. In giving the medicine you must pay attention to the strength of the patient.

21. With regard to trepanning, when there is a necessity for it, the following particulars should be known. If you have had the management of the case from the first, you must not at once saw the bone down to the meninx; for it is not proper that the membrane should be laid bare and exposed to injuries for a length of time, as in the end it may become fungous. And there is another danger if you saw the bone down to the meninx and remove it at once, lest in the act of sawing you should wound the meninx. But in trepanning, when only a very little of the bone remains to be sawed through, and the bone can be moved, you must desist from saw-

ing, and leave the bone to fall out of itself. For to a bone not sawed through, and where a portion is left of the sawing, no mischief can happen; for the portion now left is sufficiently thin. In other respects you must conduct the treatment as may appear suitable to the wound. And in trepanning you must frequently remove the trepan, on account of the heat in the bone, and plunge it in cold water. For the trepan being heated by running round, and heating and drying the bone, burns it and makes a larger piece of bone around the sawing to drop off, than would otherwise do. And if you wish to saw at once down to the membrane, and then remove the bone, you must also, in like manner, frequently take out the trepan and dip it in cold water. But if you have not charge of the treatment from the first, but undertake it from another after a time, you must saw the bone at once down to the meninx with a serrated trepan, and in doing so must frequently take out the trepan and examine with a sound (specillum), and otherwise along the tract of the instrument. For the bone is much sooner sawn through, pro-

vided there be matter below it and in it, and it often happens that the bone is more superficial, especially if the wound is situated in that part of the head where the bone is rather thinner than in other parts. But you must take care where you apply the trepan, and see that you do so only where it appears to be particularly thick, and having fixed the instrument there, that you frequently make examinations and endeavor by moving the bone to bring it up. Having removed it, you must apply the other suitable remedies to the wound. And if, when you have the management of the treatment from the first, you wish to saw through the bone at once, and remove it from the membrane, you must, in like manner, examine the tract of the instrument frequently with the sound, and see that it is fixed on the thickest part of the bone, and endeavor to remove the bone by moving it about. But if you use a perforator (*trepan?*), you must not penetrate to the membrane, if you operate on a case which you have had the charge of from the first, but must leave a thin scale of bone, as described in the process of sawing.

On the Surgery

IT IS the business of the physician to know, in the first place, things similar and things dissimilar; those connected with things most important, most easily known, and in anywise known;[1] which are to be seen, touched, and heard; which are to be perceived in the sight, and the touch, and the hearing, and the nose, and the tongue, and the understanding; which are to be known by all the means we know other things.

2. The things relating to surgery, are—the patient; the operator; the assistants; the instruments; the light, where and how; how many things, and how; where the body, and the instruments; the time; the manner; the place.

3. The operator is either sitting or standing, conveniently for himself, for the person operated upon, for the light. There are two kinds of light, the common and the artificial; the common is not at our disposal, the artificial is at our disposal. There are two modes of using

each, either to the light, or from the light (to the side?). There is little use of that which is from (*or* oblique to the light), and the degree of it is obvious. As to opposite the light, we must turn the part to be operated upon to that which is most brilliant of present and convenient lights, unless those parts which should be concealed, and which it is a shame to look upon; thus the part that is operated upon should be opposite the light, and the operator opposite the part operated upon, except in so far as he does not stand in his own light; for in this case the operator will indeed see, but the thing operated upon will not be seen. With regard to himself: when sitting, his feet should be raised to a direct line with his knees, and nearly in contact with one another; the knees a little higher than the groins, and at some distance from one another, for the elbows to rest upon them. The robe, in a neat and orderly manner, is to be thrown over the elbows and shoulders equally and proportionally. With regard to the part operated upon; we have to consider how far distant, and how near, above, below, on this side, on that side, or in the middle. The measure as to distance and proximity is, that the elbows do not press the knees before, nor the sides be-

[1] The meaning of the first clause of this sentence, according to Galen, is, that the first thing which the medical practitioner must do is to make himself well acquainted with semeiology, by comparing carefully the condition of disease with that of health.

hind; that the hands be not raised higher than the breasts, nor lower than so as that when the breast reposes on the knees he may have the hands at right angles with the arm: thus it is as regards the medium; but as concerns this side or that, the operator must not be beyond his seat, but in proportion as he may require turning he must shift the body, or part of the body, that is operated upon. When standing, he must make his inspection, resting firmly and equally on both feet; but he must operate while supporting himself upon either leg, and not the one on the same side with the hand which he makes use of; the knee being raised to the height of the groins as while sitting; and the other measures in like manner. The person operated upon should accommodate the operator with regard to the other parts of his body, either standing, sitting, or lying; so as that he may continue to preserve his figure, avoid sinking down, shrinking from, turning away; and may maintain the figure and position of the part operated upon, during the act of presentation, during the operation, and in the subsequent position.

4. The nails should be neither longer nor shorter than the points of the fingers; and the surgeon should practice with the extremities of the fingers, the index-finger being usually turned to the thumb; when using the entire hand, it should be prone; when both hands, they should be opposed to one another. It greatly promotes a dexterous use of the fingers when the space between them is large, and when the thumb is opposed to the index. But it is clearly a disease when the thumb is impaired from birth, or when, from a habit contracted during the time of nursing, it is impeded in its motions by the fingers. One should practice all sorts of work with either of them, and with both together (for they are both alike), endeavouring to do them well, elegantly, quickly, without trouble, neatly, and promptly.

5. The instruments, and when and how they should be prepared, will be treated of afterwards; so that they may not impede the work, and that there may be no difficulty in taking hold of them, with the part of the body which operates. But if another gives them, he must be ready a little beforehand, and do as you direct.

6. Those about the patient must present the part to be operated upon as may seem proper, and they must hold the rest of the body steady, in silence, and listening to the commands of the operator.

7. There are two views of bandaging: that which regards it while doing, and that which regards it when done. It should be done quickly, without pain, with ease, and with elegance; quickly, by despatching the work; without pain, by being readily done; with ease, by being prepared for everything; and with elegance, so that it may be agreeable to the sight. By what mode of training these accomplishments are to be acquired has been stated. When done, it should fit well and neatly; it is neatly done when with judgment, and when it is equal and unequal, according as the parts are equal or unequal. The forms of it (the bandage?) are the simple, the slightly winding (called ascia), the sloping (sima), the monoculus, the rhombus, and the semi-rhombus. The form of bandage should be suitable to the form and the affection of the part to which it is applied.

8. There are two useful purposes to be fulfilled by bandaging: (first,) strength, which is imparted by the compression and the number of folds. In one case the bandage effects the cure, and in another it contributes to the cure. For these purposes this is the rule—that the force of the constriction be such as to prevent the adjoining parts from separating, without compressing them much, and so that the parts may be adjusted but not forced together; and that the constriction be small at the extremities, and least of all in the middle. The knot and the thread that is passed through should not be in a downward but in an upward direction, regard being had to the circumstances under which the case is presented; to position, to the bandaging, and to the compression. The commencement of the ligatures is not to be placed at the wound, but where the knot is situated. The knot should not be placed where it will be exposed to friction, nor where it will be in the way, nor where it will be useless. The knot and the thread should be soft, and not large.

9. (Second.) One ought to be well aware that every bandage has a tendency to fall off towards the part that declines or becomes smaller; as, for example, upwards, in the case of the head, and downwards, in the case of the leg. The turns of the bandage should be made from right to left, and from left to right, except on the head, where it should be in a straight direction. When opposite parts are to be bandaged together, we must use a bandage with two heads; or if we make use of a bandage with one head, we must attach it in like manner at some fixed point: such, for example, as the middle of the head; and so in other cases. Those parts which are much exposed to motion, such as the joints, where there is a flexion, should have few

and slight bandages applied to them, as at the ham; but where there is much extension, the bandage should be single and broad, as at the kneepan; and for the maintenance of the bandage in its proper place, some turns should be carried to those parts which are not much moved, and are lank, such as the parts above and below the knee. In the case of the shoulder, a fold should be carried round by the other armpit; in that of the groin, by the flanks of the opposite side; and of the leg, to above the calf of the leg. When the bandage has a tendency to escape above, it should be secured below, and *vice versa;* and where there is no means of doing this, as in the case of the head, the turns are to be made mostly on the most level part of the head, and the folds are to be done with as little obliquity as possible, so that the firmest part being last applied may secure the portions which are more movable. When we cannot secure the bandaging by means of folds of the cloth, nor by suspending them from the opposite side, we must have recourse to stitching it with ligatures, either passed circularly or in the form of a seam.

10. The bandages should be clean, light, soft, and thin. One should practice rolling with both hands together, and with either separately. One should also choose a suitable one, according to the breadth and thickness of the parts. The heads of the bandages should be hard, smooth, and neatly put on. That sort of bandaging is the worst which quickly falls off; but those are bad bandages which neither compress nor yet come off.

11. The following are the object which the upper bandage, the under bandage, or both aim at: The object of the under bandage is either to bring together parts that are separated, or to compress such as are expanded, or to separate what are contracted, or to restore to shape what are distorted, or the contrary. It is necessary to prepare pieces of linen cloth, which are light, thin, soft, clean, having no seams nor protuberances on them, but sound, and able to bear some stretching, or even a little more than required; not dry, but wetted with a juice suitable to the purpose required. We must deal with parts separated (*in a sinus?*) in such wise, that the parts which are raised may touch the bottom without producing pressure; we must begin on the sound part, and terminate at the wound; so that whatever humor is in it may be expelled, and that it may be prevented from collecting more. And straight parts are to be bandaged in a straight direction, and oblique obliquely, in such a position as to create no pain; and so that there may be no constriction nor falling off on a change of position, either for the purpose of taking hold of anything, or laying the limb; and that muscles, veins, nerves, and bones may be properly placed and adjusted to one another. It should be raised or laid in a natural position, so as not to occasion pain. In those cases in which an abscess is formed, we must act in a contrary way. When our object is to bring together parts which have become expanded, in other respects we must proceed on the same plain; and we must commence the bringing together from some considerable distance; and after their approach, we must apply compression, at first slight, and afterwards stronger, the limit of it being the actual contact of the parts. In order to separate parts which are drawn together, when attended with inflammation, we must proceed on the opposite plan; but when without inflammation, we must use the same preparations, but bandage in the opposite direction. In order to rectify distorted parts, we must proceed otherwise on the same principles; but the parts which are separated must be brought together by an underbandage, by agglutinants, and by suspending it (*the limb?*) in its natural position. And when the deformities are the contrary, this is to be done on the contrary plan.

12. In fractures we must attend to the length, breadth, thickness, and number of the compresses. The length should be that of the bandaging; the breadth, three or four fingers; thickness, three or fourfold; number so as to encircle the limb, neither more nor less; those applied for the purpose of rectifying a deformity, should be of such a length as to encircle it; the breadth and thickness being determined by the vacuity, which is not to be filled up at once. The upper bandages are two, the first of which is to be carried from the seat of the injury upwards, and the second from the seat of the injury downwards, and from below upwards; the parts about the seat of the injury being most compressed, the extremities least, and the rest in proportion. The upper bandages should take in a considerable portion of the sound parts. We must attend to the number, length, and breadth of the bandages; the number must be such as not to be inferior to what the injury requires, nor occasion compression with the splints, nor prove cumbersome, nor occasion any slipping of them, nor render them inefficient. As to length and breadth, they should be three, four, five, or six cubits in length, and as many fingers broad. The folds of the strings (*selvages?*)

should be such as not to occasion pressure; they are to be soft and not thick; and all these things are to be proportionate to the length, breadth, and thickness of the part affected. The splints are to be smooth, even, and rounded at the extremities; somewhat less all along than the upper bandaging, and thickest at the part to which the fracture inclines. Those parts where there are tuberosities, and which are devoid of flesh, such as the ankles or fingers, we must guard from the splints which are placed over them, either by position, or by their shortness. They are to be secured by the strings in such a manner as not to occasion pressure at first. A soft, consistent, and clean cerate should be rubbed into the folds of the bandage.

13. As to the temperature and quantity of the water used, its heat should be just such as the hand can bear, and it ought to be known that a large quantity is best for producing relaxation and attenuation, whereas a moderate quantity is best for incarnating and softening. The limit to the affusion is, to stop when the parts become swelled up, and before the swelling subsides; for the parts swell up at first, and fall afterward.

14. The object on which it (*the limb?*) is laid should be soft, smooth, and sloping upwards toward the protuberant parts of the body, such as the heel or hips, so that there may be no projection, nor bending inwards, nor turning aside. The canal (*spout or gutter?*) should rather comprehend the whole limb than the half of it, attention being paid to the injury and to whatever else appears to create inconvenience.

15. The presentation of the injured part to the physician, the extension, the arrangement, and so forth, are to be regulated according to nature. What is nature in these operations is to be determined by the accomplishment of the object which we have in view, and for this purpose we must look to the part in the state of rest, in its middle state, and to habit; in regard to the state of rest and relaxation, as in the arm, that it be in a line with the hand; and with regard to the medium between flexion and extension, that the forearm be at right angles to the arm; and with regard to habit, it should be considered that some limbs bear certain positions preferably, as, for example, the thighs extension; for in such attitudes the parts can best bear to be placed for a considerable time without a change of posture. And in the change from the state of distention, the muscles, veins, nerves, and bones, when properly arranged and secured, will preserve their relations to one another while the limb is raised or placed.

16. The extension should be most powerful when the largest and thickest bones, or when both are broken; next when the under-bone, and least of all, when the upper. When immoderate, it is injurious, except in the case of children. The limb should be a little elevated. The model by which we judge if the part be properly set is the sound part of the same name, or the part which is its pair.

17. Friction can relax, brace, incarnate, attenuate: hard braces, soft relaxes, much attenuates, and moderate thickens.

18. The following should be the state of matters on the first application of the bandage. The person to whom it has been applied should say that he feels the compression particularly at the seat of the injury, but very little at the extremities; the parts should be adjusted but not pressed together, and that rather by the number of the bandages than by the force of the constriction; and the tightness should rather be on the increase during the first day and night; but on the next it should be less, and on the third the bandages should be loose. On the next day a soft swelling should be observed in the extremities; and on the third day, when the bandaging is loosed, the swelling should be found diminished in size, and this should be the case every time the bandages are removed. At the second application of the bandage, it should be ascertained whether the dressing has been properly done, and then greater compression should be made, and with more bandages; and on the third, still greater, and still more. On the seventh day from the first dressing, when the bandages are loosed, the limb should be found slender and the bones mobile. We must then have recourse to the splints, provided the limb be free of swelling, pruritus, and ulceration, and allow them to remain until twenty days after the accident; but if any suspicions arise, the bandages must be loosed in the interval. The splints should be tightened every third day.

19. The suspending of a fractured limb in a sling, the disposition of it, and the bandaging, all have for their object to preserve it in position. The principal considerations with regard to the position are the habits and the peculiar nature of each of the limbs: the varieties are shown in running, walking, standing, lying, action, repose.

20. It should be kept in mind that exercise strengthens, and inactivity wastes.

21. Compression should be produced by the number of bandages, rather than by the force

of the constriction.

22. In cases of ecchymosis, contusions, sprains, or swellings not attended with inflammations, blood is to be expelled from the wound, in greatest quantity to the upper part, and in smallest to the inferior; neither the arm nor the leg should be placed in a declining position: the head of the bandage should be placed on the wound, and there the greatest pressure should be made; the least at the extremities, and intermediately in the middle; the last fold of the bandage should be at the upper part of the body. As to binding and compression, these objects are to be attained rather by the number of the bandages than the force of the constriction; and moreover, in these cases the bandages should be thin, light, soft, clean, broad, sound, so that they may effect their purpose, even without splints. And we must use affusions.

23. Dislocations, sprains, diastases of bones, violent separation, abruption of the extremities of bones, and distrainings, so as to induce *varus* or *valgus,* in these cases we must apply the bandages so as not to compress the part whence the displacement took place, and that we may render them tight at the side to which the displacement was, and give the limb an inclination in the opposite direction, and that in an excessive degree. We employ bandages, compresses, suspension of the limb in a sling, attitude, extention, friction, rectification; and along with these the affusion of much water.

24. In treating parts which are atrophied, we must comprehend a considerable part of the sound limb with the bandage, so that by the influx thereby produced, the wasted part may ac-quire a supply greater than its loss, and may be thus disposed to growth and restoration of its fleshy parts. It is better also to bandage the parts above, as the thigh in the case of the leg, and also the thigh and leg of the opposite side, so that they may be placed in similar circumstances, and may both equally be deprived of motion; and that the supply of nourishment may be alike curtailed and open to both. The compression should be the effect rather of the number of the bandages than of their tightness. We relax first the part most requiring it, and have recourse to that kind of friction which will promote the growth of flesh, and to affusion. No splints.

25. Those things which are for the purpose of giving support and strength to the part, as to the breast, side, head, and so forth, are used in such cases as the following: for pulsations, that there may be no motion in the part; and in separation at the sutures of the skull, in order to give support; and in order to strengthen the chest and head, in coughs, sneezings, and other movements. In all these cases the same measure of bandaging is to be observed, for where the injury is, there the bandage should compress most, and something soft is to be placed below that suits with the complaint; and we must not apply the bandages tighter than just to stop the pulsations from creating disturbance, and that the separated parts at the sutures may be brought into contact, they must not be such as absolutely to stop the coughs and sneezings, but so as to give support, and, without occasioning uneasiness, prevent the parts from being shaken.

On Fractures

IN TREATING fractures and dislocations, the physician must make the extension as straight as possible, for this is the most natural direction. But if it incline to either side, it should rather turn to that of pronation, for there is thus less harm than if it be toward supination. Those, then, who act in such cases without deliberation, for the most part do not fall into any great mistake, for the person who is to have his arm bound, presents it in the proper position from necessity, but physicians who fancy themselves learned in these matters, are they who commit blunders. There is no necessity for much study, then, in order to set a broken arm, and in a word, any ordinary physician can per-form it; but I am under the necessity of giving the longer directions on this subject, because I know physicians who have the reputation of being skilled in giving the proper positions to the arm in binding it up, while in reality they are only showing their own ignorance. But many other things in our art are judged of in this manner, for people rather admire what is new, although they do not know whether it be proper or not, than what they are accustomed to, and know already to be proper; and what is strange, they prefer to what is obvious. I must now state what the mistakes of medical men are, which I wish to unteach, and what instructions I have to give as to the management of the arm; for what I have to say regarding it, will apply to the other bones in the body.

2. The arm, then, for that is the subject we were treating of, was presented in the prone position to be bound, but the physician forced his patient to hold it as the archers do when they project the shoulder, and in this position he bound it up, thinking within himself that he was acting according to Nature, and in proof of this he pointed out that all the bones in the fore-arm were thus in a straight line, and that the integuments both inside and outside, were also in a straight line, and that the flesh and nerves (*tendons?*) were thus put in their natural position, and he appealed to what happens in archery, as a proof of this. And so saying, and so doing, he is looked up to as a sage; and yet he forgets that in all the other arts and performances, whether executed by strength or dexterity, what is reckoned the natural position is not the same, and that in the same piece of work it may happen that the natural position of the right arm is not the same as that of the left. For there is one attitude in throwing the javelin, and another in slinging, another in casting stones, another in boxing, and another in a state of repose. And whatever arts one examines, it will be found that the natural position of the arms is not the same in each, but that in every case the arms are put into the attitude which suits best with the instrument that is used, and the work to be performed. In practicing archery, no doubt this is the best attitude of the left arm, for the gingly-moid extremity of the humerus being fixed in the cavity of the ulna, in this position, throws the bones of the fore-arm and arm into a line, as if they constituted a single bone, and all flexion at the joint is prevented in this position. It is no doubt certain that the member is thus put into the most unbending and extended position possible, so as not to be overcome or yield when the string is drawn by the right arm, and thus will the archer be enabled to draw the string farthest, and discharge his arrow with the greatest force and rapidity, for arrows thus discharged have the greatest swiftness and force, and are carried to the greatest distances. But there is nothing in common between the binding up of an arm and archery. Moreover, if having thus bound up the arm, the physician direct the patient to keep it thus, he will occasion him greater pain than he had from the wound itself; and thus also, if the physician order him to bend the arm, neither the bones, the nerves, nor the flesh will any longer be in the same condition, but will be

arranged differently, having overcome the bandaging. What use, then, is there of the archer's attitude? And these mistakes, the physician, conceited in his knowledge, would probably not have committed if he had allowed the patient himself to present his arm.

3. But another physician putting the arm into the state of supination, gives orders to extend the arm thus, and bandages it in this position, reckoning it the one according to nature, judging thus from the skin, and also fancying the bones to be thus in their natural position, because the bone which protrudes at the wrist, where the little finger is, appears to be in a line with the bone from which people measure the bone of the fore-arm. These things he brings forward as proofs that the parts are in their natural state, and he is supposed to speak correctly. But, indeed, if the arm be kept stretched in a supine position, it will become very painful, and this fact any one may ascertain by extending his own arm in this attitude. And also a weaker man grasping with his hands a stronger man whose arm is turned in a supine position, could lead him wherever he chose, and neither, if a man held a sword thus in his hand, could he make any proper use of it, so constrained is this position. And, moreover, if, when a physician has thus bound up the arm, he allow it to remain in the same position, the patient will endure greater pain if he walk about, but considerable, even if he remain at rest. And thus, too, if he shall bend the arm, the muscles and the bones must necessarily assume a different position. But, in addition to other mischief, he is ignorant of these facts regarding the position, that the bone which protrudes at the wrist, close to the little finger, belongs to the fore-arm, whereas the one at the joint, from which people measure the fore-arm, is the head of the humerus. He fancies that both these belong to the same bone, and many others are of this opinion. The latter, in fact, is the same part as that which is called the elbow, upon which we sometimes rest, and when he holds the arm thus in a supine position, in the first place the bone appears distorted, and in the next place the tendons which extend from the carpus along the inner side and from the fingers become distorted while the arm has a supine position; for these tendons proceed to the bone of the humerus, from which the fore-arm is measured. Such, and so many mistakes and marks of ignorance are committed, regarding the natural construction of the arm. But if one will extend a broken arm as I direct, he will turn the bone,

situated at the extremity of the little finger, into the straight line, and also the one at the elbow, and the tendons which stretch from the carpus to the extremity of the humerus will be placed in the straight line; and when the arm is suspended in a sling, it will be in the same attitude as that in which it was bound up, and will give no pain to the patient when he walks about, nor when he lies reclined, and will not become fatigued. The man should be so seated that the prominent part of the bone may be turned to the brightest light which is at hand, so that the operator in making the extension, may be at no loss to discover if it be sufficiently straight. The prominence of a broken bone could not escape being detected by the hand of an experienced person, when applied for this purpose, and, moreover, the projecting part is particularly painful to the touch.

4. In cases of fracture in either of the bones of the forearm, it is easier to effect a cure if the upper bone be broken, although it be the thicker one, both because the sound bone is situated below, and forms a support to it, and because the deformity is more easily concealed, there being a thick mass of flesh on the upper side, except near to the wrist. But the lower bone is without a covering of flesh, is not easily concealed, and requires stronger extension. If it is not this bone, but the other which is broken, a more feeble extension proves sufficient, but if both be broken, a more powerful extension is required. In the case of a young person I have known the extension made more strong than was necessary, but in general the extension made is less than what is required. And when they are extended, the physician should apply the palms of the hands, and adjust the fractured parts and then having rubbed the parts with cerate, but not in large quantity, so that the bandages may not come off, it is to be bound up in this state, care being taken that the hand be not lower than the elbow, but a little higher, so that the blood do not flow toward the extremity, but may be determined to the upper part; and then it is to be secured with the bandage, the head of which is to be placed at the fracture, and the bandage should impart firmness to the parts without occasioning strong compression. When you have carried the bandage twice or thrice round at the seat of the fracture, it is to be carried upward, so that the afflux of blood into it may be stopped, and the bandage should terminate there, and the first bandages ought not to be long. The head of the second bandage is also to be placed upon the seat of the fracture, and a single round of it being made there, it is then to be carried downward, and is not to be applied so tight as the other, and there should be greater distances between the turns, so that the bandage may prove sufficient to revert to the spot where the other terminated. The bandages may be rolled to the left hand or to the right, or to whatever side suits best with the position of the fractured arm, or according to the inclination which it may have. Afterward we must place along the arm, compresses, smeared with a little cerate, for thus they occasion less uneasiness, and are more easily arranged. And then we must apply the bandages crossways, sometimes to the right hand, and sometimes to the left, for the most part beginning below and terminating above, but sometimes commencing above and ending below. The parts which are thinly covered with flesh should be wrapped round with compresses, and inequalities should be made up, not by a number of folds at once, but by degrees. Some slack turns are also to be made around the wrist, to this side and to that. These two bandages are sufficient at first.

5. And these are the signs that the patient has been well treated and properly bandaged: if you ask him if the arm feels tight, and he says it does, but moderately so, and especially about the fracture; and this reply he should make all along, if the bandage be properly applied. And these are symptoms of the bandaging being moderately tight; if for the first day and night he fancies that the tightness does not diminish, but rather increases; and if on the next day there be a soft swelling in the hand, for this is a sign of moderate compression, but at the end of the second day the compression should feel less, and on the third day the bandaging should appear loose. And if any of these symptoms be wanting, you may conclude that the bandaging is slacker than it should be; or if any of these symptoms be in excess, you may infer that the compression is more than moderate; and judging from these, you will apply the next bandages either slacker or tighter. Having removed the bandages on the third day, you must make extension and adjust the fracture, and bind it up again; and if the first bandaging was moderately applied, the second bandaging should be made somewhat tighter. The heads of the bandages should be placed on the fractures as in the former case; for, by so doing, the humors will be driven to the extremities, whereas if you bandage any other part beforehand, the humors will be forced from it to the seat of the fracture: it

is of much importance that this should be properly understood. Thus the bandaging and compression should always commence at the seat of the fracture, and everything else should be conducted on the same principle, so that the farther you proceed from the fracture, the compression should always be the less. The bandages should never be actually loose, but should be smoothly put on. At each dressing the number of bandages should be increased; and the patient, if asked, should answer, that he feels the bandages somewhat tighter than on the former occasion, especially about the fracture, and everything else in proportion; and with respect to the swelling, the pain, and recovery, everything should proceed as after the former dressing. But on the third day the outer bandaging should appear looser. Then having removed the bandages, you should bind it up again, somewhat tighter than before, and with all the bandages which will be required on the occasion, and afterwards one ought to experience the same train of symptoms as at the former periods of bandaging.

6. When the third day arrives, that is to say, the seventh from the first dressing, if properly done, the swelling in the hand should be not very great; and the part which has been bandaged should be found more slender and less swelled at each time, and on the seventh day the swelling should be quite gone, and the broken bones should be more readily moved, and admit of being easily adjusted. And if these things be so, you should, after setting the fracture, apply the bandages so as to suit the splints, and a little more tight than formerly, unless there be more pain from the swelling in the hand. When you have applied the bandages, you must adjust the splints all around the limb, and secure them with strings so loose as just to keep them in their place, without the application of the splints contributing at all to the compression of the arm. After this the pain and recovery should proceed as in the preceding periods of the bandaging. But if, on the third day, the patient say that the bandaging is loose, you must then fasten the splints, especially at the fracture, but also elsewhere, wherever the bandaging is rather loose than tight. The splint should be thickest where the fracture protrudes, but it should not be much more so than elsewhere. Particular attention should be paid to the line of the arm corresponding to the thumb, so that no splint be laid on it, but upon each side of it, nor in the line of the little finger where the bone is prominent at the wrist, but on each

side of it. And if it be found necessary that splints should be applied in these directions at the seat of the fracture, they should be made shorter than the others, so as that they may not reach the bones which are prominent at the wrist, for otherwise there is danger of ulceration, and of the tendons being laid bare. The splints should be adjusted anew every third day, in a very gentle manner, always keeping in mind that the object of the splints is to maintain the lower bandages in their place, and that they are not needed in order to contribute to the compression.

7. If, then, you see that the bones are properly adjusted by the first dressings, and that there is no troublesome pruritus in the part, nor any reason to suspect ulceration, you may allow the arm to remain bandaged in the splints until after the lapse of more than twenty days. The bones of the fore-arm generally get consolidated in thirty days altogether; but there is nothing precise in this matter, for one constitution differs from another, and one period of life from another. When you remove the bandages, you must pour hot water on the arm and bind it up again, but somewhat slacker, and with fewer bandages than formerly: and again on the third day you undo the bandages, and bind it still more loosely, and with still fewer bandages. And if, while the arm is bound up in the splints, you should at any time suspect that the bones do not lie properly, or if anything about the bandages annoys the patient, you should loose them at the middle of the time, or a little earlier, and apply them again. A diet slightly restricted will be sufficient in those cases in which there was no external wound at first, or when the bone does not protrude; but one should live rather sparingly until the tenth day, as being now deprived of exercise; and tender articles of food should be used, such as moderately loosen the bowels; but one should abstain altogether from flesh and wine, and then by degrees resume a more nourishing diet. This doctrine may be laid down as a just rule in the treatment of fractures, both as to how they should be treated, and what will be the results of a proper plan of treatment; so that one may know, that if things do not turn out thus, there has been some defect or excess in the treatment. And in this simple plan of treatment it is necessary to attend also to the following directions, which some physicians pay little attention to, although, when improperly executed, they are capable of marring the whole process of bandaging: for if both the bones be broken, or the

lower one only, and the patient who has got his arm bandaged keep it slung in a shawl, and that the shawl is particularly loose at the fracture, so that the arm is not properly suspended at this end or that, in this case the bone must necessarily be found distorted upwards; whereas, when both bones are thus broken, if the arm recline in the shawl at the wrist and elbow, but the rest of it be not kept up, the bone in this case will be distorted to the lower side. The greater part of the arm and the wrist of the hand should therefore be equally suspended in a broad soft shawl.

8. When the arm is broken, if one stretch the fore-arm and adjust it while in this position, the muscle of the arm will be bound while extended; but when the dressing is over, and the patient bends his arm at the elbow, the muscle of the arm will assume a different shape. The following, then, is the most natural plan of setting the arm: having got a piece of wood a cubit or somewhat less in length, like the handles of spades, suspend it by means of a chain fastened to its extremities at both ends; and having seated the man on some high object, the arm is to be brought over, so that the armpit may rest on the piece of wood, and the man can scarcely touch the seat, being almost suspended; then having brought another seat, and placed one or more leather pillows under the arm, so as to keep it a moderate height while it is bent at a right angle, the best plan is to put round the arm a broad and soft skin, or broad shawl, and to hang some great weight to it, so as to produce moderate extension; or otherwise, while the arm is in the position I have described, a strong man is to take hold of it at the elbow and pull it downward. But the physician standing erect, must perform the proper manipulation, having the one foot on some pretty high object, and adjusting the bone with the palms of his hands; and it will readily be adjusted, for the extension is good if properly applied. Then let him bind the arm, commencing at the fracture, and do otherwise as directed above; let him put the same questions and avail himself of the same signs to ascertain whether the arm be moderately tight or not; and every third day let him bind it anew and make it tighter; and on the seventh or ninth day let him bind it up with splints, and leave it so until after the lapse of more than thirty days. And if he suspect that the bone is not lying properly, let him remove the bandages in the interval, and having adjusted the arm, let him bind it up again. The bone of the arm is generally consolidated in

forty days. When these are past, the dressing is to be removed, and fewer and slacker bandages applied instead of it. The patient is to be kept on a stricter diet, and for a longer space of time than in the former case; and we must form our judgment of it from the swelling in the hand, looking also to the strength of the patient. This also should be known, that the arm is naturally inclined outward; to this side, therefore, the distortion usually takes place, if not properly treated; but indeed, all the other bones are usually distorted during treatment for fracture to that side to which they naturally incline. When, therefore, anything of this kind is suspected, the arm is to be encircled in a broad shawl, which is to be carried round the breast, and when the patient goes to rest, a compress of many folds, or some such thing, is to be folded and placed between the elbow and the side, for thus the bending of the bone will be rectified, but care must be taken lest it be inclined too much inwards.

9. The human foot is composed of several small bones like the hand. These bones therefore are scarcely ever broken, unless the skin at the same time be wounded by some sharp and heavy body. The treatment of such injuries, therefore, will be delivered under the head of wounds. But if any bone be moved from its place, or a joint of the toes be luxated, or any of the bones of the part called the tarsus be displaced, it must be forced back again to its place as described with regard to the hand; and is to be treated with cerate, compresses, and bandages, like the fractures, with the exception of the splints; and is to be secured tightly in the same way, and the bandages renewed on the third day; and the patient thus bandaged should return the same answers as in fractures, as to the bandages feeling tight or slack. All these bones recover perfectly in twenty days, except those that are connected with the bones of the leg, and are in a line with them. It is advantageous to lie in bed during the whole of this time; but the patients, thinking light of the complaint, have not perseverance to do this, and they walk about before they get well; wherefore many of these do not make a perfect recovery. And often the pain puts them in mind of the injury; and deservedly, for the feet sustain the weight of the whole body. When, therefore, they walk about before they are whole, the joints which have been luxated are cured incompletely; and, on that account, while walking about, they have pains in the leg from time to time.

10. But those bones which are connected with the bones of the leg are larger than the others, and the cure of them when luxuated is more protracted. The mode of treatment then is the same; but we must use more bandages and more splints, and the bandage is to be carried round to this side and to that, and pressure is to be made as in the other cases, particularly at the seat of the luxation, and the first circles of the bandages are to be made there. And at each time the bandages are taken off, much hot water is to be used, for in all injuries at joints the affusion of hot water in large quantity is to be had recourse to. And the same symptoms of compression and relaxation should manifest themselves in the same times, as in the cases formerly treated of, and the subsequent bandagings should be conducted in like manner. These cases get completely well for the most part in forty days, if the patients have resolution to keep their bed; but if not, they are subjected to the complaints formerly described, or still worse.

11. In persons who jumping from any high object pitch upon their heel with great force, the bones are separated, and the veins pour forth their contents, owing to the contusion of the flesh surrounding the bone, and hence a swelling and much pain supervene. For this bone (os calcis) is not a small one, protrudes beyond the line of the leg, and is connected with important veins and tendons; for the back tendon of the leg is inserted into this bone. Such cases are to be treated with cerate, and with compresses and bandages; and hot water is to be used in large quantity; and they require many bandages, which ought to be particularly good and appropriate. And if the patient happen to have a tender skin about the heel, nothing is to be done to it; but if, as some have it, the skin be thick and hardened, it is to be pared down smoothly and thinned, but without wounding it. It is not everybody who can apply the bandage properly in such cases; for if one shall bind the parts, as in other accidents about the ankle, sometimes bringing a fold round the foot and sometimes round the tendon, these turns leave out the heel, which is the seat of the contusion, and thus there is danger that the os calcis may sphacelate; and if this should take place, the impediment may endure for life and also in all the other cases of sphacelus, not proceeding from such a cause as this; as when, from being carelessly allowed to lie in a certain position during confinement to bed, the heel becomes black, or when a serious wound has occurred in the leg and it is long of healing, and is connected with the heel, or when the same thing happens in the thigh, or when in any disease a protracted decubitus takes place on the back, in all such cases the sores are inveterate, troublesome, and frequently break out again, unless particular attention be paid to the cure, along with much rest, as in all the cases attended with sphacelus. And cases of sphacelus connected with this cause, in addition to other inconveniences, are attended with great danger to the whole body. For they are apt to be attended with very acute fevers, of the continual type, accompanied with tremblings, hiccup, aberration of intellect, and which prove fatal within a few days: and there may be lividities of bloody veins,[1] with nausea, and gangrene from pressure; these diseases may occur, besides the sphacelus. Those which have been described are the most violent contusion; but in general the contusions are mild, and no great care is required with regard to the treatment, and yet it must be conducted properly. But when the contusion appears to be severe, we must do as described above, making many turns of the bandage around the heel, sometimes carrying it to the extremity of the foot, sometimes to the middle, and sometimes around the leg; and, in addition, all the surrounding parts are to be bandaged in this direction and that, as formerly described; and the compression should not be made strong, but we should make use of many bandages, and it is better also to administer hellebore the same day or on the morrow; and the bandages should be removed on the third day and reapplied. And these are the symptoms by which we discover whether the case will get worse or not: when the extravasated blood, the lividities, and the surrounding parts become red and hard, there is danger of an exacerbation. But if there be no fever, we must give emetics, as has been said, and administer the other remedies which are applicable when the fever is not of a continual type; but if continual fever be present, we must not give strong medicines, but enjoin abstinence from solid food and soups, and give water for drink, and not allow wine but *oxyglyky* (a composition from vinegar and honey?). But if the case be not going to get worse, the ecchymosed and livid parts, and those surrounding them become greenish and not hard; for this is a satisfactory proof in all cases of ecchymosis, that they are not to get worse; but when lividity is complicated

[1] By bloody veins is meant veins of a large size, as Galen explains.

with hardness, there is danger that the part may become blackened. And we must so manage the foot as that it may be generally raised a little higher than the rest of the body. Such a patient will get well in sixty days if he keep quiet.

12. The leg consists of two bones, of which the one is much more slender than the other at one part, but not much more slender at another. These are connected together at the foot, and form a common epiphysis, but they are not united together along the line of the leg; and at the thigh they are united together and form an epiphysis, and this epiphysis has a diaphysis; but the other bone in a line with the little toe is a little longer. Such is the nature of the bones of the leg.

13. Sometimes the bones connected with the foot are displaced, sometimes both bones with their epiphysis; sometimes the whole epiphysis is slightly moved, and sometimes the other bone. These cases are less troublesome than the same accidents at the wrist, if the patients will have resolution to give them rest. The mode of treatment is the same as that of the other, for the reduction is to be made, as of the other, by means of extension, but greater force is required, as the parts of the body concerned are stronger in this case. But, for the most part, two men will be sufficient, by making extension in opposite directions, but, if they are not sufficiently strong, it is easy to make more powerful extension in the following way: having fixed in the ground either the nave of a wheel, or any such object, something soft is to be bound round the foot, and then some broad thongs of ox-skin being brought round it, the heads of the thongs are to be fastened to a pestle or any other piece of wood, the end of which is to be inserted into the nave, and it, the pestle, is to be pulled away, while other persons make counter-extension by grasping the shoulders and the ham. It is also sometimes necessary to secure the upper extremity otherwise; this if you desire to effect, fasten deeply in the ground a round, smooth piece of wood, and place the upper extremity of the piece of wood at the perineum, so that it may prevent the body from yielding to the pulling at the foot, and, moreover, to prevent the leg while stretched, from inclining downward; some person seated at his side should push back the hip, so that the body may not turn round with the pulling, and for this purpose, if you think fit, pieces of wood may be fastened about the armpits on each side, and they are to be stretched by the hands, and thus secured, while another person takes hold of the limb at the knee, and aids in thus making counter-extension. Or thus, if you prefer it: having bound other thongs of leather about the limb, either at the knee, or around the thigh, and having fastened another nave of a wheel in the ground above the head, and adjusted the thongs to some piece of wood adapted to the nave, extension may thus be made in the opposite direction to the feet. Or if you choose, it may be done thus: instead of the naves, lay a moderate-sized beam under the couch, and then having fastened pieces of wood in this beam, both before and behind the head, make counter-extension by means of thongs, or place windlasses at this extremity and that, and make extension by means of them. There are many other methods of making extension. But the best thing is, for any physician who practices in a large city, to have prepared a proper wooden machine, with all the mechanical powers applicable in cases of fractures and dislocation, either for making extension, or acting as a lever. For this purpose it will be sufficient to possess a board in length, breadth, and thickness, resembling the quadrangular threshing-boards made of oak.

14. When you have made proper extension, it is easy to reduce the joint, for the displaced bone is thus raised into a line with the other. And the bones are to be adjusted with the palms of the hands, pressing upon the projecting bone with the one, and making counter-pressure below the ankle with the other. When you have replaced the bones, you must apply the bandages while the parts are upon the stretch, if you possibly can; but if prevented by the thongs, you must loose them, and make counter-extension until you get the bandages applied. The bandage is to be applied in the manner formerly described, the heads of the bandages being placed on the projecting part, and the first turns made in like manner, and so also with regard to the number of compresses and the compression; and turns of the bandages are to be brought frequently round on this and on that side of the ankle. But this joint must be bound more tight at the first dressing than in the case of the hand. But when you have applied the bandage, you must place the bandaged part somewhat higher than the rest of the body, and in such a position that the foot may hang as little as possible. The attenuation of the body is to be made proportionate to the magnitude of the luxation, for one luxation is to be a small, and another to a great extent. But in general we must reduce more, and for a longer time,

in injuries about the legs, than in those about the hands; for the former parts are larger and thicker than the latter, and it is necessary that the body should be kept in a state of rest, and in a recumbent position. There is nothing to prevent or require the limb to be bandaged a-new on the third day. And all the treatment otherwise is to be conducted in like manner, as in the preceding cases. And if the patient have resolution to lie quiet, forty days will be suffici-ent for this purpose, if only the bones be prop-erly reduced, but if he will not lie quiet, he will not be able to use the limb with ease, and he will find it necessary to wear a bandage for a long time. When the bones are not properly re-placed, but there has been some defect in this respect, the hip, the thigh, and the leg become wasted, and if the dislocation be inward, the external part of the thigh is wasted, and *vice versa*. But for the most part the dislocation is inward.

15. And when both bones of the leg are brok-en without a wound of the skin, stronger ex-tension is required. We may make extension by some of the methods formerly described, pro-vided the bones ride over one another to a con-siderable degree. But extension by men is also sufficient, and for the most part two strong men will suffice, by making extension and counter-extension. Extension must naturally be made straight in a line with the leg and thigh, wheth-er on account of a fracture of the bones of the leg or of the thigh. And in both cases they are to be bandaged while in a state of extension, for the same position does not suit with the leg and the arm. For when the fractured bones of the arm or fore-arm are bandaged, the fore-arm is suspended in a sling, and if you bind them up while extended, the figures of the fleshy parts will be changed in bending the arm at the el-bow, for the elbow cannot be kept long extend-ed, since persons are not in the custom of keep-ing the joint long in this form, but in a bent position, and persons who have been wounded in the arm, and are still able to walk about, re-quire to have the arm bent at the elbow-joint. But the leg, both in walking and standing, is habitually extended, either completely or near-ly so, and is usually in a depending position from its construction, and in order that it may bear the weight of the rest of the body. Where-fore it readily bears to be extended when neces-sary, and even when in bed the limb is often in this position. And when wounded, necessity sub-dues the understanding, since the patients be-come incapable of raising themselves up, so that

they neither think of bending the limb nor of getting up erect, but remain lying in the same position. For these reasons, neither the same position nor the same mode of bandaging ap-plies to the arm and to the leg. If, then, exten-sion by means of men be sufficient, we should not have recourse to any useless contrivances, for it is absurd to employ mechanical means when not required; but if extension by men be not sufficient, you may use any of the mechan-ical powers which is suitable. When sufficiently extended, it will be easy to adjust the bones and bring them into their natural position, by straightening and arranging them with the palms of the hand.

16. When the parts are adjusted, you should apply the bandages while the limb is in a stretched position, making the first turns to the right or to the left, as may be most suitable; and the end of the bandage should be placed over the fracture, and the first turns made at that place; and then the bandage should be carried up the leg, as described with regard to the other fractures. But the bandages should be broader and longer, and more numerous, in the case of the leg than in that of the arm. And when it is bandaged it should be laid upon some smooth and soft object, so that it may not be distorted to the one side or the other, and that there may be no protrusion of the bones either forward or backward; for this purpose nothing is more convenient than a cushion, or something similar, either of linen or wool, and not hard; it is to be made hollow along its mid-dle, and placed below the limb. With regard to the canals (*gutters?*) usually placed below frac-tured legs, I am at a loss whether to advise that they should be used or not. For they certainly are beneficial, but not to the extent which those who use them suppose. For the canals do not preserve the leg at rest as they suppose; nor, when the rest of the body is turned to the one side or the other, does the canal prevent the leg from following, unless the patient himself pay attention; neither does the canal prevent the limb from being moved without the body to the one side or the other. And a board is an un-comfortable thing to have the limb laid upon, unless something soft be placed above it. But it is a very useful thing in making any subsequent arrangements of the bed and in going to stool. A limb then may be well or ill arranged with or without the canal. But the common people have more confidence, and the surgeon is more like-ly to escape blame, when the canal is placed un-der the limb, although it is not *secundum ar-*

tem. For the limb should by all means lie straight upon some level and soft object, since the bandaging must necessarily be overcome by any distortion in the placing of the leg, whenever or to whatever extent it may be inclined. The patient, when bandaged, should return the same answers as formerly stated, for the bandaging should be the same, and the same swellings should arise in the extremities, and the slackening of the bandages in like manner, and the new bandaging on the third day; and the bandaged part should be found reduced in swelling; and the new bandagings should be more tightly put on, and more pieces of cloth should be used; and the bandages should be carried loosely about the foot, unless the wound be near the knee. Extension should be made and the bones adjusted at every new bandaging; for, if properly treated, and if the swelling progress in a suitable manner, the bandaged limb will have become more slender and attenuated, and the bones will be more mobile, and yield more readily to extension. On the seventh, the ninth, or the eleventh day, the splints should be applied as described in treating of the other fractures. Attention should be paid to the position of the splints about the ankles and along the tendon of the foot which runs up the leg. The bones of the leg get consolidated in forty days, if properly treated. But if you suspect that anything is wanting to the proper arrangement of the limb, or dread any ulceration, you should loose the bandages in the interval, and having put everything right, apply them again.

17. But if the other bone (*fibula?*) of the leg be broken, less powerful extension is required, and yet it must not be neglected, nor be performed slovenly, more especially at the first bandaging. For in all cases of fracture this object should be attained then as quickly as possible. For when the bandage is applied tight while the bones are not properly arranged, the part becomes more painful. The treatment otherwise is the same.

18. Of the bones of the leg, the inner one, called the tibia, is the more troublesome to manage, and requires the greater extension; and if the broken bones are not properly arranged, it is impossible to conceal the distortion, for the bone is exposed and wholly uncovered with flesh; and it is much longer before patients can walk on the leg when this bone is broken. But if the outer bone be broken, it causes much less trouble, and the deformity, when the bones are not properly set, is much more easily concealed, the bone being well covered with flesh;

and the patients speedily get on foot, for it is the inner bone of the leg which supports the most of the weight of the body. For along with the thigh, as being in a line with weight thrown upon the thigh, the inner bone has more work to sustain; inasmuch as it is the head of the thigh-bone which sustains the upper part of the body, and it is on the inner and not on the outer side of the thigh, being in a line with the tibia; and the other half of the body approximates more to this line than to the external one; and at the same time the inner bone is larger than the outer, as in the fore-arm the bone in the line of the little finger is the slenderer and longer. But in the joint of the inferior extremity, the disposition of the longer bone is not alike, for the elbow and the ham are bent differently. For these reasons when the external bone is broken, the patients can soon walk about; but in fractures of the inner, it is a long time before they can walk.

19. When the thigh-bone is broken, particular pains should be taken with regard to the extension that it may not be insufficient, for when excessive, no great harm results from it. For, if one should bandage a limb while the extremities of the bone are separated to a distance from one another by the force of the extension, the bandaging will not keep them separate, and so the bones will come together again as soon as the persons stretching it let go their hold; for the fleshy parts (*muscles?*) being thick and strong, are more powerful than the bandaging, instead of being less so. In the case then which we are now treating of, nothing should be omitted in order that the parts may be properly distended and put in a straight line; for it is a great disgrace and an injury to exhibit a shortened thigh. For the arm, when shortened, might be concealed, and the mistake would not be great; but a shortened thigh-bone would exhibit the man maimed. For when the sound limb is placed beside it, being longer than the other, it exposes the mistake, and therefore it would be to the advantage of a person who would be improperly treated that both his legs should be broken, rather than either of them; for in this case the one would be of the same length as the other. When, then, proper extension has been made, you must adjust the parts with the palms of the hands, and bandage the limb in the manner formerly described, placing the hands of the bandages as was directed, and making the turns upward. And the patient should return the same answers to the same questions as formerly, should be pained and recover in like

manner, and should have the bandaging renewed in the same way; and the application of the splints should be the same. The thigh-bone is consolidated in forty days.

20. But this also should be known, that the thigh-bone is curved rather to the outside than to the inside, and rather forward than backward; when not properly treated, then, the distortions are in these directions; and the bone is least covered with flesh at the same parts, so that the distortion cannot be concealed. If, therefore, you suspect anything of this kind, you should have recourse to the mechanical contrivances recommended in distortion of the arm. And a few turns of the bandage should be brought round by the hip and the loins, so that the groin and the articulation near the perineum may be included in the bandage; and moreover, it is expedient that the extremities of the splints should not do mischief by being placed on parts not covered with the bandages. The splints, in fact, should be carefully kept off the naked parts at both ends; and the arrangement of them should be so managed, as that they may not be placed on the natural protuberances of the bone at the knee-joint, nor on the tendon which is situated there.

21. The swellings which arise in the ham, at the foot, or in any other part from the pressure, should be well wrapped in unscoured and carded wool, washed with wine and oil, and anointed with cerate, before bandaging; and if the splints give pain they should be slackened. You may sooner reduce the swellings, by laying aside the splints, and applying plenty of bandages to them, beginning from below and rolling upward; for thus the swellings will be most speedily reduced, and the humors be propelled to the parts above the former bandages. But this form of bandaging must not be used unless there be danger of vesications or blackening in the swelling, and nothing of the kind occurs unless the fracture be bound too tight, or unless the limb be allowed to hang, or it be rubbed with the hand, or some other thing of an irritant nature be applied to the skin.

22. More injury than good results from placing below the thigh a canal which does not pass farther down than the ham, for it neither prevents the body nor the leg from being moved without the thigh. And it creates uneasiness by being brought down to the ham, and has a tendency to produce what of all things should be avoided, namely, flexion at the knee, for this completely disturbs the bandages; and when the thigh and leg are bandaged, if one bend the limb at the knee, the muscles necessarily assume another shape, and the broken bones are also necessarily moved. Every endeavor then should be made to keep the ham extended. But it appears to me, that a canal which embraces the limb from the nates to the foot is of use. And moreover, a shawl should be put loosely round at the ham, along with the canal, as children are swathed in bed; and then, if the thigh-bone gets displaced either upward or to the side, it can be more easily kept in position by this means along with the canal. The canal then should be made so as to extend all along the limb or not used at all.

23. The extremity of the heel should be particularly attended to, so that it may be properly laid, both in fractures of the leg and of the thigh. For if the foot be placed in a dependent position, while the rest of the body is supported, the limb must present a curved appearance at the forepart of the leg; and if the heel be placed higher than is proper, and if the rest of the leg be rather too low, the bone at the forepart of the leg must present a hollow, more especially if the heel of the patient be naturally large. But all the bones get consolidated more slowly, if not laid properly, and if not kept steady in the same position, and in this case the callus is more feeble.

24. These things relate to cases in which there is fracture of the bones without protrusion of the same or wound of any other kind. In those cases in which the bones are simply broken across, and are not comminuted, but protrude, if reduced the same day or next, and secured in their place, and if there be no reason to anticipate that any splintered bones will come away; and in those in which the broken bones do not protrude, nor is the mode of fracture such that there is reason to expect the splinters will come out, some physicians heal the sores in a way which neither does much good nor harm, by means of a cleansing application, applying pitch ointment, or some of the dressings for fresh wounds, or anything else which they are accustomed to do, and binding above them compresses wetted with wine, or greasy wool, or something else of the like nature. And when the wounds become clean and are new healed, they endeavor to bind up the limb with plenty of bandages, and keep it straight with splints. This treatment does some good, and never much harm. The bones, however, can never be equally well restored to their place, but the part is a little more swelled than it should be; and the limb will be somewhat shortened, provided

both bones either of the leg or fore-arm have been fractured.

25. There are others who treat such cases at first with bandages, applying them on both sides of the seat of the injury, but omit them there, and leave the wound uncovered, and afterward they apply to the wound some cleansing medicine, and complete the dressing with compresses dipped in wine and greasy wool. This plan of treatment is bad, and it is clear that those who adopt this mode of practice are guilty of great mistakes in other cases of fracture as well as these. For it is a most important consideration to know in what manner the head of the bandage should be placed and at what part the greatest pressure should be, and what benefits would result from applying the end of the bandage and the pressure at the proper place, and what mischiefs would result from applying the head of the bandage and the pressure otherwise than at the proper place. Wherefore it has been stated in the preceding part of the work what are the results of either; and the practice of medicine bears witness to the truth of it, for in a person thus bandaged, a swelling must necessarily arise on the wound. For, if even a sound piece of skin were bandaged on either side, and a part were left in the middle, the part thus left unbandaged would become most swelled, and would assume a bad color; how then could it be that a wound would not suffer in like manner? The wound then must necessarily become discolored and its lips everted, the discharge will be ichorous and without pus, and the bones, which should not have got into a state of necrosis, exfoliate; and the wound gets into a throbbing and inflamed condition. And they are obliged to apply a cataplasm on account of the swelling, but this is an unsuitable application to parts which are bandaged on both sides, for a useless load is added to the throbbing which formerly existed in it. At last they loose the bandages when matters get very serious, and conduct the rest of the treatment without bandaging; and notwithstanding, if they meet with another case of the same description, they treat it in the same manner, for they do not think that the application of the bandages on both sides, and the exposure of the wound are the cause of what happened, but some other untoward circumstance. Wherefore I would not have written so much on this subject, if I had not well known that this mode of bandaging is unsuitable, and yet that many conduct the treatment in this way, whose mistake it is of vital importance to correct, while what is here said is a proof, that what

was formerly written as to the circumstances under which bandages should be tightly applied to fractures or otherwise has been correctly written.

26. As a general rule it may be said, that in those cases in which a separation of bone is not expected, the same treatment should be applied as when the fractures are not complicated with an external wound; for the extension, adjustment of the bones, and the bandaging, are to be conducted in the same manner. To the wound itself a cerate mixed with pitch is to be applied, a thin folded compress is to be bound upon it, and the parts around are to be anointed with white cerate. The cloths for bandages and the other things should be torn broader than in cases in which there is no wound, and the first turn of the bandage should be a good deal broader than the wound. For a narrower bandage than the wound binds the wound like a girdle, which is not proper, or the first turn should comprehend the whole wound, and the bandaging should extend beyond it on both sides. The bandage then should be put on in the direction of the wound, and should be not quite so tight as when there is no wound, but the bandage should be otherwise applied in the manner described above. The bandages should be of a soft consistence, and more especially so in such cases than in those not complicated with a wound. The number of bandages should not be smaller, but rather greater than those formerly described. When applied, the patient should have the feeling of the parts being properly secured, but not too tight, and in particular he should be able to say that they are firm about the wound. And the intervals of time during which the parts seem to be properly adjusted, and those in which they get loose, should be the same as those formerly described. The bandages should be renewed on the third day, and the after treatment conducted in the same manner as formerly described, except that in the latter case the compression should be somewhat less than in the former. And if matters go on properly, the parts about the wound should be found at every dressing always more and more free of swelling, and the swelling should have subsided on the whole part comprehended by the bandages. And the suppurations will take place more speedily than in the case of wounds treated otherwise; and the pieces of flesh in the wound which have become black and dead, will sooner separate and fall off under this plan of treatment than any other, and the sore will come more quickly to cicatrization when thus treated than

otherwise. The reason of all this is, that the parts in which the wound is situated, and the surrounding parts, are kept free of swelling. In all other respects the treatment is to be conducted as in cases of fracture without a wound of the integuments. Splints should not be applied. On this account the bandages should be more numerous than in the former case, both because they must be put on less tight, and because the splints are later of being applied. But if you do apply the splints, they should not be applied along the wound, and they are to be put on in a loose manner, especial care being taken that there may be no great compression from the splints. This direction has been formerly given. And the diet should be more restricted, and for a longer period, in those cases in which there is a wound at the commencement, and when the bones protrude through the skin; and, in a word, the greater the wound, the more severe and protracted should the regimen be.

27. The treatment of the sores is the same in those cases of fracture in which there was no wound of the skin at first, but one has formed in the course of treatment, owing to the pressure of the splints occasioned by the bandages, or from any other cause. In such cases it is ascertained that there is an ulcer, by the pain and the throbbing; and the swelling in the extremities becomes harder than usual, and if you apply your finger the redness disappears, but speedily returns. If you suspect anything of the kind you must loose the dressing, if there be any itching below the under-bandages, or in any other part that is bandaged, and used a pitched cerate instead of the other. If there be nothing of that, but if the ulcer be found in an irritable state, being very black and foul, and the fleshy parts about to suppurate, and the tendons to slough away, in these cases no part is to be exposed to the air, nor is anything to be apprehended from these suppurations, but the treatment is to be conducted in the same manner as in those cases in which there was an external wound at first. You must begin to apply the bandages loosely at the swelling in the extremities, and then gradually proceed upward with the bandaging, so that it may be tight at no place, but particularly firm at the sore, and less so elsewhere. The first bandages should be clean and not narrow, and the number of bandages should be as great as in those cases in which the splints were used, or somewhat fewer. To the sore itself a compress, anointed with white cerate, will be sufficient, for if a piece of flesh or nerve (*tendon?*) become black, it will fall

off; for such sores are not to be treated with acrid, but with emollient applications, like burns. The bandages are to be renewed every third day, and no splints are to be applied, but rest is to be more rigidly maintained than in the former cases, along with a restricted diet. It should be known, that if any piece of flesh or tendon be to come away, the mischief will spread much less, and the parts will much more speedily drop off, and the swelling in the surrounding parts will much more completely subside, under this treatment, than if any of the cleansing applications be put upon the sore. And if any part that is to come away shall fall off, the part will incarnate sooner when thus treated than otherwise, and will more speedily cicatrize. Such are the good effects of knowing how a bandage can be well and moderately applied. But a proper position, the other parts of the regimen, and suitable bandages co-operate.

28. If you are deceived with regard to a recent wound, supposing there will be no exfoliation of the bones, while they are on the eve of coming out of the sore, you must not hesitate to adopt this mode of treatment; for no great mischief will result, provided you have the necessary dexterity to apply the bandages well and without doing any harm. And this is a symptom of an exfoliation of bone being about to take place under this mode of treatment; pus runs copiously from the sore, and appears striving to make its escape. The bandage must be renewed more frequently on account of the discharge, since otherwise fevers come on; if the sore and surrounding parts be compressed by the bandages they become wasted. Cases complicated with the exfoliation of very small bones, do not require any change of treatment, only the bandages should be put on more loosely, so that the discharge of pus may not be intercepted, but left free, and the dressings are to be frequently renewed until the bone exfoliate, and the splints should not be applied until then.

29. Those cases in which the exfoliation of a larger piece of bone is expected, whether you discover this at the commencement, or perceive subsequently that it is to happen, no longer require the same mode of treatment, only that the extension and arrangement of the parts are to be performed in a manner that has been described; but having formed double compresses, not less than half a fathom in breadth (being guided in this by the nature of the wound), and considerably shorter than what would be required to go twice round the part that is wounded, but considerably longer than to go

once round, and in number what will be sufficient, these are to be dipped in a black austere wine; and beginning at the middle, as is done in applying the double-headed bandage, you are to wrap the part around and proceed crossing the heads in the form of the bandage called "ascia." These things are to be done at the wound, and on both sides of it; and there must be no compression, but they are to be laid on so as to give support to the wound. And on the wound itself is to be applied the pitched cerate, or one of the applications to recent wounds, or any other medicine which will suit with the embrocation. And if it be the summer season, the compresses are to be frequently damped with wine; but if the winter season, plenty of greasy wool, moistened with wine and oil, should be applied. And a goat's skin should be spread below, so as to carry off the fluids which run from the wound; these must be guarded against, and it should be kept in mind, that parts which remain long in the same position are subject to excoriations which are difficult to cure.

30. In such cases as do not admit of bandaging according to any of the methods which have been described, or which will be described, great pains should be taken that the fractured part of the body be laid in a right position, and attention should be paid that it may incline upward rather than downward. But if one would wish to do the thing well and dexterously, it is proper to have recourse to some mechanical contrivance, in order that the fractured part of the body may undergo proper and not violent extension; and this means is particularly applicable in fractures of the leg. There are certain physicians who, in all fractures of the leg, whether bandages be applied or not, fasten the sole of the foot to the couch, or to some other piece of wood which they have fixed in the ground near the couch. These persons thus do all sorts of mischief but no good; for it contributes nothing to the extension that the foot is thus bound, as the rest of the body will no less sink down to the foot, and thus the limb will no longer be stretched, neither will it do any good toward keeping the limb in a proper position, but will do harm, for when the rest of the body is turned to this side or that, the bandaging will not prevent the foot and the bones belonging to it from following the rest of the body. For if it had not been bound it would have been less distorted, as it would have been the less prevented from following the motion of the rest of the body. But one should sew two balls of Egyptian leather,

such as are worn by persons confined for a length of time in large shackles, and the balls should have coats on each side, deeper toward the wound, but shorter toward the joints; and the balls should be well stuffed and soft, and fit well, the one above the ankles, and the other below the knee. Sideways it should have below two appendages, either of a single or double thong, and short, like loops, the one set being placed on either side of the ankle, and the other on the knee. And the other upper ball should have others of the same kind in the same line. Then taking four rods, made of the cornel tree, of equal length, and of the thickness of a finger, and of such length that when bent they will admit of being adjusted to the appendages, care should be taken that the extremities of the rods bear not upon the skin, but on the extremities of the balls. There should be three sets of rods, or more, one set a little longer than another, and another a little shorter and smaller, so that they may produce greater or less distention, if required. Either of these sets of rods should be placed on this side and that of the ankles. If these things be properly contrived, they should occasion a proper and equable extension in a straight line, without giving any pain to the wound; for the pressure, if there is any, should be thrown at the foot and the thigh. And the rods are commodiously arranged on either side of the ankles, so as not to interfere with the position of the limb; and the wound is easily examined and easily arranged. And, if thought proper, there is nothing to prevent the two upper rods from being fastened to one another; and if any light covering be thrown over the limb, it will thus be kept off from the wound. If, then, the balls be well made, handsome, soft, and newly stitched, and if the extension by the rods be properly managed, as has been already described, this is an excellent contrivance; but if any of them do not fit properly, it does more harm than good. And all other mechanical contrivances should either be properly done, or not be had recourse to at all, for it is a disgraceful and awkward thing to use mechancial means in an unmechanical way.

31. Moreover, the greater part of physicians treat fractures, both with and without an external wound, during the first days, by means of unwashed wool, and there does not appear to be anything improper in this. It is very excusable for those who are called upon to treat newly-received accidents of this kind, and who have no cloth for bandages at hand, to do them up with wool; for, except cloth for bandages,

one could not have anything better than wool in such cases; but a good deal should be used for this purpose, and it should be well carded and not rough, for in small quantity and of a bad quality it has little power. But those who approve of binding up the limb with wool for a day or two, and on the third and fourth apply bandages, and make the greatest compression and extension at that period, such persons show themselves to be ignorant of the most important principles of medicine; for, in a word, at no time is it so little proper to disturb all kinds of wounds as on the third and fourth day; and all sort of probing should be avoided on these days in whatever other injuries are attended with irritation. For, generally, the third and fourth day in most cases of wounds, are those which give rise to exacerbations, whether the tendency be to inflammation, to a foul condition of the sore, or to fevers. And if any piece of information be particularly valuable this is; to which of the most important cases in medicine does it not apply? and that not only in wounds but in many other diseases, unless one should call all other diseases wounds. And this doctrine is not devoid of a certain degree of plausibility, for they are allied to one another in many respects. But those who maintain that wool should be used until after the first seven days, and then that the parts should be extended and adjusted, and secured with bandages, would appear not to be equally devoid of proper judgment, for the most dangerous season for inflammation is then past, and the bones being loose can be easily set after the lapse of these days. But still this mode of treatment is far inferior to that with bandages from the commencement; for, the latter method exhibits the patient on the seventh day free from inflammation, and ready for complete bandaging with splints; while the former method is far behind in this respect, and is attended with many other bad effects which it would be tedious to describe.

31a. In those cases of fracture in which the bones protrude and cannot be restored to their place, the following mode of reduction may be practiced:—Some small pieces of iron are to be prepared like the levers which the cutters of stone make use of, one being rather broader and another narrower; and there should be three of them at least, and still more, so that you may use those that suit best; and then, along with extension, we must use these as levers, applying the under surface of the piece of iron to the under fragment of the bone, and the upper surface to the upper bone; and, in a word, we

must operate powerfully with the lever as we would do upon a stone or a piece of wood. The pieces of iron should be as strong as possible, so that they may not bend. This is a powerful assistance, provided the pieces of iron be suitable, and one use them properly as levers. Of all the mechanical instruments used by men, the most powerful are these three, the axis in peritrochio, the lever, and the wedge. Without these, one or all, men could not perform any of their works which require great force. Wherefore, reduction with the lever is not to be despised, for the bones will be reduced in this way, or not at all. But if the upper fragment which rides over the other does not furnish a suitable point of support for the lever, but the protruding part is sharp, you must scoop out of the bone what will furnish a proper place for the lever to rest on. The lever, along with extension, may be had recourse to on the day of the accident, or next day, but by no means on the third, the fourth, and the fifth. For if the limb is disturbed on these days, and yet the fractured bones not reduced, inflammation will be excited, and this no less if they are reduced; for convulsions are more apt to occur if reduction take place, than if the attempt should fail. These facts should be well known, for if convulsions should come on when reduction is effected, there is little hope of recovery; but it is of use to displace the bones again if this can be done without trouble. For it is not at the time when the parts are in a particularly relaxed condition that convulsions and tetanus are apt to supervene, but when they are more than usually tense. In the case we are now treating of, we should not disturb the limb on the aforesaid days, but strive to keep the wound as free from inflammation as possible, and especially encourage suppuration in it. But when seven days have elapsed, or rather more, if there be no fever, and if the wound be not inflamed, then there will be less to prevent an attempt at reduction, if you hope to succeed; but otherwise you need not take and give trouble in vain.

32. When you have reduced the bones to their place, the modes of treatment, whether you expect the bones to exfoliate or not, have been already described. All those cases in which an exfoliation of bone is expected, should be treated by the method of bandaging with cloths, beginning for the most part at the middle of the bandage, as is done with the double-headed bandage; but particular attention should be paid to the shape of the wound, so that its lips may gape or be distorted as little as possible under the band-

age. Sometimes the turns of the bandage have to be made to the right, and sometimes to the left, and sometimes a double-headed bandage is to be used.

33. It should be known that bones, which it has been found impossible to reduce, as well as those which are wholly denuded of flesh, will become detached. In some cases the upper part of the bone is laid bare, and in others the flesh dies all around; and, from a sore of long standing, certain of the bones become carious, and some not, some more, and some less; and in some the small, and in others the large bones. From what has been said it will be seen, that it is impossible to tell in one word when the bones will separate. Some come away more quickly, owing to their smallness, and some from being merely fixed at the point; and some, from pieces not separating, but merely exfoliating, become dried up and putrid; and besides, different modes of treatment have different effects. For the most part, the bones separate most quickly in those cases in which suppuration takes place most quickly, and when new flesh is most quickly formed, and is particularly sound, for the flesh which grows up below in the wound generally elevates the pieces of bone. It will be well if the whole circle of the bone separate in forty days; for in some cases it is protracted to sixty days, and in some to more; for the more porous pieces of bone separate more quickly, but the more solid come away more slowly; but the other smaller splinters in much less time, and others otherwise. A portion of bone which protrudes should be sawn off for the following reasons: if it cannot be reduced, and if it appears that only a small piece is required in order that it may get back into its place; and if it be such that it can be taken out, and if it occasions inconvenience and irritates any part of the flesh, and prevents the limb from being properly laid, and if, moreover, it be denuded of flesh, such a piece of bone should be taken off. With regard to the others, it is not of much consequence whether they be sawed off or not. For it should be known for certain, that such bones as are completely deprived of flesh, and have become dried, all separate completely. Those which are about to exfoliate should not be sawn off. Those that will separate completely must be judged of from the symptoms that have been laid down.

34. Such cases are to be treated with compresses and vinous applications, as formerly laid down regarding bones which will separate. We must avoid wetting it at the beginning with anything cold; for there is danger of febrile rig-

ors, and also of convulsions; for convulsions are induced by cold things, and also sometimes by wounds. It is proper to know that the members are necessarily shortened in those cases in which the bones have been broken, and have healed the one across the other, and in those cases in which the whole circle of the bone has become detached.

35. Those cases in which the bone of the thigh, or of the arm, protrudes, do not easily recover. For the bones are large, and contain much marrow; and many important nerves, muscles, and veins are wounded at the same time. And if you reduce them, convulsions usually supervene; and, if not reduced, acute bilious fevers come on, with singultus and mortification. The chances of recovery are not fewer in those cases in which the parts have not been reduced, nor any attempts made at reduction. Still more recover in those cases in which the lower, than those in which the upper part of the bone protrudes; and some will recover when reduction has been made, but very rarely indeed. For modes of treatment and peculiarity of constitution make a great difference as to the capability of enduring such an injury. And it makes a great difference if the bones of the arm and of the thigh protrude to the inside; for there are many and important vessels situated there, some of which, if wounded, will prove fatal; there are such also on the outside, but of less importance. In wounds of this sort, then, one ought not to be ignorant of the dangers, and should prognosticate them in due time. But if you are compelled to have recourse to reduction, and hope to succeed, and if the bones do not cross one another much, and if the muscles are not contracted (for they usually are contracted), the lever in such cases may be advantageously employed.

36. Having effected the reduction, you must give an emollient draught of hellebore the same day, provided it has been reduced on the day of the accident, but otherwise it should not be attempted. The wound should be treated with the same things as are used in fractures of the bones of the head, and nothing cold should be applied; the patient should be restricted from food altogether, and if naturally of a bilious constitution, he should have for a diet a little fragrant *oxyglyky* sprinkled on water; but if he is not bilious, he should have water for drink; and if fever of the continual type come on, he is to be confined to this regimen for fourteen days at least, but if he be free of fever, for only seven days, and then you must bring him back by de-

grees to a common diet. To those cases in which the bones have not been reduced, a similar course of medicine should be administered, along with the same treatment of the sores and regimen; and in like manner the suspended part of the body should not be stretched, but should rather be contracted, so as to relax the parts about the wound. The separation of the bones is protracted, as also was formerly stated. But one should try to escape from such cases, provided one can do so honourably, for the hopes of recovery are small, and the dangers many; and if the physician do not reduce the fractured bones he will be looked upon as unskillful, while by reducing them he will bring the patient nearer to death than to recovery.

37. Luxations and subluxations at the knee are much milder accidents than subluxations and luxations at the elbow. For the knee-joint, in proportion to its size, is more compact than that of the arm, and has a more even conformation, and is rounded, while the joint of the arm is large, and has many cavities. And in addition, the bones of the leg are nearly of the same length, for the external one overtops the other to so small an extent as hardly to deserve being mentioned, and therefore affords no great resistance, although the external nerve (*ligament?*) at the ham arises from it; but the bones of the fore-arm are unequal, and the shorter is considerably thicker than the other, and the more slender (*ulna?*) protrudes, and passes up above the joint, and to it (the *olecranon?*) are attached the nerves (*ligaments?*) which go downward to the junction of the bones; and the slender bone (*ulna?*) has more to do with the insertion of the ligaments in the arm than the thick bone (*radius?*). The configuration then of the articulations, and of the bones of the elbow, is such as I have described. Owing to their configuration, the bones at the knee are indeed frequently dislocated, but they are easily reduced, for no great inflammation follows, nor any constriction of the joint. They are displaced for the most part to the inside, sometimes to the outside, and occasionally into the ham. The reduction in all these cases is not difficult, but in the dislocations inward and outward, the patient should be placed on a low seat, and the thigh should be elevated, but not much. Moderate extension for the most part sufficeth, extension being made at the leg, and counter-extension at the thigh.

38. Dislocations at the elbow are more troublesome than those at the knee, and, owing to the inflammation which comes on, and the con-figuration of the joint, are more difficult to reduce if the bones are not immediately replaced. For the bones at the elbow are less subject to dislocation than those of the knee, but are more difficult to reduce and keep in their position, and are more apt to become inflamed and ankylosed.

39. For the most part the displacements of these bones are small, sometimes toward the ribs, and sometimes to the outside; and the whole articulation is not displaced, but that part of the humerus remains in place which is articulated with the cavity of the bone of the fore-arm that has a protuberance (*ulna?*). Such dislocations, to whatever side, are easily reduced, and the extension is to be made in the line of the arm, one person making extension at the wrist, and another grasping the armpit, while a third, applying the palm of his hand to the part of the joint which is displaced, pushes it inward, and at the same time makes counter-pressure on the opposite side near the joint with the other hand.

40. The end of the humerus at the elbow gets displaced (*subluxated?*) by leaving the cavity of the ulna. Such luxations readily yield to reduction, if applied before the parts get inflamed. The displacement for the most part is to the inside, but sometimes to the outside, and they are readily recognized by the shape of the limb. And often such luxations are reduced without any powerful extension. In dislocations inward, the joint is to be pushed into its place, while the fore-arm is brought round to a state of pronation. Such are most of the dislocations at the elbow.

41. But if the articular extremity of the humerus be carried to either side above the bone of the fore-arm, which is prominent, into the hollow of the arm (?), this rarely happens; but if it does happen, extension in the straight line is not so proper under such circumstances; for in such a mode of extension, the process of the ulna (*olecranon?*) prevents the bone of the arm (*humerus?*) from passing over it. In dislocations of this kind, extension should be made in the manner described when treating of the bandaging of fractured bones of the arm, extension being made upward at the armpit, while the parts at the elbow are pushed downward, for in this manner can the humerus be most readily raised above its cavity; and when so raised, the reduction is easy with the palms of the hand, the one being applied so as to make pressure on the protuberant part of the arm, and the other making counter-pressure, so as to

push the bone of the fore-arm into the joint. This method answers with both cases. And perhaps this is the most suitable mode of reduction in such a case of dislocation. The parts may be reduced by extension in a straight line, but less readily than thus.

42. If the arm be dislocated forward—this rarely happens, indeed, but what would a sudden shock not displace? for many other things are removed from their proper place, notwithstanding a great obstacle,—in such a violent displacement the part (*olecranon?*) which passes above the prominent part of the bones is large, and the stretching of the nerves (*ligaments?*) is intense; and yet the parts have been so dislocated in certain cases. The following is the symptom of such a displacement: the arm cannot be bent in the least degree at the elbow, and upon feeling the joint the nature of the accident becomes obvious. If, then, it is not speedily reduced, strong and violent inflammation, attended with fever, will come on, but if one happen to be on the spot at the time it is easily reduced. A piece of hard linen cloth (or a piece of hard linen, not very large, rolled up in a ball, will be sufficient) is to be placed across the bend of the elbow, and the arm is then to be suddenly bent at the elbow, and the hand brought up to the shoulder. This mode of reduction is sufficient in such displacements; and extension in the straight line can rectify this manner of dislocation, but we must use at the same time the palms of the hands, applying the one to the projecting part of the humerus at the bend of the arm for the purpose of pushing it back, and applying the other below to the sharp extremity of the elbow, to make counter-pressure, and incline the parts into the straight line. And one may use with advantage in this form of dislocation the method of extension formerly described, for the application of the bandages in the case of fracture of the arm; but when extension is made, the parts are to be adjusted, as has been also described above.

43. But if the arm be dislocated backward (but this very rarely happens, and it is the most painful of all, and the most subject to bilious fevers of the continual type, which prove fatal in the course of a few days), in such a case the patient cannot extend the arm. If you are quickly present, by forcible extension the parts may return to their place of their own accord; but if fever have previously come on, you must no longer attempt reduction, for the pain will be rendered more intense by any such violent attempt. In a word, no joint whatever should be reduced during the prevalence of fever, and least of all the elbow-joint.

44. There are also other troublesome injuries connected with the elbow-joint; for example, the thicker bone (*radius?*) is sometime partially displaced from the other, and the patient can neither perform extension nor flexion properly. This accident becomes obvious upon examination with the hand at the bend of the arm near the division of the vein that runs up the muscle. In such a case it is not easy to reduce the parts to their natural state, nor is it easy, in the separation of any two bones united by symphysis, to restore them to their natural state, for there will necessarily be a swelling at the seat of the diastasis. The method of bandaging a joint has been already described in treating of the application of bandages to the ankle.

45. In certain cases the process of the ulna (*olecranon?*) behind the humerus is broken; sometimes its cartilaginous part, which gives origin to the posterior tendon of the arm, and sometimes its fore part, at the base of the anterior coronoid process; and when this displacement takes place, it is apt to be attended with malignant fever. The joint, however, remains in place, for its whole base protrudes at that point. But when the displacement takes place where its head overtops the arm, the joint becomes looser if the bone be fairly broken across. To speak in general terms, all cases of fractured bones are less dangerous than those in which the bones are not broken, but the veins and important nerves (*tendons?*) situated in these places are contused; for the risk of death is more immediate in the latter class of cases than in the former, if continual fever come on. But fractures of this nature seldom occur.

46. It sometimes happens that the head of the humerus is fractured at its epiphysis; and this, although it may appear to be a much more troublesome accident, is in fact a much milder one than the other injuries at the joint.

47. The treatment especially befitting each particular dislocation has been described; and it has been laid down as a rule, that immediate reduction is of the utmost advantage, owing to the rapid manner in which inflammation of the tendons supervenes. For even when the luxated parts are immediately reduced, the tendons usually become stiffened, and for a considerable time prevent extension and flexion from being performed to the ordinary extent. All these cases are to be treated in a similar way, whether the extremity of the articulating bone be snapped off, whether the bones be separated, or whether

they be dislocated; for they are all to be treated with plenty of bandages, compresses, and cerate, like other fractures. The position of the joint in all these cases should be the same, as when a fractured arm or fore-arm has been bound up. For this is the most common position in all dislocations, displacements, and fractures; and it is the most convenient for the subsequent movements, whether of extension or flexion, as being the intermediate stage between both. And this is the position in which the patient can most conveniently carry or suspend his arm in a sling. And besides, if the joint is to be stiffened by callus, it were better that this should not take place when the arm is extended, for this position will be a great impediment and little advantage; if the arm be wholly bent, it will be more useful; but it will be much more convenient to have the joint in the intermediate position when it becomes ankylosed. So much with regard to position.

48. In bandaging, the head of the first bandage should be placed at the seat of the injury, whether it be a case of fracture, of dislocation, or of diastasis (*separation?*), and the first turns should be made there, and the bandages should be applied most firmly at that place, and less so on either side. The bandaging should comprehend both the arm and the fore-arm, and on both should be to a much greater extent than most physicians apply it, so that the swelling may be expelled from the seat of the injury to either side. And the point of the fore-arm should be comprehended in the bandaging, whether the injury be in that place or not, in order that the swelling may not collect there. In applying bandages, we must avoid as much as possible accumulating many turns of the bandage at the bend of the arm. For the principal compression should be at the seat of the injury, and the same rules are to be observed, and at the same periods, with regard to compression and relaxation, as formerly described respecting the treatment of broken bones; and the bandages should be renewed every third day; and they should appear loose on the third day, as in the other case. And splints should be applied at the proper time (for there is nothing unsuitable in them, whether the bones be fractured or not, provided there is no fever); they should be particularly loose, whether applied to the arm or the fore-arm, but they must not be thick. It is necessary that they should be of unequal size, and that the one should ride over the other, whenever from the flexion it is judged proper. And the application of the compresses should be regulated in the same manner as has been stated with regard to the splints; and they should be put on in a somewhat more bulky form at the seat of the injury. The periods are to be estimated from the inflammation, and from what has been written on them above.

On the Articulations

I AM acquainted with one form in which the shoulder-joint is dislocated, namely, that into the armpit; I have never seen it take place upward nor outward; and yet I do not positively affirm whether it might be dislocated in these directions or not, although I have something which I might say on this subject. But neither have I ever seen what I considered to be a dislocation forward. Physicians, indeed, fancy that dislocation is very apt to occur forward, and they are more particularly deceived in those persons who have the fleshy parts about the joint and arm much emaciated; for, in all such cases, the head of the arm appears to protrude forward. And I in one case of this kind having said that there was no dislocation, exposed myself to censure from certain physicians and common people on that account, for they fancied that I alone was ignorant of what everybody else was acquainted with, and I could not convince them but with difficulty, that the matter was so. But if one will strip the point of the shoulder of the fleshy parts, and where the muscle (*deltoid?*) extends, and also lay bare the tendon that goes from the armpit and clavicle to the breast (*pectoral muscle?*), the head of the humerus will appear to protrude strongly forward, although not dislocated, for the head of the humerus naturally inclines forward, but the rest of the bone is turned outward. The humerus is connected obliquely with the cavity of the scapula, when the arm is stretched along the sides; but when the whole arm is stretched forward, then the head of the humerus is in a line with the cavity of the humerus, and no longer appears to protrude forward. And with regard to the variety we are now treating of, I have never seen a case of dislocation forward; and yet I do not speak decidedly respecting it, whether such a dislocation may take place or not. When, then, a dislocation into the armpit takes place, seeing it is of frequent occurrence, many persons know how to reduce it, for it is an easy thing to teach all the methods by which physicians effect the reductions, and the best manner of applying them. The strongest of those methods should be used when the difficulty of reduction is particularly great. The strongest is the method to be last described.

2. Those who are subject to frequent dislocations at the shoulder-joint, are for the most part competent to effect the reduction themselves; for, having introduced the knuckles of the other hand into the armpit, they force the joint upward, and bring the elbow toward the breast. The physician might reduce it in the same manner, if having introduced his fingers into the armpit on the inside of the dislocated joint, he would force it from the ribs, pushing his own head against the acromion, in order to make counter-pressure, and with his knees applied to the patient's elbow pushing the arm to the sides. It will be of advantage if the operator has strong hands, or the physician may do as directed with his head and hands, while another person brings the elbow toward the breast. Reduction of the shoulder may also be effected by carrying the fore-arm backward to the spine, and then with the one hand grasping it at the elbow, to bend the arm upward, and with the other to support it behind at the articulation. This mode of reduction, and the one formerly described, are not natural, and yet by rotating the bone of the joint, they force it to return.

3. Those who attempt to perform reduction with the heel, operate in a manner which is an approach to the natural. The patient must lie on the ground upon his back, while the person who is to effect the reduction is seated on the ground upon the side of the dislocation; then the operator, seizing with his hand the affected arm, is to pull it, while with his heel in the armpit he pushes in the contrary direction, the right heel being placed in the right armpit, and the left heel in the left armpit. But a round ball of a suitable size must be placed in the hollow of the armpit; the most convenient are very small and hard balls, formed from several pieces of leather sewed together. For without something of the kind the heel cannot reach to the head of the humerus, since, when the arm is stretched, the armpit becomes hollow, the tendons on both sides of the armpit making counter-contraction so as to oppose the reduction. But another person should be seated on the other side of the patient to hold the sound shoulder, so that the

body may not be dragged along when the arm of the affected side is pulled; and then, when the ball is placed in the armpit, a supple piece of thong sufficiently broad is to be placed round it, and some person taking hold of its two ends is to seat himself above the patient's head to made counter-extension, while at the same time he pushes with his foot against the bone at the top of the shoulder. The ball should be placed as much on the inside as possible, upon the ribs, and not upon the head of the humerus.

4. There is another method of reduction performed by the shoulder of a person standing. The person operating in this way, who should be taller than the patient, is to take hold of his arm and place the sharp point of his own shoulder in the patient's armpit, and push it in so that it may lodge there, and having for his object that the patient may be suspended at his back by the armpit, he must raise himself higher on this shoulder than the other; and he must bring the arm of the suspended patient as quickly as possible to his own breast. In this position he should shake the patient when he raises him up, in order that the rest of the body may be a counterpoise to the arm which is thus held. But if the patient be very light, a light child should be suspended behind along with him. These methods of reduction are all of easy application in the palestra, as they can all be performed without instruments, but they may also be used elsewhere.

5. Those who accomplish the reduction by forcibly bending it round a pestle, operate in a manner which is nearly natural. But the pestle should be wrapped in a soft shawl (for thus it will be less slippery), and it should be forced between the ribs and the head of the humerus. And if the pestle be short, the patient should be seated upon something, so that his arm can with difficulty pass above the pestle. But for the most part the pestle should be longer, so that the patient when standing may be almost suspended upon the piece of wood. And then the arm and forearm should be stretched along the pestle, whilst some person secures the opposite side of the body by throwing his arms round the neck, near the clavicle.

6. But the method with a ladder is another of the same kind, and still better, since by it the body can be more safely counterpoised on this side; and that, while in the method which the piece of wood resembling a pestle, there is danger of the body tumbling to either side. But some round thing should be tied upon the step of the ladder which may be fitted to the armpit,

whereby the head of the bone may be forced into its natural place.

7. The following, however, is the strongest of all the methods of reduction. We must get a piece of wood, five, or at least four inches broad, two inches in thickness, or still thinner, and two cubits in length, or a little less; and its extremity at one end should be rounded, and made very narrow and very slender there, and it should have a slightly projecting edge (*ambe*) on its round extremity, not on the part that is to be applied to the side, but to the head of the humerus, so that it may be adjusted in the armpit at the sides under the head of the humerus; and a piece of soft shawl or cloth should be glued to the end of the piece of wood, so as to give the less pain upon pressure. Then having pushed the head of this piece of wood as far inward as possible between the ribs and the head of the humerus, the whole arm is to be stretched along this piece of wood, and is to be bound round at the arm, the fore-arm, and the wrist, so that it may be particularly well secured; but great pains should be taken that the extremity of this piece of wood should be introduced as far as possible into the armpit, and that it is carried past the head of the humerus. Then a cross-beam is to be securely fastened between two pillars, and afterward the arm with the piece of wood attached to it is to be brought over this cross-beam, so that the arm may be on the one side of it and the body on the other, and the cross-beam in the armpit; and then the arm with the piece of wood is to be forced down on the one side of the cross-beam, and the rest of the body on the other. The cross-beam is to be bound so high that the rest of the body may be raised upon tip-toes. This is by far the most powerful method of effecting reduction of the shoulder; for one thus operates with the lever upon the most correct principles, provided only the piece of wood be placed as much as possible within the head of the humerus, and thus also the counter-balancing weights will be most properly adjusted, and safely applied to the bone of the arm. Wherefore recent cases in this way may be reduced more quickly than could be believed, before even extension would appear to be applied; and this is the only mode of reduction capable of replacing old dislocations, and this it will effect, unless flesh has already filled up the (glenoid) cavity, and the head of the humerus has formed a socket for itself in the place to which it has been displaced; and even in such an old case of dislocation, it appears to me that we could effect reduction (for what object would a lever power properly applied not move?), but it would not remain in its place, but would be again displaced as formerly. The same thing may be effected by means of the ladder, by preparing it in the same manner. If the dislocation be recent, a large Thessalian chair may be sufficient to accomplish this purpose; the wood, however, should be dressed up as described before; but the patient should be seated sideways on the chair, and then the arm, with the piece of wood attached to it, is to be brought over the back of the chair, and force is to be applied to the arm, with the wood on the one side, and the body on the other side. The same means may be applied with a double door. One should always use what happens to be at hand.

8. Wherefore it should be known that one constitution differs much from another as to the facility with which dislocations in them may be reduced, and one articular cavity differs much from another, the one being so constructed that the bone readily leaps out of it, and another less so; but the greatest difference regards the binding together of the parts by the nerves (*ligaments?*) which are slack in some and tight in others. For the humidity in the joints of men is connected with the state of the ligaments, when they are slack and yielding; for you may see many people who are so humid (*flabby?*) that when they choose they can disarticulate their joints without pain, and reduce them in like manner. The habit of the body also occasions a certain difference, for in those who are in a state of embonpoint and fleshy the joint is rarely dislocated, but is more difficult to reduce; but when they are more attenuated and leaner than usual, then they are more subject to dislocations which are more easily reduced. And the following observation is a proof that matters are so; for in cattle the thighs are most apt to be dislocated at the hip-joint, when they are most particularly lean, which they are at the end of winter, at which time then they are particularly subject to dislocations (if I may be allowed to make such an observation while treating of a medical subject); and therefore Homer has well remarked, that of all beasts oxen suffer the most at that season, and especially those employed at the plow as being worked in the winter season. In them, therefore, dislocations happen most frequently, as being at that time most particularly reduced in flesh. And other cattle can crop the grass when it is short, but the ox cannot do so until it becomes long; for, in the others, the projection of the lip is slender, and so is the upper lip, but in the ox the projection of the lip

is thick, and the upper jaw is thick and obtuse, and therefore they are incapable of seizing short herbs. But the *solidungula* as having prominent teeth in both their front jaws, can crop the grass and grasp it with their teeth while short, and delight more in short grass than in rank; for, in general, short grass is better and more substantial than rank, as having not yet given out its fructification. Wherefore the poet has the following line:

As when to horned cattle dear the vernal season comes,[1]

because rank grass appears to be most sought after by them. But otherwise in the ox, this joint is slacker than in other animals, and, therefore, this animal drags his foot in walking more than any other, and especially when lank and old. For all these reasons the ox is most particularly subject to dislocations; and I have made the more observations respecting him, as they confirm all that was said before on this subject. With regard, then, to the matter on hand, I say that dislocations occur more readily, and are more speedily reduced in those who are lean than in those who are fleshy; and in those who are humid and lank there is less inflammation than in such as are dry and fleshy, and they are less compactly knit hereafter, and there is more mucosity than usual in cases not attended with inflammation, and hence the joints are more liable to luxations; for, in the main, the articulations are more subject to mucosities in those who are lean than in those who are fleshy; and the flesh of lean persons who have not been reduced by a proper course of discipline abounds more with mucosity than that of fat persons. But in those cases in which the mucosity is accompanied with inflammation, the inflammation binds (*braces?*) the joint, and hence those who have small collections of mucosities are not very subject to dislocations, which they would be if the mucosity had not been accompanied with more or less inflammation.

9. In cases of dislocation those persons who are not attacked with inflammation of the surrounding parts, can use the shoulder immediately without pain, and do not think it necessary to take any precautions with themselves; it is therefore the business of the physician to warn them beforehand that dislocation is more likely to return in such cases than when the tendons have been inflamed. This remark applies to all the articulations, but particularly to those of the

[1] There is no such line in the works of Homer as they have come down to us.

shoulder and knee, for these are the joints most subject to luxations. But those who have inflammation of the ligaments cannot use the shoulder, for the pain and the tension induced by the inflammation prevent them. Such cases are to be treated with cerate, compresses, and plenty of bandages; but a ball of soft clean wool is to be introduced into the armpit, to fill up the hollow of it, that it may be a support to the bandaging, and maintain the joint *in situ*. The arm, in general, should be inclined upward as much as possible, for thus it will be kept at the greatest possible distance from the place at which the head of the humerus escaped. And when you bandage the shoulder you must fasten the arms to the sides with a band, which is to be carried round the body. The shoulder should be rubbed gently and softly. The physician ought to be acquainted with many things, and among others with friction; for from the same name the same results are not always obtained; for friction could brace a joint when unseasonably relaxed, and relax it when unseasonably hard; but we will define what we know respecting friction in another place. The shoulder, then, in such a state, should be rubbed with soft hands; and, moreover, in a gentle manner, and the joint should be moved about, but not roughly, so as to excite pain. Things get restored sometimes in a greater space of time, and sometimes in a smaller.

10. A dislocation may be recognized by the following symptoms:—Since the parts of a man's body are proportionate to one another, as the arms and the legs, the sound should always be compared with the unsound, and the unsound with the sound, not paying regard to the joints of other individuals (for one person's joints are more prominent than another's), but looking to those of the patient, to ascertain whether the sound joint be unlike the unsound. This is a proper rule, and yet it may lead to much error; and on this account it is not sufficient to know this art in theory, but also by actual practice; for many persons from pain, or from any other cause, when their joints are not dislocated, cannot put the parts into the same positions as the sound body can be put into; one ought therefore to know and be acquainted beforehand with such an attitude. But in a dislocated joint the head of the humerus appears lying much more in the armpit than it is in the sound joint; and also, above, at the top of the shoulder, the part appears hollow, and the acromion is prominent, owing to the bone of the joint having sunk into the part below; there is a source of error in this case also, as will be de-

scribed afterward, for it deserves to be described; and also, the elbow of the dislocated arm is farther removed from the ribs than that of the other; but by using force it may be approximated, though with considerable pain; and also they cannot, with the elbow extended, raise the arm to the ear, as they can the sound arm, nor move it about as formerly in this direction and that. These, then, are the symptoms of dislocation at the shoulder. The methods of reduction and the treatment are as described.

11. It deserves to be known how a shoulder which is subject to frequent dislocations should be treated. For many persons owing to this accident have been obliged to abandon gymnastic exercises, though otherwise well qualified for them; and from the same misfortune have become inept in warlike practices, and have thus perished. And this subject deserves to be noticed, because I have never known any physician treat the case properly; some abandon the attempt altogether, and others hold opinions and practice the very reverse of what is proper. For many physicians have burned the shoulders subject to dislocation, at the top of the shoulder, at the anterior part where the head of the humerus protrudes, and a little behind the top of the shoulder; these burnings, if the dislocation of the arm were upward, or forward, or backward, would have been properly performed; but now, when the dislocation is downward, they rather promote than prevent dislocations, for they shut out the head of the humerus from the free space above. The cautery should be applied thus: taking hold with the hands of the skin at the armpit, it is to be drawn into the line, in which the head of the humerus is dislocated; and then the skin thus drawn aside is to be burnt to the opposite side. The burnings should be performed with irons, which are not thick nor much rounded, but of an oblong form (for thus they pass the more readily through), and they are to be pushed forward with the hand; the cauteries should be red-hot, that they may pass through as quickly as possible; for such as are thick pass through slowly, and occasion eschars of a greater breadth than convenient, and there is danger that the cicatrices may break into one another; which, although nothing very bad, is most unseemly, or awkward. When you have burnt through, it will be sufficient, in most cases, to make eschars only in the lower part; but if there is no danger of the ulcers passing into one another, and there is a considerable piece of skin between them, a thin spatula is to be pushed through these holes which have been burned,

while, at the same time, the skin is stretched, for otherwise the instrument could not pass through; but when you have passed it through you must let go the skin, and then between the two eschars you should form another eschar with a slender iron, and burn through until you come in contact with the spatula. The following directions will enable you to determine how much of the skin of the armpit should be grasped; all men have glands in the armpit greater or smaller, and also in many other parts of the body. But I will treat in another work of the whole constitution of the glands, and explain what they are, what they signify, and what are their offices. The glands, then, are not to be taken hold of, nor the parts internal to the glands; for this would be attended with great danger, as they are adjacent to the most important nerves. But the greater part of the substances external to the glands are to be grasped, for there is no danger from them. And this, also, it is proper to know, that if you raise the arm much, you will not be able to grasp any quantity of skin worth mentioning, for it is all taken up with the stretching; and also the nerves, which by all means you must avoid wounding, become exposed and stretched in this position; but if you only raise the arm a little, you can grasp a large quantity of skin, and the nerves which you ought to guard against are left within, and at a distance from the operation. Should not, then, the utmost pains be taken in the whole practice of the art to find out the proper attitude in every case? So much regarding the armpit, and these contractions will be sufficient, provided the eschars be properly placed. Without the armpit there are only two places where one might place the eschars to obviate this affection; the one before and between the head of the humerus and the tendon at the armpit; and then the skin may be fairly burned through, but not to any great depth, for there is a large vein adjacent, and also nerves, neither of which must be touched with the heat. But externally, one may form another eschar considerably above the tendon at the armpit, but a little below the head of the humerus; and the skin must be burned fairly through, but it must not be made very deep, for fire is inimical to the nerves. Through the whole treatment the sores are to be so treated, as to avoid all strong extension of the arm, and this is to be done moderately, and only as far as the dressing requires; for thus they will be less cooled (for it is of importance to cover up all sorts of burns if one would treat them mildly), and then the lips of them will be less turned aside; there will be less hemorrhage and fear of convulsions. But when the sores have become clean, and are going on to cicatrization, then by all means the arm is to be bound to the side night and day; and even when the ulcers are completely healed, the arm must still be bound to the side for a long time; for thus more especially will cicatrization take place, and the wide space into which the humerus used to escape will become contracted.

12. When attempts to reduce a dislocated shoulder have failed, if the patient be still growing, the bone of the affected arm will not increase like the sound one, for although it does increase in so far it becomes shorter than the other; and those persons called *weasel-armed,* become so from two accidents, either from having met with this dislocation *in utero,* or from another accident, which will be described afterward. But those who while they were children have had deep-seated suppurations about the head of the bone, all become weasel-armed; and this, it should be well known, will be the issue, whether the abscess be opened by an incision or cautery, or whether it break spontaneously. Those who are thus affected from birth are quite able to use the arm, yet neither can they raise the arm to the ear, by extending the elbow, but they do this much less efficiently than with the sound arm. But in those who have had the shoulder dislocated after they were grown up, and when it has not been reduced, the top of the shoulder becomes much less fleshy, and the habit of body at that part is attenuated; but when they cease to have pain, whatever they attempt to perform by raising the elbow from the sides obliquely, they can no longer accomplish as formerly; but whatever acts are performed by carrying the arm around by the sides, either backward or forward, all those they can perform; for they can work with an auger or a saw, or with a hatchet, and can dig, by not raising the elbow too much, and do all other kinds of work which are done in similar attitudes.

13. In those cases where the acromion has been torn off, the bone which is thus separated appears prominent. The bone is the bond of connection between the clavicle and scapula, for in this respect the constitution of man is different from that of other animals; physicians are particularly liable to be deceived in this accident (for as the separated bone protrudes, the top of the shoulder appears low and hollow), so that they make preparations as if for dislocation of the shoulder; for I have known many physicians, otherwise not inexpert at the art, who have done much mischief by attempting to re-

duce such shoulders, thus supposing it a case of dislocation; and they did not desist until they gave over hopes of succeeding, or committed the mistake of supposing that they had reduced the shoulder. The treatment, in these cases, is similar to that which is applicable in others of a like kind, namely, cerate, compresses, and suitable bandaging with linen cloths. The projecting part must be pushed down, and the greater number of compresses are to be placed on it, and most compression is to be applied at that part, and the arm being fastened to the side is to be kept elevated; for thus the parts which had been torn asunder are brought into closest proximity with one another. All this should be well known, and if you choose you may prognosticate safely that no impediment, small or great, will result from such an injury at the shoulder, only there will be a deformity in the place, for the bone cannot be properly restored to its natural situation, but there must necessarily be more or less tumefaction in the upper part. For neither can any other bone be made exactly as it was, which having become incorporated with another bone, and having grown to it as an apophysis, has been torn from its natural situation. If properly bandaged, the acromion becomes free of pain in a few days.

14. When a fractured clavicle is fairly broken across it is more easily treated, but when broken obliquely it is more difficult to manage. Matters are different in these cases from what one would have supposed; for a bone fairly broken across can be more easily restored to its natural state, and with proper care the upper part may be brought down by means of suitable position and proper bandaging, and even if not properly set, the projecting part of the bone is not very sharp. But in oblique fractures the case is similar to that of bones which have been torn away, as formerly described; for they do not admit of being restored to their place, and the prominence of the bone is very sharp. For the most part, then, it should be known, no harm results to the shoulder or to the rest of the body from fracture of the clavicle, unless it sphacelate, and this rarely happens. A deformity, however, may arise from fracture of the clavicle, and in these cases it is very great at first, but by and by it becomes less. A fractured clavicle, like all other spongy bones, gets speedily united; for all such bones form callus in a short time. When, then, a fracture has recently taken place, the patients attach much importance to it, as supposing the mischief greater than it really is, and the physicians bestow great pains in order that it may be proper-

ly bandaged; but in a little time the patients, having no pain, nor finding any impediment to their walking or eating, become negligent; and the physicians finding they cannot make the parts look well, take themselves off, and are not sorry at the neglect of the patients, and in the meantime the callus is quickly formed. The method of dressing which is most appropriate, is similar to that used in ordinary cases, consisting of cerate, compresses, and bandages; and it should be most especially known in this operation, that most compresses should be placed on the projecting bone, and that the greatest pressure should be made there. There are certain physicians who make a show of superior skill by binding a heavy piece of lead on the part in order to depress the projecting bone; but this mode of treatment does not apply to the clavicle, for it is impossible to depress the projecting part to any extent worth mentioning. There are others who, knowing the fact that the bandages are apt to slip off, and that they do not keep the projecting parts in their place, apply compresses and bandages like the others, and then having girt the patient with a girdle, where it is usually applied with most effect, they make a heap of the compresses upon the projecting bone when they apply them, and having fastened the head of the bandage to the girdle in front, they apply it so as to bring the turns of it into the line of the clavicle, carrying them to the back, and then bringing them around the girdle they carry them to the fore part and again backward. There are others who do not apply the bandage round the girdle, but carry the rounds of it by the perineum and anus, and along the spine, so as to compress the fracture. To an inexperienced person these methods will appear not far from natural, but when tied, they will be found of no service; for they do not remain firm any length of time, even if the patient keep his bed, although in this position they answer best; and yet even when lying in bed, should he bend his leg, or should his trunk be bent, all the bandages will be displaced; and, moreover, the bandaging is inconvenient, inasmuch as the anus is comprehended by it, and many turns of the bandage are crowded there in a narrow space. And in the method with the girdle, the girdle cannot be so firmly girt around, but that the turns of the bandage force the girdle to ascend, and hence of necessity all the other bandages must be slackened. He would seem to me to come nearest his purpose, although after all he effects but little, who would take a few turns round the girdle, but would use the bandage principally to secure the former bandaging; for in this manner the bandages would be most secure, and would mutually assist one another. Every thing now almost has been said which applies to fracture of the clavicle. But this also should be known, that in fractures of the clavicle, it is the part attached to the breast which is uppermost, and that the piece attached to the acromion is the lowermost. The cause of this is, that for the most part the breast can neither be depressed nor raised, there being but a slight movement of the joint at the breast, for the sternum is connected together on both sides with the spine. The clavicle admits of most motion at the joint of the shoulder, and this arises from its connection with the acromion. And, moreover, when broken, the part which is connected with the sternum flies upward, and is not easily forced downward; for it is naturally light, and there is more room for it above than below. But the shoulder, the arm, and the parts connected with them, are easily moved from the sides and breast, and, on that account, they admit of being considerably elevated and depressed. When, therefore, the clavicle is broken, the fragment attached to the shoulder inclines downward, for it inclines much more readily with the shoulder and arm downward than upward. Matters being as I have stated, they act imprudently who think to depress the projecting end of the bone. But it is clear that the under part ought to be brought to the upper, for the former is the movable part, and that which has been displaced from its natural position. It is obvious, therefore, that there is no other way of applying force to it (for the bandages no more force it to than they force it from); but if one will push the arm when at the sides as much as possible upward, so that the shoulder may appear as sharp as possible, it is clear that in this way it will be adjusted to the fragment of the bone connected with the breast from which it was torn. If one then will apply a bandage, *secundum artem*, for the purpose of promoting a speedy cure, and will reckon everything else of no value, except the position as described, he will form a correct opinion of the case, and will effect a cure in the speediest and most appropriate manner. It is of great importance, however, that the patient should lie in a recumbent posture. Fourteen days will be sufficient if he keep quiet, and twenty at most.

15. But if the clavicle be fractured in the opposite manner (which does not readily happen), so that the fragment of bone connected with the breast is depressed, while the piece connected with the acromion is raised up and rides over the

other, this case does not require much management, for if the shoulder and arm be let go, the fragments of the bone will be adjusted to one another, and an ordinary bandage will suffice, and the callus will be formed in the course of a few days.

16. If the fracture be not thus, but if it incline either forward or backward, it may be restored to its natural position, by raising the shoulder with the arm as formerly described, and brought back to its natural place, when the cure will be speedily accomplished. Most of the varieties of displacement may be rectified by raising the arm upward. When the upper bone is displaced laterally or downward, it would favor the adaptation of the parts if the patient would lie on his back, and if some elevated substance were placed between the shoulder-blades, so that the breast may be depressed as much as possible upon the two sides; and if, while another person raised the arm extended along the sides, the physician, applying the palm of the one hand to the head of the bone, would push it away, and with the other would adjust the broken bones, he would thus reduce the parts most readily to their natural position. But, as formerly stated, the upper bone (*sternal fragment?*) is rarely depressed downward. In most cases, after the bandages have been applied, that position is beneficial in which the elbow is fixed to the same side, and the shoulder is kept elevated; but in certain cases, the shoulder is to be raised, as has been directed, and the elbow is to be brought forward to the breast, and the hand laid on the acromion of the sound side. If the patient has the resolution to lie in bed, something should be placed so as to support the shoulder, and keep it as much elevated as possible. But if he walk about, the arm should be slung in a shawl, which embraces the point of the elbow, and is passed round the neck.

17. When the elbow-joint is displaced or dislocated to the side or outward, while its sharp point (*olecranon?*) remains in the cavity of the humerus, extension is to be made in a straight line, and the projecting part is to be pushed backward and to the side.

18. In complete dislocations toward either side, extension is to be made as in bandaging fracture of the arm; for thus the rounded part of the elbow will not form an obstacle to it. Dislocation, for the most part, takes place toward the sides (*inwardly?*). Reduction is to be effected by separating (the bones) as much as possible, so that the end (of the humerus) may not come in contact with the olecranon, and it is to be carried up, and turned round, and not forced in a straight line, and, at the same time, the opposite sides are to be pushed together, and propelled into their proper place. It will further assist if rotation of the fore-arm be made at the elbow, sometimes turning it into a supine position, and sometimes into a prone. The position for the treatment consists in keeping the hand a little higher than the elbow, and the arm at the sides; then it may either be suspended or laid at rest, for either position will answer; and nature and the usage of common means will accomplish the cure, if the callus does not form improperly: it is formed quickly. The treatment is to be conducted with bandages according to the rule for bandaging articulations, and the point of the elbow is to be included in the bandage.

19. Dislocations at the elbow give rise to the most serious consequences, such as fevers, pain, nausea, vomitings of pure bile, and more especially when the humerus is displaced backward from pressure on the nerve, which occasions numbness; next to it is the dislocation forward; the treatment is the same; reduction in dislocation backward is by extension and adaptation; the symptom of this variety—loss of the power of extension; or of dislocation forward—loss of the power of flexion, and in this case reduction is to be accomplished by placing a hard ball (in the bend of the elbow), and bending the fore-arm about it, along with sudden extension.

20. Diastasis of the bones may be recognized by examining the part where the vein that runs along the arm divides.

21. In those cases callus is quickly formed. In congenital dislocations the bones below the seat of the injury are shorter than natural, and, mostly, those nearest to the place; namely, the bones of the fore-arm, next those of the hand; and, third, those of the fingers. The arm and shoulder are stronger, owing to the nourishment which they receive, and the other arm, from the additional work which it has to perform, is still more strong. Wasting of the flesh takes place on the inside if the dislocation be on the outside; or otherwise, on the side opposite the dislocation.

22. When the elbow is dislocated either inward or outward, extension is to be made with the fore-arm at a right angle to the arm; the arm, suspended by means of a shawl passed through the armpit, and a weight attached to the extremity of the elbow; or force may be applied with the hands; when the articular extremity has been cleared, the displaced parts are

to be rectified with the palms of the hand, as in dislocations of the hands. It is to be bandaged, suspended in a sling, and placed while in this attitude.

23. Dislocations backward are to be rectified by the palms of the hands, along with sudden extension; the two acts are to be performed together, as in other cases of the kind. But in dislocation forward the arm is to be bent around a ball of cloth of proper size, and at the same time replaced.

24. But if the displacement be on the other side, both these operations are to be performed in effecting the adjustment. For conducting the treatment, the position and bandaging are the same as in the other cases. But all these cases may be reduced by ordinary distention.

25. Of the methods of reduction, some operate by raising up the part, some by extension, and some by rotation: the last consists in rapidly turning the fore-arm to this side and that.

26. The joint of the hand is dislocated either inward or outward, most frequently inward. The symptoms are easily recognized: if inward, the patient cannot at all bend his fingers; and if outward, he cannot extend them. With regard to the reduction,—by placing the fingers above a table, extension and counter-extension are to be made by other persons, while with the palm or heel of the hand on the projecting bone one pushes forward, and another from behind on the other bone; some soft substance is to be applied to it, and the arm is to be turned to the prone position if the dislocation was forward, but to the supine, if backward. The treatment is to be conducted with bandages.

27. The whole hand is dislocated either inward or outward, or to this side or that, but more especially inward; and sometimes the epiphysis is displaced, and sometimes the other of these bones is separated. In these cases strong extension is to be applied, and pressure is to be made on the projecting bone, and counter-pressure on the opposite side, both at the same time, behind and at the side, with the hands upon a table, or with the heel. These accidents give rise to serious consequences and deformities; but in the course of time the part gets strong, and admits of being used. The cure is with bandages, which ought to embrace both the hand and fore-arm; and splints are to be applied as far as the fingers; and when they are used they should be more frequently unloosed than in fractures, and more copious affusions of water should be used.

28. In congenital dislocations (at the wrist) the hand becomes shortened, and the atrophy of the flesh occurs, for the most part, on the side opposite to the dislocation. In an adult the bones remain of their natural size.

29. Dislocation at the joint of a finger is easily recognized. Reduction is to be effected by making extension in a straight line, and applying pressure on the projecting bone, and counter-pressure on the opposite side of the other. The treatment is with bandages. When not reduced, callus is formed outside of the joint. When the dislocation takes place at birth, during adolescence the bones below the dislocation are shortened, and the flesh is wasted rather on the opposite than on the same side with the dislocation. When it occurs in an adult the bones remain of their proper size.

30. The jaw-bone, in few cases, is completely dislocated, for the zygomatic process formed from the upper jaw-bone (*malar?*) and the bone behind the ear (*temporal?*) shuts up the heads of the under jaw, being above the one (*condyloid process?*), and below the other (*coronoid process?*). Of these extremities of the lower jaw, the one, from its length, is not much exposed to accidents, while the other, the coronoid, is more prominent than the zygoma, and from both these heads nervous tendons arise, with which the muscles called temporal and masseter are connected; they have got these names from their actions and connections; for in eating, speaking, and the other functional uses of the mouth, the upper jaw is at rest, as being connected with the head by synarthrosis, and not by diarthrosis (*enarthrosis?*): but the lower jaw has motion, for it is connected with the upper jaw and the head by enarthrosis. Wherefore, in convulsions and tetanus, the first symptom manifested is rigidity of the lower jaw; and the reason why wounds in the temporal region are fatal and induce coma, will be stated in another place. These are the reasons why complete dislocation does not readily take place, and this is another reason, because there is seldom a necessity for swallowing so large pieces of food as would make a man gape more than he easily can, and dislocation could not take place in any other position than in great gaping, by which the jaw is displaced to either side. This circumstance, however, contributes to dislocation there; of nerves (*ligaments?*) and muscles around joints, or connected with joints, such as are frequently moved in using the member are the most yielding to extension, in the same manner as well-dressed hides yield the most. With regard, then, to the matter on hand, the jaw-bone is rarely dislocated, but is frequently slackened (*partially dis-*

placed?) in gaping, in the same manner as many other derangements of muscles and tendons arise. Dislocation is particularly recognized by these symptoms: the lower jaw protrudes forward, there is displacement to the opposite side, the coronoid process appears more prominent than natural on the upper jaw, and the patient cannot shut his lower jaw but with difficulty. The mode of reduction which will apply in such cases is obvious: one person must secure the patient's head, and another, taking hold of the lower jaw with his fingers within and without at the chin, while the patient gapes as much as he can, first moves the lower jaw about for a time, pushing it to this side and that with the hand, and directing the patient himself to relax the jaw, to move it about, and yield as much as possible; then all of a sudden the operator must open the mouth, while he attends at the same time to three positions: for the lower jaw is to be moved from the place to which it is dislocated to its natural position; it is to be pushed backward, and along with these the jaws are to be brought together and kept shut. This is the method of reduction, and it cannot be performed in any other way. A short treatment suffices, a waxed compress is to be laid on, and bound with a loose bandage. It is safer to operate with the patient laid on his back, and his head supported on a leather cushion well filled, so that it may yield as little as possible, but some person must hold the patient's head.

31. When the jaw is dislocated on both sides, the treatment is the same. The patients are less able to shut the mouth than in the former variety; and the jaw protrudes farther in this case, but is not distorted; the absence of distortion may be recognized by comparing the corresponding rows of the teeth in the upper and lower jaws. In such cases reduction should be performed as quickly as possible; the method of reduction has been described above. If not reduced, the patient's life will be in danger from continual fevers, coma attended with stupor (for these muscles, when disordered and stretched preternaturally, induce coma); and there is usually diarrhea attended with bilious, unmixed, and scanty dejections; and the vomitings, if any, consist of pure bile, and the patients commonly die on the tenth day.

32. In fracture of the lower jaw, when the bone is not fairly broken across, and is still partially retained, but displaced, it should be adjusted by introducing the fingers at the side of the tongue, and making suitable counter-pressure on the outside; and if the teeth at the wound be distorted and loosened, when the bone is adjusted, they should be connected together, not only two, but more of them, with a gold thread, if possible, but otherwise, with a linen thread, until the bone be consolidated, and then the part is to be dressed with cerate, a few compresses, and a few bandages, which should not be very tight, but rather loose. For it should be well known that in fracture of the jaw, dressing with bandages, if properly performed, is of little advantage, but occasions great mischief if improperly done. Frequent examinations should be made about the tongue, and prolonged pressure should be applied with the fingers, in order to rectify the displaced bone. It would be best if one could do so constantly, but that is impossible.

33. But if the bone be fairly broken across (this, however, rarely happens), it is to be set in the manner now described. When adjusted, the teeth are to be fastened together as formerly described, for this will contribute much toward keeping the parts at rest, especially if properly fastened, and the ends of the thread secured with knots. But it is not easy to describe exactly in writing the whole manipulation of the case; but the reader must figure the thing to himself from the description given. Then one must take a piece of Carthaginian leather; if the patient be a younger person, it will be sufficient to use the outer skin, but if an adult, the whole thickness of the hide will be required; it is to be cut to the breadth of about three inches, or as much as will be required, and having smeared the jaw with a little gum (for thus it sticks more pleasantly), the end of the skin is to be fastened with the glue near the fractured part of the jaw, at the distance of an inch or a little more, from the wound. This piece is to be applied below the jaw; but the thong should have a cut in it, in the direction of the chin, so that it may go over the sharp point of the chin. Another piece of thong like this, or somewhat broader, is to be glued to the upper part of the jaw, at about the same distance from the wound as the other thong; this thong should be so cut as to encircle the ear. The thongs should be sharp-pointed at the part where they unite, and in gluing them, the flesh of the thong should be turned to the patient's skin, for in this way it will be more tenacious; then we must stretch this thong, but still more so the one at the chin, in order to prevent the fragments of the jaw from riding over each other, and the thongs are to be fastened at the vertex, and then a bandage is to be bound round the forehead, and a

proper apparatus is to be put over all, to prevent the bandages from being displaced. The
patient should lie upon the sound side of the
jaw, not resting upon the jaw, but upon the
head. He is to be kept on a spare diet for ten
days, and then nourished without delay. If there
be no inflammation during the first days, the
jaw is consolidated in twenty days; for callus
quickly forms in this, as in all the other porous
bones, provided there be no sphacelus (*exfoliation?*). But much remains to be said on the
sphacelus of bones in another place. This method of distention with glued substances is mild,
of easy application, and is useful for many dislocations in many parts of the body. Those physicians who have not judgment combined with
their dexterity, expose themselves in fractures
of the jaws, as in other cases, for they apply a
variety of bandages to a fractured jaw-bone,
sometimes properly, and sometimes improperly. For all such bandaging of a fractured jaw-
bone has a tendency rather to derange the bones
connected with the fracture, than to bring them
into their natural position.

34. But if the lower jaw be disjointed at its
symphysis in the chin (there is but one symphysis in the lower jaw, but there are several in
the upper; but I am unwilling to digress from the
subject, as these matters will have to be touched
upon in other kinds of disease)—if, then, the
symphysis be separated at the chin, it is the work
which anybody can perform, to rectify it; for
the part which protrudes is to be pushed inward by pressure with the fingers, and the part
that inclines inward is to forced outward by
pushing with the fingers from within. It is after having applied extension to separate the fragments that this is to be done, for they will thus
be more easily restored to their natural position,
than if one should bring them together by using force. This is proper to be known as applying to all such cases. When you have set the
parts, you must fasten the teeth on both sides to
one another, as formerly directed. The treatment is to be accomplished with cerate, a few
compresses, and bandages. This part, in particular, requires a short but complex (?) bandaging, for it is nearly cylindrical, though not
exactly so; but the turn of the bandage is to be
made, if the right jaw was dislocated, to the
right hand (that is said to be to the right hand
when the right hand conducts the bandaging);
but if the other jaw be the seat of the dislocation, the bandaging is to be made in the other
direction. And if matters be properly adjusted,
and the patient keep quiet, there will be a speedy

recovery, and the teeth will be uninjured; but
if not, the recovery will be more protracted, the
teeth will be distorted, will give trouble, and become useless.

35. Of fractures of the nose there are more
than one variety, but those who, without judgment, delight in fine bandagings, do much mischief, most especially in injuries about the nose.
For this is the most complex of all the forms of
bandaging, having most of the turns of the bandage called "ascia," and rhomboidal intervals and
uncovered spaces of the skin. As has been said,
those who practice manipulation without judgment are fond of meeting with a case of fractured nose, that they may apply the bandage.
For a day or two, then, the physician glories in
his performance, and the patient who has been
bandaged is well pleased, but speedily the patient complains of the incumbrance of the bandage, and the physician is satisfied, because he
has had an opportunity of showing his skill in
applying a complex bandage to the nose. Such
a bandaging does everything the very reverse
of what is proper; for, in the first place, those
who have their nose flattened by the fracture,
will clearly have the part rendered still more
flat, if pressure above be applied to it; and further, those cases in which the nose is distorted
to either side, whether at the cartilage or higher
up, will evidently derive no benefit from bandaging above it, but will rather be injured; for
it will not admit of having compresses properly
arranged on either side of the nose, and indeed,
persons applying this bandage do not seek to
do this.

36. This bandaging would appear to me to
answer best when the skin surrounding the bone
is contused on its ridge near the middle, or if
the bone itself have sustained some injury, but
not a great one, in such cases, redundant callus
forms in the nose, and the part becomes a little
too prominent; and yet, even in these cases, the
bandaging need not require much trouble, if,
indeed, any bandage be applied at all; for it is
enough if one lay a waxed compress on the contusion, and then apply the double-headed bandage, thus taking one turn with it. The best application to such accidents is a small cataplasm
of wheaten flour, washed, and mixed up into a
viscid mass. If the flour be made from good
wheat, and if it be glutinous, it should be used
alone for all such cases, but if it be not very
glutinous, a little of the manna of frankincense,
well pulverized, is to be moistened with water,
and the flour is to be mixed up with it, or a very
little gum may be mixed in like manner.

37. In those cases in which the fractured portions are depressed and flattened, if it is depressed in front at the cartilage, something may be introduced into the nostrils to rectify the parts. If not, all such deformities may be restored by introducing the fingers into the nostrils, if this can be managed, but if not, a thick spatula is to be introduced with the fingers, not to the fore part of the nose, but to the depressed portion, and the physician is to take hold of the nose externally on both sides, and at the same time raise it up. And if the fracture be much in the fore part one may introduce into the nostrils as already stated, either caddis scraped from a linen towel, or something such wrapped up in a piece of cloth, or rather stitched in Carthaginian leather, and moulded into a shape suitable to the place into which it is to be introduced. But if the fracture be at a greater distance, it is not possible to introduce anything within, for if it was irksome to bear anything of the kind in the fore part, how is it not to be so when introduced farther in? At first, then, by rectifying the parts from within, and sparing no pains upon them from without, they are to be brought to their natural position, and set. A fractured nose may be readily restored to shape, especially on the day of the accident, or even a little later, but the physicians act irresolutely, and touch it more delicately at first than they should; for the fingers should be applied on both sides along the natural line of the nose, and it is to be pushed downward, and thus, with pressure from within, the displacement is to be rectified. But for these purposes no physician is equal to the index-fingers of the patient himself, if he will pay attention and has resolution, for they are the most natural means. Either of the fingers is to be placed firmly along the whole nose, and thus it is to be gently held, and steadily, if possible until it become firm, but if not, he himself is to hold it for as long a time as possible, in the manner described; or if he cannot, a child or woman should do it, for the hands ought to be soft. Thus may a fracture of the nose, attended with depression, and not with displacement to the side, but in a straight line, be most properly treated. I have never seen a case of fractured nose which could not be rectified when attempted, before callus is formed, provided the treatment be properly applied. But although men would give a great price to escape being deformed, yet at the same time they do not know how to take care, nor have resolution, if they do not experience pain, nor fear death, although the formation of callus in the nose speedily takes place, for the most part is consolidated in ten days, provided sphacelus do not take place.

38. When the fractured bone is displaced laterally, the treatment is the same, but it is obvious that the reduction is to be made, not by applying equal force on both sides, but by pushing the displaced portion into its natural position, and pressing on it from without, and introducing something into the nostrils, and boldly rectifying the fragments which incline inward, until the whole be properly adjusted, well knowing that if you do not restore the parts at once, it is impossible but that the nose must be distorted. But when you restore the parts to their natural position, either the patient himself, or some other person, is to apply one finger or more to the part which protrudes, and keep it in position until the fracture be consolidated; but the little finger is, from time to time, to be pushed into the nostril, to rectify the parts which incline inward. When any inflammation supervenes, dough must be used, but attention must still be equally paid to the application of the fingers, although the dough be on the part. But if the fracture be in the cartilage, with lateral displacement, the end of the nose must necessarily be distorted. In such cases some of the aforementioned means of reduction, or whatever suits, is to be introduced into the nostril; but there are many convenient things to be found which have no smell, and are appropriate in other respects; thus, on one occasion, I introduced a slice of sheep's lung, as it happened to be at hand; for sponges, if introduced, imbibe humidities. Then the outer skin of Carthaginian leather is to be taken, and a piece of the size of the thumb, or what will answer, is to be cut off and glued to the outside of the nostril which is turned aside, and then this piece of thong is to be stretched to the proper degree, or rather a little more than what will be sufficient to make the nose straight and regular. Then (for the thong must be long) it is to be brought below the ear and round the head, and the end of the thong may either be glued to the forehead, or a still longer one may be carried all round the head, and secured. This is a natural mode of setting the nose, is of easy application, and is calculated to enable the counter-extension on the nose to be made greater or less, as you may incline. In a case where the fractured nose is turned to the side, the treatment is to be conducted otherwise, as already described; and in most of them the thong ought to be glued to the end of the nose, in order to make extension in the opposite direction.

39. When the fracture is complicated with a wound, one need not be troubled on that account, but pitch-cerate or any of the applications for fresh wounds is to be applied to the sores; for, in general, they admit of easy cure, even when there is reason to apprehend that pieces of bone will come out. The parts, at first, are to be adjusted fearlessly, taking care that nothing is omitted, and, subsequently, they are also to be adjusted with the fingers; more softly, indeed, but still it must be done; and of all parts of the body the nose is modeled with the greatest ease. And there is nothing to prevent us from having recourse to the practice of gluing on the thongs, and drawing the nose to the opposite side, even if there be a wound or the parts be inflamed, for these thongs give no pain.

40. In fractures of the ear all sorts of bandages do harm. For one would not think of applying it quite loose, and if applied more tightly, it only does the more harm, for even the sound ear, when confined with a bandage, becomes painful, throbs, and gets into a febrile state. With regard to cataplasms, the heaviest, on the whole, are the worst; but almost all kinds are bad, form abscesses, occasion an increase of humors, and afterward troublesome suppurations; and a fractured ear stands in less need of such applications than any other part; the most ready, if required, is the paste of meal, but neither should it have weight. It should touch as little as possible; for it is a good remedy sometimes to apply nothing at all, both to the ear and to many other cases. Attention must be paid to the patient's position during sleep. And the body must be reduced, more especially if there be danger lest the ear suppurate; it will also be better to open the bowels, and if the patient can be readily made to vomit, this may be accomplished by means of the *syrmaïsm*. If the part come to suppuration, it should not be hastily opened; for often when matter appears to be formed it is absorbed again, even when no cataplasm is applied. But if forced to open it, the part will get soonest well if transfixed with a cautery, and yet it should be well understood that the ear gets maimed, and is less than the other if burned through. If not burned through, an incision, and not a very small one, should be made on the upper side; for the pus is found to be surrounded with a thicker covering than one would have supposed; and it may be said, in general, that all parts of a mucous nature and which form mucus, as being all viscid, when touched, slip from below the fingers to either side; and on

that account the physician, in such cases, finds that he has to pass his instrument through a thicker substance than he supposed; and in certain ganglionic cases, when the skin is flabby and mucous, many physicians open them, expecting to find a collection in them; here the physician forms a wrong judgment, but by such a procedure no great harm results to the patient from having had the part opened. But with regard to watery parts, and such as are filled with mucus, and which are situated in regions where every one of the parts, if opened, will occasion death or some other injury, these will be treated of in another work. When, therefore, incision is made in the ear, all sorts of cataplasms and pledges should be avoided, and it is to be treated either with applications for recent wounds, or anything else which is neither heavy nor will occasion pain, for if the cartilage be laid bare and abscesses form, the case will be troublesome; this happens from such modes of treatment. In all aggravated cases, the most effectual remedy is the transfixing of the part with a hot iron.

41. The vertebræ of the spine when contracted into a hump behind from disease, for the most part cannot be remedied, more especially when the gibbosity is above the attachment of the diaphragm to the spine. Certain of those below the diaphragm are carried off by varices in the legs, more especially by such as occur in the vein at the ham; and in those cases where the gibbosities are removed, the varices take place also in the groin; and some have been carried off by a dysentery when it becomes chronic. And when the gibbosity occurs in youth before the body has attained its full growth, in these cases the body does not usually grow along the spine, but the legs and the arms are fully developed, whilst the parts (about the back) are arrested in their development. And in those cases where the gibbosity is above the diaphragm, the ribs do not usually expand properly in width, but forward, and the chest becomes sharp-pointed and not broad, and they become affected with difficulty of breathing and hoarseness; for the cavities which inspire and expire the breath do not attain their proper capacity. And they are under the necessity of keeping the neck bent forward at the great vertebra, in order that their head may not hang downward; this, therefore, occasions great contraction of the pharynx by its inclination inward; for, even in those who are erect in stature, dyspnœa is induced by this bone inclining inward, until it be restored to its place. From this frame of body, such persons appear to have more prominent necks than per-

sons in good health, and they generally have hard and unconcocted tubercles in the lungs, for the gibbosity and the distension are produced mostly by such tubercles, with which the neighboring nerves communicate. When the gibbosity is below the diaphragm, in some of these cases nephritic diseases and affections of the bladder supervene, but abscesses of a chronic nature, and difficult to cure, occur in the loins and groins, and neither of these carries off the gibbosity; and in these cases the hips are more emaciated than when the gibbosity is seated higher up; but the whole spine is more elongated in them than in those who have the gibbosity seated higher up, the hair of the pubes and chin is of slower growth and less developed, and they are less capable of generation than those who have the gibbosity higher up. When the gibbosity seizes persons who have already attained their full growth, it usually occasions a crisis of the then existing disease, but in the course of time some of them attack, as in the case of younger persons, to a greater or less degree; but, for the most part, all these diseases are less malignant. And yet many have borne the affection well, and have enjoyed good health until old age, more especially those persons whose body is inclined to be plump and fat; and a few of them have lived to beyond sixty years of age, but the most of them are more short-lived. In some cases the curvature of the spine is lateral, that is to say, either to the one side or the other; the most of such cases are connected with tubercles (*abscesses?*) within the spine; and in some, the positions in which they have been accustomed to lie co-operate with the disease. But these will be treated of among the chronic affections of the lungs; for these the most suitable prognostics of what will happen in these cases are given.

42. When the spine protrudes backward, in consequence of a fall, it seldom happens that one succeeds in straightening it. Wherefore succussion on a ladder has never straightened anybody, as far as I know, but it is principally practiced by those physicians who seek to astonish the mob—for to such persons these things appear wonderful, for example, if they see a man suspended or thrown down, or the like; and they always extol such practices, and never give themselves any concern whatever may result from the experiment, whether bad or good. But the physicians who follow such practices, as far as I have known them, are all stupid. The device, however, is an old one, and I give great praise to him who first invented this, and any

other mechanical contrivance which is according to nature. For neither would I despair, but that if succussion were properly gone about, the spine, in certain cases, might be thereby rectified. But, indeed, for my own part, I have been ashamed to treat all such cases in this way, because such modes of procedure are generally practiced by charlatans.

43. Those cases in which the gibbosity is near the neck, are less likely to be benefited by these succussions with the head downward, for the weight of the head, and tops of the shoulders, when allowed to hang down, is but small; and such cases are more likely to be made straight by succussion applied with the feet hanging down, since the inclination downward is greater in this way. When the hump is lower down, it is more likely in this case that succussion with the head downward should do good. If one, then, should think of trying succussion, it may be applied in the following manner:—The ladder is to be padded with leather lined cushions, laid across, and well secured to one another, to a somewhat greater extent, both in length and breadth, than the space which the man's body will occupy; he is then to be laid on the ladder upon his back, and the feet, at the ankles, are to be fastened, at no great distance from one another, to the ladder, with some firm but soft band; and he is further to be secured, in like manner, both above and below the knee, and also at the nates; and at the groins and chest loose shawls are to be put round in such a fashion as not to interfere with the effect of the succussion; and his arms are to be fastened along his sides to his own body, and not to the ladder. When you have arranged these matters thus, you must hoist up the ladder, either to a high tower or to the gable-end of a house; but the place where you make the succussion should be firm, and those who perform the extension should be well instructed, so that they may let go their hold equally to the same extent, and suddenly, and that the ladder may neither tumble to the ground on either side, nor they themselves fall forward. But, if the ladder be let go from a tower, or the mast of a ship, fastened into the ground with its cordage, it will be better, so that the ropes run upon a pulley or axle-tree. But it is disagreeable even to enlarge upon these matters; and yet, by the contrivances now described, the proper succussion may be made.

44. But if the hump be situated very high up, and if succussion be by all means to be used, it will be better to do it with the feet downward, as has been said, for the force downward will

be the greater in this case. The patient is to be well fastened to the ladder by cords at the breast, at the neck by means of a very loose shawl so as merely to keep the part properly on the ladder, and the head is to be fastened to the ladder at the forehead, the arms are to be stretched along and attached to the patient's body, and not to the ladder, and the rest of the body is not to be bound, except so as to keep it in place by means of a loose shawl wrapped round it and the ladder; attention, moreover, should be paid that these ligatures do not interfere with the force of the succussion, and the legs are not to be fastened to the ladder, but should be placed near one another, so as to be in line with the spine. These matters should be thus arranged, if recourse is to be had at all to succussion on a ladder; for it is disgraceful in every art, and more especially in medicine, after much trouble, much display, and much talk, to do no good after all.

45. In the first place, the structure of the spine should be known, for this knowledge is requisite in many diseases. Wherefore, on the side turned to the belly (*the anterior?*) the vertebræ are in a regular line, and are united together by a pulpy and nervous band of connection, originating from the cartilages, and extending to the spinal marrow. There are certain other nervous cords which decussate, are attached (*to the vertebræ?*), and are extended from both sides of them. But we will describe in another work the connections of the veins and arteries, their numbers, their qualities, their origin, their functional offices in particular parts, in what sort of sheaths the spinal marrow is inclosed, where they arise, where they terminate, how they communicate, and what their uses. On the opposite side (*behind?*) the vertebræ are connected together by a ginglymoid articulation. Common cords (*nerves?*) are extended to all parts, both those within and without. There is an osseous process from the posterior part of all and each of the vertebræ, whether greater or smaller; and upon these processes there are cartilaginous epiphyses, and from them arise nervous productions (*ligaments?*), akin to the external nerves (τόνοι). The ribs are united to them, having their heads inclined rather to the inside than the out, and every one of them is articulated with the vertebræ; and the ribs in man are very curved, and, as it were, arched. The space between the ribs and the processes of the vertebræ is filled on both sides by muscles, which arise from the neck and extend to the loins (?). The spine, longitudinally, is a straight line slightly curved; from the os sacrum

to the great vertebra which is connected with the articulation of the femur, the spine inclines backward, for the bladder, the organs of generation, and the loose portion of the rectum, are situated there. From this, to the attachment of the diaphragm, the spine inclines inward, and this portion alone, from the internal parts, gives origin to muscles, which are called *psoæ*. From this to the great vertebra (*seventh cervical?*) which is above the tops of the shoulders, it is convex behind lengthways; but it is more in appearance than it really is, for the spinous processes are highest in the middle, and less so above and below. The region of the neck is convex before.

46. In cases of displacement backward along the vertebræ, it does not often happen, in fact, it is very rare, that one or more vertebræ are torn from one another and displaced. For such injuries do not readily occur, as the spine could not easily be displaced backward but by a severe injury on the fore part through the belly (which would prove fatal), or if a person falling from a height should pitch on the nates, or shoulders (and even in this case he would die, but not immediately); and it also would not readily happen that such a displacement could take place forward, unless some very heavy weight should fall upon it behind; for each of the posterior spinal processes is so constructed, that it would sooner be broken than undergo any great inclination forward from a force which would have to overcome the ligaments and the articulations mutually connecting them. And the spinal marrow would suffer, if from the displacement of a vertebra it were to be bent even to a small extent; for the displaced vertebra would compress the spinal marrow, if it did not break it; and if compressed and strangled, it would induce insensibility of many great and important parts, so that the physician need not give himself any concern about rectifying the displacement of the vertebra, accompanied, as it is, by many other ill consequences of a serious nature. It is evident, then, that such a case could not be reduced either by succussion or by any other method, unless one were to cut open the patient, and then, having introduced the hand into one of the great cavities, were to push outward from within, which one might do on the dead body, but not at all on the living. Wherefore, then, do I write all this? Because certain persons fancy that they have cured patients in whom the vertebra had undergone complete dislocation forward. Some, indeed, suppose that this is the easiest of all these dislocations to be

recovered from, and that such cases do not stand in need of reduction, but get well spontaneously. Many are ignorant, and profit by their ignorance, for they obtain credit from those about them. These are deceived in this way, for they suppose the spinous processes to be the vertebræ themselves, because every one of them appears round to the touch, not knowing that these bones are processes from the vertebræ, as formerly stated; but the vertebræ are at a considerable distance before them; for of all animals, man, in proportion to his bulk, has the belly (*internal cavity?*) the narrowest from behind to before, especially at the breast. When, therefore, any of these processes are severely fractured, whether one or more, the part there appears lower than on either side, and for that reason they are deceived, supposing that the vertebræ are displaced inward. And the attitudes of the patient contribute also to deceive them; for if they attempt to put themselves into a bent position, they are pained, from the skin being stretched at the seat of the injury, and at the same time the fragments of the bones wound the skin still more; but if they bend forward, they feel easier, for the skin at the wound is thus relaxed, and the bones are less disposed to hurt them; and if touched, they shrink and bend forward, and the part which is touched appears empty and soft. All the circumstances now mentioned contribute to deceive the physician. Such patients speedily get well without any bad effects, for callus readily forms in all such bones as are porous.

47. There are many varieties of curvature of the spine even in persons who are in good health; for it takes place from natural conformation and from habit, and the spine is liable to be bent from old age, and from pains. Gibbosities (*or projections backward*) from falls generally take place when one pitches on the nates, or falls on the shoulders. In this case some one of the vertebræ must necessarily appear higher than natural, and those on either side to a less degree; but yet no one generally has started out of the line of the others, but every one has yielded a little, so that a considerable extent of them is curved. On this account the spinal marrow easily bears such distortions, because they are of a circular shape, and not angular. The apparatus for the reduction in this case must be managed in the following manner: a strong and broad board, having an oblong furrow in it, is to be fastened in the ground, or, in place of the board, we may scoop out an oblong furrow in the wall, about a cubit above the floor, or at any suitable height, and then something like an oaken bench, of a quadrangular shape, is to be laid along (the wall?) at a distance from the wall, which will admit of persons to pass round if necessary, and the bench is to be covered with robes, or anything else which is soft, but does not yield much; and the patient is to be stoved with vapor, if necessary, or bathed with much hot water, and then he is to be stretched along the board on his face, with his arms laid along and bound to his body; the middle, then, of a thong which is soft, sufficiently broad and long, and composed of two cross straps of leather, is to be twice carried along the middle of the patient's breast, as near the armpits as possible, then what is over of the thongs at the armpits is to be carried round the shoulders, and afterward the ends of the thong are to be fastened to a piece of wood resembling a pestle; they are to be adapted to the length of the bench laid below the patient, and so that the pestle-like piece of wood resting against this bench may make extension. Another such band is to be applied above the knees and the ankles, and the ends of the thongs fastened to a similar piece of wood; and another thong, broad, soft, and strong, in the form of a swathe, having breadth and length sufficient, is to be bound tightly round the loins, as near the hips as possible; and then what remains of this swathe-like thong, with the ends of the thongs, must be fastened to the piece of wood placed at the patient's feet, and extension in this fashion is to be made upward and downward, equally and at the same time, in a straight line. For extension thus made could do no harm, if properly performed, unless one sought to do mischief purposely. But the physicians, or some person who is strong, and not uninstructed, should apply the palm of one hand to the hump, and then, having laid the other hand upon the former, he should make pressure, attending whether this force should be applied directly downward, or toward the head, or toward the hips. This method of applying force is particularly safe; and it is also safe for a person to sit upon the hump while extension is made, and raising himself up, to let himself fall again upon the patient. And there is nothing to prevent a person from placing a foot on the hump, and supporting his weight on it, and making gentle pressure; one of the men who is practiced in the palestra would be a proper person for doing this in a suitable manner. But the most powerful of the mechanical means is this: if the hole in the wall, or in the piece of wood fastened into the ground, be made as much below the man's back as may be judged proper, and if a board, made of lime-

tree, or any other wood, and not too narrow, be put into the hole, then a rag, folded several times or a small leather cushion, should be laid on the hump; nothing large, however, should be laid on the back, but just as much as may prevent the board from giving unnecessary pain by its hardness; but the hump should be as much as possible on a line with the hole made in the wall, so that the board introduced into it may make pressure more especially at that spot. When matters are thus adjusted, one person, or two if necessary, must press down the end of the board, whilst others at the same time make extension and counter-extension along the body, as formerly described. Extension may also be made with axles, which may either be fastened in the ground beside the bench, or the post of the axles may be attached to the bench itself, if you will make them perpendicular and over-topping (*the bench?*) a little at both ends, or at either end of the bench. These powers are easily regulated, so as to be made stronger or weaker, and they are of such force, that if one were to have recourse to them for a mischievous purpose, and not as a remedy, they would operate strongly in this way also; for by making merely extension and counter-extension longitudinally, without any additional force, one might make sufficient extension; and if, without making extension at all, one were only to press down properly with the board, sufficient force might be applied in this way. Such powers, then, are excellent which admit of being so regulated, that they can be made weaker and stronger as required. And the forces are applied in the natural way; for the pressure above forces the displaced parts into their place. Natural extension restores parts which have come too near one another to their natural position. I, then, am acquainted with no powers which are better or more appropriate than these; for extension along the spine downward has no proper hold at the bone called the os sacrum; and extension upward, along the neck and head, has indeed a hold; but extension thus made is unseemly to behold, and, besides, if increased, may occasion much mischief otherwise. I once made trial of the following plan. Having placed the patient on his back, I put below the hump a bladder, not inflated, and afterward introduced air into the bladder by means of a brass pipe connected with it. But the experiment did not succeed; for, when the man was fairly extended, the bladder yielded, and the air could not be forced into it; and, besides, the hump of the patient was apt to slip off the distended bladder when they were pressed together. But when I did not extend the man strongly, the bladder was swelled up by the air, and the man became more bent forward than proper. I have written this expressly; for it is a valuable piece of knowledge to learn what things have been tried and have proved ineffectual, and wherefore they did not succeed.

48. In curvatures forward of the vertebræ from a fall, or from some heavy body falling upon them, in general no one of them is displaced far beyond the others, but if one or more be so displaced, the case proves fatal; but, as formerly stated, the displacement is circular, and not angular. In such cases, then, the urine and fæces are more apt to be retained than in displacement outward, the feet and the whole inferior extremities are colder, and the symptoms are more fatal than in the former case; and if they do survive, they are more subject to retention of the urine, and to loss of strength, and to torpor in their legs. But if the displacement be in the upper part, they experience loss of strength and torpor of the whole body. I know no mechanical contrivance by which such a displacement could be reduced, unless that one might be benefited by succussion on a bladder, or any other similar plan of treatment, such as extension, as formerly described. I am not aware of any mode of pressure which might be applied along with the extension, like that of the board in displacement backward; for how could one apply pressure from before through the belly? (*internal cavity?*) The thing is impossible. But neither coughing nor sneezing has any power so as to co-operate with the extension, nor would the injection of air into the bowels have any effect. And to apply large cupping instruments with the view of drawing back the vertebræ which have protruded forward, shows a great error of judgment; for they rather propel than attract, and those who apply them are not aware even of this fact, for the greater will be the inclination forward the greater the instrument applied, the skin being forcibly drawn into the cupping-instrument. I could tell of other modes of succussion than those formerly described, which one might fancy would be more applicable in such an affection; but I have no great confidence in them, and therefore I do not describe them. On the main, it should be known, respecting the accidents which I have briefly described, that displacements forward are of a fatal and injurious nature; but that displacements backward, for the most part, do not prove fatal, nor occasion retention of urine nor torpor of

the limbs, for they do not stretch the ducts leading toward the intestines, nor occasion obstruction of the same; but displacements forward produce both these bad effects, and many others in addition. And truly they are more apt to lose the power of their legs and arms, to have torpor of the body, and retention of urine, who experience no displacement either forward or backward, but merely a violent concussion along the spine, while those who have displacement backward are least subject to these symptoms.

49. And one might observe many other instances in medicine, of considerable injuries not proving serious, but producing a crisis in some affection, while less considerable injuries prove more serious, give rise to chronic diseases, and extend their effects to the whole system. Now something similar may happen in fracture of the ribs; for in fracture of one or more ribs, in general, if the fractured bones are not driven inward, nor are laid bare, fever rarely supervenes, neither does it often happen that there is hæmoptysis, empyema, and suppurating sores, which require treatment with pledgets, nor necrosis of the bones; and in these cases the ordinary regimen is sufficient. For, unless they be seized with continual fever, a strict diet does more harm than good, by inducing inanition, and increasing the pain, fever, and cough; for moderate fullness of the intestines has a tendency to replace the ribs, while evacuation leads to suspension of the ribs, and suspension induces pain. Ordinary bandaging, externally, is sufficient in such cases; the bandages should be applied moderately tight, along with cerate and compresses, or a pad of wool may be applied. The rib is consolidated in twenty days, for callus soon forms in such bones.

50. But when there is contusion of the flesh about the ribs, either from a blow, or a fall, or a bruise, or any like cause, there is often copious vomiting of blood, for there are canals stretched along the vacuity of each rib (*intercostal space?*), and nerves proceeding from the most important parts of the body have their origin there. Many of these, therefore, are troubled with coughs, tubercles, empyema, external suppurations, and sphacelus of the ribs. And even when no such symptoms supervene from contusion of the skin about the ribs, still in such cases there is, generally, more combined pain than in fractures of the ribs, and relapses of pain in the seat of the injury are more apt to occur. Wherefore some physicians pay much less attention to such injuries, than where the rib is fractured, whereas, if they were wise, they would treat such cases with far greater care than the other; for it is proper that the diet should be restricted, that the patients should remain at rest as much as possible, and abstain from venery, from fat articles of food, from such as excite cough, and from everything strong; they should be bled in the arm, speak as little as possible, should have the contused part bound round with folded compresses, plenty of bandages, broader than the contusion, and which should be smeared with cerate; in applying the bandages, broad and soft shawls should be used, and they should be put on moderately firm, so that the patient will say that they are neither too tight nor loose, and the bandaging should commence at the seat of the injury, and be made more particularly tight there, and the bandaging should be conducted as is done with a double-headed roller, so that the skin about the ribs may not be ruffled, but may lie smooth, and the bandaging should be renewed every day, or every alternate day. It is better also to open the bowels with some gentle medicine, so as just to produce an evacuation of the food, and the diet is to be restricted for ten days, and then the body is to be recruited and filled up; while you are upon the reducing system, the bandaging should be tighter, but when you are making him up again, it must be looser; and, if he spit blood from the commencement, the treatment and bandaging should be continued for forty days; but if there be no hæmoptysis, treatment for twenty days will generally be sufficient; but the length of time must be regulated by the magnitude of the injury. When such contusions are neglected, if no greater mischief result therefrom, at all events the bruised part has its flesh more pulpy than it had formerly. When, therefore, any such thing is left behind, and is not properly dissipated by the treatment, it will be worse if the mucosity be lodged near the bone, for the flesh no longer adheres to the bone as formerly, the bone becomes diseased, and chronic sloughings of the bone in many cases arise from such causes. But if the mischief be not upon the bone, but it is the flesh itself which is pulpy, relapses and pains will return from time to time, if there happen to be any disorder in the body; wherefore proper bandaging, and for a considerable time, must be had recourse to, until the extravasated blood forming in the bruise be dried up and absorbed, and the part be made up with sound flesh, and the flesh adhere to the bone. The best cure is the cautery in those cases which, from neglect, have become chronic, and the

place turns painful, and the flesh is pulpy. And when the flesh itself is pulpy, the burning should be carried as far as the bone, but the bone itself should not be heated; but if it be in the inter-costal space, you need not make the burning so superficial, only you must take care not to burn quite through. But if the contusion appear to be at the bone, if it be still recent, and the bone has not yet become necrosed, if it be very small, it is to be burned as has been described; but if the rising along the bone be oblong, several es-chars are to be burned over it. Necrosis of the rib will be described along with the treatment of suppurating sores.

51. There are four modes of dislocation at the hip-joint: of which modes, dislocation inward takes place most frequently, outward, the most frequently of all the other modes; and it some-times takes place backward and forward, but seldom. When, therefore, dislocation takes place inward, the leg appears longer than natural, when compared with the other leg, for two rea-sons truly; for the bone which articulates with the hip-joint is carried from above down to the ischium where it rises up to the pubes, upon it, then, the head of the femur rests, and the neck of the femur is lodged in the cotyloid foramen (*foramen thyroideum?*). The buttock appears hollow externally, from the head of the thigh-bone having shifted inward, and the extremity of the femur at the knee is turned outward, and the leg and foot in like manner. The foot then being turned outward, physicians, from igno-rance, bring the sound leg to it and not it to the sound leg; on this account, the injured limb ap-pears to be much longer than the sound one, and in many other cases similar circumstances lead to error in judgment. Neither does the limb at the groin admit of flexion as in the sound limb, and the head of the bone is felt at the perineum too prominent. These, then, are the symptoms attending dislocation of the thigh inward.

52. When, then, a dislocation has not been re-duced, but has been misunderstood or neglected, the leg, in walking, is rolled about as is the case with oxen, and the weight of the body is most-ly supported on the sound leg, and the limb at the flank, and the joint where the dislocation has occurred is necessarily hollow and bent, while on the sound side the buttock is necessarily rounded. For if one should walk with the foot of the sound leg turned outward, the weight of the body would be thrown upon the injured limb, but the injured limb could not carry it, for how could it? One, then, is forced in walking to turn the leg inward, and not outward, for

thus the sound leg best supports its own half of the body, and also that of the injured side. But being hollow at the flank and the hip-joint, they appear small in stature, and are forced to rest on a staff at the side of the sound leg. For they require the support of a staff there, since the nates inclines to this side, and the weight of the body is carried to it. They are forced also to stoop, for they are obliged to rest the hand on the side of the thigh against the affected limb; for the limb which is injured cannot support the body in changing the legs, unless it be held when it is applied to the ground. They who have got an unreduced dislocation inward are forced to put themselves into these attitudes, and this from no premeditation on their part how they should assume the easiest position, but the im-pediment itself teaches them to choose that which is most conformable to their present cir-cumstances. For persons who have a sore on the foot, or leg, and cannot rest upon the limb, all, even children, walk in this way; for they turn the injured limb outward in walking, and they derive two advantages therefrom, to sup-ply two wants; the weight of the body is not equally thrown upon the limb turned outward, as upon the one turned inward, for neither is the weight in a line with it, but is much more thrown upon the one under the body; for the weight is in a straight line with it, both in walk-ing and in the shifting of the legs. In this po-sition one can most quickly turn the sound limb under the body, by walking with the un-sound limb outward, and the sound inward. In the case we are now treating of, it is well that the body finds out the attitudes which are the easiest for itself. Those persons, then, who have not attained their growth at the time when they met with a dislocation which is not re-duced, become maimed in the thigh, the leg, and the foot, for neither do the bones grow prop-erly, but become shortened, and especially the bone of the thigh; and the whole limb is emaci-ated, loses its muscularity, and becomes ener-vated and thinner, both from the impediment at the joint, and because the patient cannot use the limb, as it does not lie in its natural position, for a certain amount of exercise will relieve ex-cessive enervation, and it will remedy in so far the deficiency of growth in length. Those per-sons, then, are most maimed who have experi-enced the dislocation *in utero,* next those who have met with it in infancy, and least of all, those who are full grown. The mode of walking adopted by adults has been already described; but those who are children when this accident befalls them, generally lose the erect position of the body, and crawl about miserably on the sound leg, supporting themselves with the hand of the sound side resting on the ground. Some, also, who had attained manhood before they met with this accident, have also lost the faculty of walking erect. Those who were children when they met with the accident, and have been properly instructed, stand erect upon the sound leg, but carry about a staff, which they apply under the armpit of the sound side, and some use a staff in both arms; the unsound limb they bear up, and the smaller the unsound limb, the greater facility have they in walking, and their sound leg is no less strong than when both are sound. The fleshy parts of the limb are enervated in all such cases, but those who have dislocation inward are more subject to this loss of strength than, for the most part, those who have it outward.

53. Some tell a story how the Amazonian women dislocate the joints of their male children while mere infants, some at the knee, and others at the hip-joint, that they may be maimed, and that the male sex may not conspire against the female, and that they use them as artisans to perform any sedentary work, such as that of a shoemaker or brazier. Whether these things be true or not I do not know, but this I know, that matters would be such as is represented, provided their children, while infants, were to have their joints dislocated. The consequences of dislocation inward at the hip-joint are much greater than of dislocation outward at the hip-joint, but at the knee, although there be some difference, it is less; but the mode of either impediment is peculiar, their legs are more bandied when the dislocation is outward, but those who have dislocation inward stand erect on their feet with less freedom. In like manner, when the dislocation is at the ankle-joint, if outward they become *vari* (*their toes are turned inward?*), but they can stand; but if the dislocation be inward they become *valgi* (*their toes are turned outward?*), but they have less freedom of standing. The proportional growth of their bones is as follows: in those cases in which the bone of the leg is dislocated, the bones of the feet grow very little, as being very near the injury, but the bones of the leg increase in size, and with very little defect, but the fleshy parts (*muscles?*) are wasted. But when the ankle-joint is in its natural state, but the knee is dislocated, in these cases the bones of the leg do not grow in like manner, but become shortened, as being nearest the seat of the injury,

and the bones of the feet also are atrophied, but not in the same proportion; because, as was said a little while ago, the ankle-joint is safe, and if they could use it, as in the case of club-foot, the bones of the foot would be still less atrophied. When the dislocation takes place at the hip-joint, the bone of the thigh, in this case, does not generally grow in like manner, as being the one nearest the seat of the injury, but becomes shorter than the sound one; but the growth of the bones of the leg is not arrested in like manner; nor of those of the feet, for this reason, that there is no displacement between the bones of the thigh and leg, nor between those of the leg and foot; in those cases, however, the fleshy parts of the whole limb are atrophied; but if they could make use of the limb, the growth of the bones would be still more developed, as formerly stated, only the thigh, although its flesh would be much less wasted, would still be by no means so fleshy as the sound limb. The following observations are a proof of this: those persons who are weasel-armed (*galiancones*) from birth, owing to dislocation of the humerus, or when the accident has happened to them before they have attained their full growth, such persons have the bone of the arm shortened, but those of the fore-arm and hand are little inferior in size to the sound, for the reasons which have been stated, because the humerus is the bone nearest to the joint affected, and, on that account, it is shorter than natural; but the fore-arm is not equally affected by the accident, because the joint at which the bones of the arm and fore-arm are articulated remains in its natural condition, and the hand is still further distant than the fore-arm from the seat of the injury. Such are the reasons why certain of the bones in this case increase in growth, and certain do not. The laborious office of the hand contributes much to the development of the flesh in the fore-arm and hand, for whatever work is done by the hand, these weasel-armed persons strive to do no less effectually with the other hand than with the sound; for the arms do not support the weight of the body like the legs, and the work performed by them is light. From exercise, then, the fleshy parts on the hand and fore-arm are not atrophied in weasel-armed persons, and by these means the arm, too, gains flesh. But in dislocation inward at the hip-joint, whether from birth or from childhood, the fleshy parts, on that account, are much more atrophied than those of the hand, because the patients cannot exercise the leg. Another proof will be given in the observations which will be presently stated, that these things are such as I have represented.

54. When the head of the femur is dislocated outward, the limb in these cases, when compared with the other, appears shortened, and this is natural, for the head of the femur no longer rests on a bone as in dislocation inward, but along the side of a bone which naturally inclines to the side, and it is lodged in flesh of a pulpy and yielding nature, and on that account it appears more shortened. Inwardly, the thigh about the perineum appears more hollow and flabby, but externally the buttock is more rounded, from the head of the thigh having slipped outward, but the nates appear to be raised up, owing to the flesh there having yielded to the head of the thigh-bone; but the extremity of the thigh-bone, at the knee, appears to be turned inward, and the leg and foot in like manner, neither does it admit of flexion like the sound limb. These, then, are the symptoms of dislocation outward.

55. When such a dislocation is not reduced in adults, the whole limb appears to be shortened, and in walking they cannot reach the ground with the heel, but they walk with the ball of the foot on the ground, and the points of their toes incline a little inward. But the injured limb, in this case, can support the body much better than in dislocation inward, both because the head of the femur and the neck of its articular extremity, being naturally oblique, have formed a bed under a considerable portion of the hip, and because the extremity of the foot is not forcibly turned outward, but is nearly in a line with the body, and is even inclined more inwardly. When, then, the articular extremity of the femur has worn out a socket for itself in the flesh where it was lodged, and the flesh is lubricated, it ceases to be painful in the course of time, and when it becomes free from pain, they can walk without a staff, if so inclined, and they can support the body on the injured limb. From usage then, in such cases, the fleshy parts are less enervated than in those which have been mentioned a little before, still, however, they lose their strength more or less; but in general there is more enervation when the dislocation is inward than when it is outward. Some of them, then, cannot wear their shoes, owing to the unbending state of their leg, and some of them can. But when this dislocation takes place *in utero,* and when the dislocation having occurred at any time before manhood, from violence, has not been replaced, or when from disease the articular extremity has started from its socket, and is displaced (for many such cases occur,

and from some of them, if the femur become necrosed, obstinate suppurations requiring the use of tents are formed, and in certain of them the bone is laid bare), whether the bone become necrosed or not, the bone of the thigh is much shortened, and does not usually grow like the sound one, the bones, too, of the leg, become shorter than those of the other, but in a small degree, for the same reasons that were formerly stated; such persons can walk, some of them in the same fashion as adults having an unreduced dislocation, and some of them walk with the whole foot on the ground, but limp in walking, being obliged to do so by the shortness of the limb. Such is the result, even though they be carefully and properly trained in the attitudes before they have strength for walking, and in like manner also, after they have acquired the necessary strength; but those persons require the most care who were very young when they met with the accident, for, if neglected while children, the limb becomes entirely useless and atrophied. The fleshy parts of the entire limb are more wasted than those of the sound limb, but this is much less apt to happen in their case than in dislocation inward, owing to usage and exercise, as they are speedily able to make use of the limb, as was stated a little before with regard to the weasel-armed (*galiancones*).

56. There are persons who, from birth or from disease, have dislocations outward of both the thighs; in them, then, the bones are affected in like manner, but the fleshy parts in their case lose their strength less; the legs, too, are plump and fleshy, except that there is some little deficiency at the inside, and they are plump because they have the equal use of both their legs, for in walking they totter equally to this side and that. Their nates appear very prominent, from the displacement of the bones of the joint. But if in their case the bones do not sphacelate (*become carious?*) and if they do not become bent above the hip-joint, if nothing of this kind happen to them, they become otherwise sufficiently healthy, but the growth of all the rest of the body, with the exception of the head, is arrested.

57. In dislocations of the head of the femur backward, which rarely occur, the patient cannot extend the leg, either at the dislocated joint, or at the ham, to any extent, and of all the dislocations, this is the variety in which the patients have the least power of making extension at the groin and the ham. But, moreover, this also should be known (for it is a valuable piece of knowledge, and of much importance, and yet most people are ignorant of it), that persons in

health cannot extend the joint at the ham, if they do not extend the joint at the groin at the same time, unless they raise the foot very high, for in this way they could do it; neither also could they bend the joint at the ham, but with much greater difficulty, if they do not bend the joint at the groin at the same time. There are many other things in the body which have similar connections, both with regard to the contractions of nerves (*ligaments?*), and the positions of muscles, and many of them more worthy of being known than is generally supposed, and with regard to the nature of the intestine and that of the whole internal cavity, and with regard to the displacements and contractions of the uterus; but all these things will be treated of elsewhere, in a work akin to the present one. But with regard to the matter on hand, they cannot make extension, as has been already stated; and the limb appears shortened, for two reasons—first, because it cannot be extended, and also because the bone has slipped into the flesh of the nates; for the head and neck of the femur, in this dislocation, are carried downward from their natural situation, to the outside of the nates. But yet they can bend the limb, unless prevented by pain, and the leg and foot appear pretty straight, and not much inclined toward either side, but at the groin the flesh, when felt, appears looser, from the bone of the joint having slipped to the other side, but at the nates the head of the femur may be felt to be more prominent than natural. Such are the symptoms accompanying dislocation of the thigh backward.

58. When this dislocation occurs in an adult, and is not reduced, he can walk, indeed, after a time, and when the pain has abated, and when he has been accustomed to rotate the articular bone in the flesh; he finds it necessary, however, to make strong flexion at the groin in walking, for two reasons, both because the limb, for the causes already stated, becomes much shorter, and he is far from touching the ground with his heel, and he can barely reach it with the ball of his foot, and not even thus, unless he bend himself at the groins, and also bend with the other leg at the ham. And in this case, he is under the necessity of supporting the upper part of the thigh with his hand at each step: this also contributes, in a certain degree, to make him bend the body at the groins; for, during the shifting of the feet in walking, the body cannot be supported on the unsound limb, unless it be pressed to the ground by the hand,—the end of the femur not being placed properly under the body, but having slipped backward to the nates;

and if he should try to rest the weight of his body for a little, upon the foot, without any other support, he would fall backward, for there would be a great inclination in this direction, from the hips having protruded backward far beyond the line of the foot, and the spine inclining toward the hips. Such persons can walk, indeed, without a staff, if so accustomed, for because the sole of the foot is in its old line, and is not inclined outward, they do not require anything to balance them. Such, however, as, instead of grasping the thigh, prefer resting their weight upon a staff introduced into the armpit of the affected side, these, if they use a longer staff, will walk, indeed, more erect, but will not be able to reach the ground with the foot, or if they wish to rest upon the foot, they must take a shorter staff, and will require to bend the body at the groins. The wasting of the fleshy parts is analogous to what happens in the cases formerly described, for the wasting is greatest in those cases in which the patients keep the limb up, and do not exercise it, whilst those who practice walking, have the least atrophy. The sound leg, however, is not benefited, but is rather rendered more deformed, if the injured limb be applied to the ground, for it is forced to co-operate with the other, being protruded at the hip, and bent at the ham. But if the patient does not use the injured limb by applying it to the ground, but carries it up, and rests upon a staff, the sound leg thereby gains strength, for it is employed in its natural position, and further, the exercise gives it strength. But it may be said, these things are foreign to medicine; for what is the use of enlarging upon cases which are already past remedy? This is far from being the case, for it belongs to the knowledge of medicine to be acquainted also with these, and they cannot possibly be separated from one another; for to such as are curable, means are to be used to prevent them from becoming incurable, studying how they may best be prevented from getting into an incurable state. And incurable cases should be known, that they may not be aggravated by useless applications, and splendid and creditable prognostics are made by knowing where, how, and when every case will terminate, and whether it will be converted into a curable or an incurable disease. When then, from birth, or during one's youth, this dislocation backward occurs, and is not reduced, whether it be connected with violence or disease (for many such dislocations occur in diseases, but the nature of the diseases in which dislocations take place, will be described afterward); if, then, the dislocated limb be not re-duced, the bone of the thigh becomes short-ened, the whole limb is impaired, is arrested in its growth, and loses its flesh from want of use; the articulation at the ham is also impaired, for the nerves (*ligaments?*) become stretched, from the causes formerly stated, wherefore those who have this dislocation, cannot make extension at the knee-joint. In a word, all parts of the body which were made for active use, if moderately used and exercised at the labor to which they are habituated, become healthy, increase in bulk, and bear their age well, but when not used, and when left without exercise, they become dis-eased, their growth is arrested, and they soon become old. Among these parts the joints and nerves (*ligaments?*), if not used, are not the least liable to be so affected; they are impaired, then, for the reasons we have stated, more in this variety of dislocation than in the others, for the whole limb is wasted, both in its bones and in its fleshy parts. Such persons, then, when they attain their full growth, keep the limb raised and flexed, rest the weight of the body on the other leg, and support themselves with a staff, some with one, and others with two.

59. In dislocations of the head of the thigh-bone forward (they are of rare occurrence), the patients cannot extend the leg completely, but least of all can they bend it at the groin; they are pained, also, if forced to bend the limb at the ham. The length of the leg, if compared at the heel, is the same as that of the other; but the extremity of the foot inclines less to project forward. But the whole limb has its natural direction, and inclines neither to this side nor to that. These cases are particularly attended with severe pain, and they are more apt to be accompanied with retention of urine at first than any of the other dislocations; for the head of the thigh-bone is lodged very near to impor-tant nerves. And the region of the groin appears swelled out and stretched, while that of the na-tes is more wrinkled and flabby. The symptoms now stated are those which attend this disloca-tion of the thigh-bone.

60. When persons have attained their full growth before meeting with this dislocation, and when it has not been reduced, upon the subsidence of the pain, and when the bone of the joint has been accustomed to be rotated in the place where it is lodged, these persons can walk almost erect without a staff, and with the injured leg almost quite straight, as it does not admit of easy flexion at the groin and the ham; owing, then, to this want of flexion at the groin,

they keep the limb more straight in walking than they do the sound one. And sometimes they drag the foot along the ground, as not be-ing able to bend the upper part of the limb, and they walk with the whole foot on the ground; for in walking they rest no less on the heel than on the fore part of the foot; and if they could take great steps, they would rest entirely on the heel in walking; for persons whose limbs are sound, the greater the steps they take in walk-ing, rest so much the more on the heel, while they are putting down the one foot and raising the opposite. In this form of dislocation, per-sons rest their weight more on the heel than on the anterior part of the foot, for the fore part of the foot cannot be bent forward equally well when the rest of the limb is extended as when it is in a state of flexion; neither, again, can the foot be arched to the same degree when the limb is bent as when it is extended. The natural state of matters is such as has been now described; and in an unreduced dislocation, persons walk in the manner described, for the reasons which have been stated. The limb, moreover, is less fleshy than the other, at the nates, the calf of the leg, and the whole of its posterior part. When this dislocation occurs in infancy, and is not reduced, or when it is congenital, in these cases the bone of the thigh is more atrophied than those of the leg and foot; but the atrophy of the thigh-bone is least of all in this form of dislocation. The fleshy parts, however, are ev-erywhere attenuated, more especially behind, as has been stated above. If properly trained, such persons, when they grow up, can use the limb, which is only a little shorter than the other, and yet they support themselves on a staff at the affected side. For, not being able to use proper-ly the ball of the foot without the heel, nor to put it down as some can in the other varieties of dislocation (the cause of which has been just now stated), on this account they require a staff. But those who are neglected, and are not in the practice of putting their foot to the ground, but keep the limb up, have the bones more atro-phied than those who use the limb; and, at the articulations, the limb is more maimed in the direct line than in the other forms of disloca-tion.

61. In a word, luxations and subluxations take place in different degrees, being some-times greater and sometimes less; and those cases in which the bone has slipped or been dis-placed to a much greater extent, are in general more difficult to rectify than otherwise; and if not reduced, such cases have greater and more

striking impairment and lesion of the bones, fleshy parts, and attitudes; but when the bone has slipped, or been displaced to a less extent, it is easier to reduce such cases than the other; and if the attempts at reduction have failed, or have been neglected, the impairment in such cases is less, and proves less injurious than in the cases just mentioned. The other joints present great differences as to the extent of the displacements which they are subject to. But the heads of the femur and humerus are very similar to one another as to their dislocations. For the heads of the bones are rounded and smooth, and the sockets which receive the heads are also circular, and adapted to the heads; they do not admit then of being dislocated in any intermediate degree, but, from their rounded shape, the bones slip either outward or inward. In the case we are now treating of, then, there is either a complete dislocation or none at all, and yet these bones admit of being displaced to a greater or less extent; and the thigh is more subject to these differences than the arm.

62. Wherefore, then, some of these congenital displacements, if to a small extent, may be reduced to their natural condition, and especially those at the ankle-joint. Most cases of congenital club-foot are remediable, unless the declination be very great, or when the affection occurs at an advanced period of youth. The best plan, then, is to treat such cases at as early a period as possible, before the deficiency of the bones of the foot is very great, and before there is any great wasting of the flesh of the leg. There is more than one variety of club-foot, the most of them being not complete dislocations, but impairments connected with the habitual maintenance of the limb in a certain position. In conducting the treatment, attention must be paid to the following points: to push back and rectify the bone of the leg at the ankle from without inward, and to make counter-pressure on the bone of the heel in an outward direction, so as to bring it into line, in order that the displaced bones may meet at the middle and side of the foot; and the mass of the toes, with the great toe, are to be inclined inward, and retained so; and the parts are to be secured, with cerate containing a full proportion of resin, with compresses, and soft bandages in sufficient quantity, but not applied too tight; and the turns of the bandages should be in the same direction as the rectifying of the foot with the hand, so that the foot may appear to incline a little outward. And a sole made of leather not very hard, or of lead, is to be bound on, and it is not to be applied to the skin but when you are about to make the last turns of the bandages. And when it is all bandaged, you must attach the end of one of the bandages that are used to the bandages applied to the inferior part of the foot on the line of the little toe; and then this bandage is to be rolled upward in what is considered to be a sufficient degree, to above the calf of the leg, so that it may remain firm when thus arranged. In a word, as if moulding a wax model, you must bring to their natural position the parts which were abnormally displaced and contracted together, so rectifying them with your hands, and with the bandaging in like manner, as to bring them into their position, not by force, but gently; and the bandages are to be stitched so as to suit the position in which the limb is to be placed, for different modes of the deformity require different positions. And a small shoe made of lead is to be bound on externally to the bandaging, having the same shape as the Chian slippers had. But there is no necessity for it if the parts be properly adjusted with the hands, properly secured with the bandages, and properly disposed of afterward. This, then, is the mode of cure, and it neither requires cutting, burning, nor any other complex means, for such cases yield sooner to treatment than one would believe. However, they are to be fairly mastered only by time, and not until the body has grown up in the natural shape; when recourse is had to a shoe, the most suitable are the buskins, which derive their name from being used in traveling through mud; for this sort of shoe does not yield to the foot, but the foot yields to it. A shoe shaped like the Cretan is also suitable.

63. In cases of complete dislocation at the ankle-joint, complicated with an external wound, whether the displacement be inward or outward, you are not to reduce the parts, but let any other physician reduce them if he choose. For this you should know for certain, that the patient will die if the parts are allowed to remain reduced, and that he will not survive more than a few days, for few of them pass the seventh day, being cut off by convulsions, and sometimes the leg and foot are seized with gangrene. It should be well known that such will be the results; and it does not appear to me that hellebore will do any good, though administered the same day, and the draught repeated, and yet it is the most likely means, if any such there be; but I am of opinion that not even it will be of service. But if not reduced, nor any attempts at first made to reduce them, most of such cases recover. The leg and foot are to be

arranged as the patient wishes, only they must not be put in a dependent position, nor moved about; and they are to be treated with pitched cerate, a few compresses dipped in wine, and not very cold, for cold in such cases induces convulsions; the leaves also of beet, or of colt's foot, of any such, when boiled in dark-colored austere wine, form a suitable application to the wound and the surrounding parts; and the wound may further be anointed with cerate in a tepid state. But if it be the winter season, the part is to be covered with unscoured wool, which is to be sprinkled from above with tepid wine and oil, but on no account is either bandage or compress to be applied; for this should be known most especially, that whatever compresses, or is heavy, does mischief in such cases. And certain of the dressings used to recent wounds are suitable in such cases; and wool may be laid upon the sore, and sprinkled with wine, and allowed to remain for a considerable time; but those dressings for recent wounds which only last for a few days, and into which resin enters as an ingredient, do not agree with them; for the cleansing of the sores is a slow process, and the sore has a copious discharge for a long time. Certain of these cases it may be advantageous to bandage. It ought also to be well understood, that the patient must necessarily be much maimed and deformed, for the foot is retracted outward, and the bones which have been displaced outward protrude: these bones, in fact, not being generally laid bare, unless to a small extent; neither do they exfoliate, but they heal by thin and feeble cicatrices, provided the patient keeps quiet for a length of time; but otherwise there is danger that a small ulcer may remain incurable. And yet in the case we are treating of, those who are thus treated are saved; whereas, when the parts are reduced and allowed to remain in place, the patients die.

64. The same rule applies to dislocations at the wrist, attended with a wound and projection of the bone, whether the bones of the arm be displaced inward or outward. For this should be well understood, that the patient will die in the course of a few days, by the same mode of death as formerly described, if the bone be reduced, and allowed to remain so. But in those cases in which they are not reduced, nor any attempt made to reduce them, the patients, for the most part, recover; and the same mode of treatment as has been described will be applicable; but the deformity and impediment of the limb must necessarily be great, and the fingers of the hand will be weak and useless; for if the bones have slipped inward, they cannot bend the fingers, or if outward, they cannot extend them.

65. When the os tibiæ, having made a wound at the knee, has protruded through the skin, whether the dislocation be outward or inward, in such a case, if the bone be reduced, death will be even more speedy than in the other cases, although speedy also in them. But the only hope of recovery is if you treat them without reduction. These cases are more dangerous than the others, as being so much higher up, as being so much stronger joints, and displaced from bones which are so much stronger. But if the os femoris form a wound at the knee, and slip through it, provided it be reduced and left so, it will occasion a still more violent and speedy death than in the cases formerly described; but if not reduced, it will be much more dangerous than those cases mentioned before, and yet this is the only hope of recovery.

66. The same rule applies to the elbow-joint, and with regard to the bones of the fore-arm and arm. For when these bones protrude through a wound which they have made in the skin, all cases in which they are reduced prove fatal; but if not reduced, there is a chance of recovery; but to those that survive there is certain impediment. And if in any instance the bones of the upper articulations (*shoulder-joint?*), should be dislocated, and project through a wound which they have made in the skin, these, if reduced, are followed by more speedy death; and if not reduced, they are more dangerous than the others. But the mode of treatment which appears to me most suitable has been already described.

67. When the joints of the toes or hands are dislocated, and the bones protrude through a wound which they have made, and when there is no fracture of the bone, but merely displacement of the joint, in these cases, if the reduction be made and allowed to remain, there is some danger of spasms (*tetanus?*) if not properly treated, and yet it may be worth while to reduce them, having warned the patient beforehand that much caution and care will be required. The easiest, the most efficient method, and the one most conformable to art, is that by the lever, as formerly described when treating of bones which have been fractured and protruded; then the patient must be as quiet as possible, lie in a recumbent position, and observe a restricted regimen. And it will be better also that he should get some gentle emetics. The sore is to be treated with dressings for fresh wounds,

which permit of affusions, or with the leaves of camomile, or with the applications for fractured bones of the head, but nothing very cold must be applied. The first (*most distant?*) joints are least dangerous, but those still higher, are more so. Reduction should be made the same day, or the next, but by no means on the third or fourth, for it is on the fourth day that exacerbations especially attack. In those cases, then, where immediate reduction cannot be accomplished, we must wait until after the aforesaid days; for whatever you reduce within ten days, may be expected to induce spasm. But if the spasm supervene on its being reduced, the joint should be quickly displaced, and bathed frequently with warm water, and the whole body should be kept in a warm, soft, and easy condition, and more especially about the joints, for the whole body should rather be in a bent than in an extended state. Moreover, it is to be expected, that the articular extremities of the bones of the fingers will exfoliate, for this generally happens, if even the least degree of inflammation take place, so that if it were not that the physician would be exposed to censure, owing to the ignorance of the common people, no reduction should be made at all. The reduction of the bones of joints which have protruded through the skin, is attended with the dangers which have been described.

68. When the articular bones of the fingers are fairly chopped off, these cases are mostly unattended with danger, unless deliquium come on in consequence of the injury, and ordinary treatment will be sufficient to such sores. But when resection is made, not at the articulations, but at some other point in the bones, these cases also are free from danger, and are still more easily cured than the others; and the fractured bones of the fingers which protrude otherwise than at the joint admit of reduction without danger. Complete resections of bones at the joints, whether the foot, the hand, the leg, the ankle, the forearm, the wrist, for the most part, are not unattended with danger, unless one be cut off at once by deliquium animi, or if continual fever supervene on the fourth day.

69. With regard to the sphacelus of fleshy parts, it takes place in wounds where there are large blood-vessels, which have been strongly compressed, and in fractures of bones which have been bound too tight, and in other cases of immoderate constriction, when the parts which have been strangulated generally drop off; and the most of such patients recover, even when a portion of the thigh comes away, or of the arm,

both bones and flesh, but less so in this case; and when the fore-arm and leg drop off, the patients readily recover. In cases then, of fracture of the bones, when strangulation and blackening of the parts take place at first, the separation of the dead and living parts quickly occurs, and the parts speedily drop off, as the bones have already given way; but when the blackening (*mortification*) takes place while the bones are entire, the fleshy parts, in this case, also quickly die; but the bones are slow in separating at the boundary of the blackening, and where the bones are laid bare. Those parts of the body which are below the boundaries of the blackening are to be removed at the joint, as soon as they are fairly dead and have lost their sensibility; care being taken not to wound any living part; for if the part which is cut off give pain, and if it should prove not to be quite dead, there is great danger lest the patient may swoon away from the pain, and such swoonings often are immediately fatal. I have known the thigh-bones, when denuded in this manner, drop off on the eightieth day; but in the case of this patient, the parts below were separated at the knee on the twentieth day, and, as I thought, too early, for it appeared to me that this should be done more guardedly. In a case which I had of such blackening in the leg, the bones of the leg, as far as they were denuded, separated at its middle on the sixtieth day. But the separation of denuded bones is quicker or slower, according to the mode of treatment; something, too, depends upon whether the compression be stronger or weaker, and whether the nerves, flesh, arteries, and veins are quicker or slower in becoming blackened and in dying; since, when the parts are not strongly compressed, the separation is more superficial, and does not go the length of laying the bones bare, and in some cases it is still more superficial, so as not even to expose the nerves. For the reasons now stated, it is impossible to define accurately the time at which each of these cases will terminate. The treatment of such cases, however, is to be readily undertaken, for they are more formidable to look at than to treat; and a mild treatment is sufficient in all such cases, for they come to a crisis of themselves; only the diet must be attended to, so that it may be as little calculated to create fever as possible, and the body is to be placed in the proper positions: these are, neither raised very high up, nor inclined much downward, but rather upward, until the separation be completed; for at that time there is most danger of hemorrhage; on this account, wounds should not be laid in a declining position, but the contrary. But after a while, and when the sores have become clean, the same positions will no longer be appropriate; but a straight position, and one inclining downward, may be proper; and in the course of time, in some of these cases, abscesses form, and require bandages. One may also expect that such patients will be attacked with dysentery; for dysentery usually supervenes in cases of mortification and of hemorrhage from wounds; it comes on generally when the blackening and hemorrhage have arrived at a crisis, and is profuse and intense, but does not last many days; neither is it of a fatal nature, for such patients do not usually lose their appetite, nor is it proper to put them on a restricted diet.

70. Dislocation inward at the hip-joint is to be reduced in the following manner: (it is a good, proper, and natural mode of reduction, and has something of display in it, if any one takes delight in such ostentatious modes of procedure). The patient is to be suspended by the feet from a cross-beam with a strong, soft, and broad cord; the feet are to be about four inches or less from one another; and a broad and soft leather collar connected with the cross-beam is to be put on above the knees; and the affected leg should be so extended as to be two inches longer than the other; the head should be about two cubits from the ground, or a little more or less; and the arms should be stretched along the sides, and bound with something soft; all these preparations should be made while he is lying on his back, so that he may be suspended for as short a time as possible. But when the patient is suspended, a person properly instructed and not weak, having introduced his arm between his thighs, is to place his fore-arm between the perineum and the dislocated head of the os femoris; and then, having joined the other hand to the one thus passed through the thighs, he is to stand by the side of the suspended patient, and suddenly suspend and swing himself in the air as perpendicularly as possible. This method comprises all the conditions which are natural; for the body being suspended by its weight, produces extension, and the person suspended from him, along with the extension, forces the head of the thigh-bone to rise up above the acetabulum; and at the same time he uses the bone of the fore-arm as a lever, and forces the os femoris to slip into its old seat. The cords should be properly prepared, and care should be taken that the person suspended along with the patient have a sufficiently strong hold.

71. Wherefore, as formerly stated, men's constitutions differ much from one another as to the facility or difficulty with which dislocations are reduced; and the cause of this was also stated formerly in treating of the shoulder. In some the thigh is reduced with no preparation, with slight extension, directed by the hands, and with slight movement; and in some the reduction is effected by bending the limb at the joint, and making rotation. But much more frequently it does not yield to any ordinary apparatus, and therefore one should be acquainted with the most powerful means which can be applied in each case, and use whatever may be judged most proper under all circumstances. The modes of extension have been described in the former parts of the work, so that one may make use of whatever may happen to be at hand. For, extension and counter-extension are to be made in the direction of the limb and the body; and if this be properly effected, the head of the thigh-bone will be raised above its ancient seat; and if thus raised, it will not be easy to prevent it from settling in its place, so that any ordinary impulse with the lever and adjustment will be quite sufficient; but some apply insufficient extension, and hence the reduction gives much trouble. The bands then should be fastened, not only at the foot, but also above the knee, so that the force of the extension may not be expended on the knee-joint more than upon the hip-joint. The extension in the direction of the foot is to be thus contrived. But the counter-extension is not only to be managed by means of something carried round the chest and armpits, but also by a long, double, strong, and supple thong applied to the perineum, and carried behind along the spine, and in front along the collar-bone and fixed to the point from which counter-extension is made; and then force is to be so applied, by means of this extension and counter-extension, that the thong at the perineum may not pass over the head of the thigh-bone, but between it and the perineum; and during the extension one should strike the head of the femur with the fist, so as to drive it outward. And when the patient is raised up by the stretching, you should pass a hand through (*between the legs?*) and grasp it with the other hand, so as at the same time to make extension, and force the dislocated limb outward; while some other person sitting by the knee quietly directs it inward.

72. It has been formerly stated by us that it will be of importance for any person who practices medicine in a populous city to get prepared a quadrangular board, about six cubits or a little

more in length, and about two cubits in breadth; a fathom will be sufficient thickness for it; and then along it from the one end to the other, an excavation must be made, so that the working of the levers may not be higher than is proper; then at both sides we are to raise short, strong, and strongly-fixed posts, having axles; and in the middle of the bench five or six long grooves are to be scooped out about four inches distant from one another, three inches will be a sufficient breadth for them, and the depth in like manner; and although the number of grooves I have mentioned will be sufficient, there is nothing to prevent their being made all over the bench. And the bench should have in its middle a pretty deep hole, of a square shape, and of about three inches in size; and into this hole, when judged necessary, is to be adjusted a corresponding piece of wood, rounded above, which, at the proper time, is to be adjusted between the perineum and the head of the thigh-bone. This upright piece of wood prevents the body from yielding to the force dragging downward by the feet; for sometimes this piece of wood serves the purpose of counter-extension upward; and sometimes, too, when extension and counter-extension are made, this piece of wood, if susceptible of some motion to this side or that, will serve the purpose of a lever for pushing the head of the thigh-bone outward. It is on this account that several grooves are scooped out on the bench, so that this piece of wood, being erected at the one which answers, may act as a lever, either on the sides of the articular heads of bones, or may make pressure direct on the heads along with the extension, according as it may suit to push inward or outward with the lever; and the lever may be either of a round or broad form, as may be judged proper; for sometimes the one form and sometimes the other suits with the articulation. This mode of applying the lever along with extension is applicable in the reduction of all dislocations of the thigh. In the case now on hand, a round lever is proper; but in dislocations outward a flat lever will be the suitable one. By means of such machines and of such powers, it appears to me that we need never fail in reducing any dislocation at a joint.

73. And one might find out other modes of reduction for this joint. If the large bench were to have raised on it two posts about a foot (*in diameter?*), and of a suitable height, on each side near its middle, and if a transverse piece of wood like the step of a ladder, were inserted in the posts, then if the sound leg were carried through between the posts, and the injured limb

were brought over the transverse piece of wood, which should be exactly adapted in height to the joint which is dislocated (and it is an easy matter so to adjust it, for the step of the ladder should be made a little higher than required, and a convenient robe, folded several times, is to be laid below the patient's body), then a piece of wood, of suitable breadth and length, is to be laid below the limb, and it should reach from the ankle to beyond the head of the thigh-bone, and should be bound moderately tight to the limb. Then the limb being extended, either by means of the pestle-like piece of wood (formerly described), or by any of the other methods of extension, the limb which is carried over the step with the piece of wood attached to it, is to be forced downward, while somebody grasps the patient above the hip-joint. In this manner the extension will carry the head of the thigh-bone above the acetabulum, while the lever power that is exercised will push the head of the thigh-bone into its natural seat. All the above-mentioned powers are strong, and more than sufficient to rectify the accident, if properly and skillfully applied. For, as formerly stated, in most cases reduction may be effected by much weaker extension, and an inferior **apparatus.**

74. If the head of the bone slip outward, extension and counter-extension must be made as described, or in a similar manner. But along with the extension a broad lever is to be used to force the bone from without inward, the lever being placed at the nates or a little farther up, and some person is to steady the patient's body, so that it may not yield, either by grasping him at the buttocks with his hands, or this may be effected by means of another similar lever, adjusted to one of the grooves, while the patient has something laid below him, and he is secured, and the dislocated thigh is to be turned gently from within outward at the knee. Suspension will not answer in this form of dislocation, for, in this instance, the arm of the person suspended from him, would push the head of the thigh-bone from the acetabulum. But one might use the piece of wood placed below him as a lever, in such a manner as might suit with this mode of dislocation; it must work from without. But what use is there for more words? For if the extension be well and properly done, and if the lever be properly used, what dislocation of the joint could occur, that might not be thus reduced?

75. In dislocation of the thigh, backward, extension and counter-extension should be made as has been described; and having laid on the

bench a cloth which has been folded several times, so that the patient may lie soft, he is to be laid on his face, and extension thus made, and, along with the extension, pressure is to be made with a board, as in the case of humpback, the board being placed on the region of the nates, and rather below than above the hip-joint; and the hole made in the wall for the board should not be direct over, but should be inclined a little downward, toward the feet. This mode of reduction is particularly appropriate to this variety of dislocation, and at the same time is very strong. But perhaps, instead of the board, it might be sufficient to have a person sitting (*on the seat of luxation?*), or pressing with his hands, or with his foot, and suddenly raising himself up, along with the extension. None of the other aforementioned modes of reduction are natural in this form of dislocation.

76. In dislocation forward, the same mode of extension should be made; but a person who has very strong hands, and is well trained, should place the palm of the one hand on the groin, and taking hold of this hand with the other, is at the same time to push the dislocated part downward, and at the same time to the fore part of the knee. This method of reduction is most especially conformable to this mode of dislocation. And the mode of suspension is also not far removed from being natural, but the person suspended should be well trained, so that his arm may not act as a lever upon the joint, but that the force of the suspension may act about the middle of the perineum, and at the os sacrum.

77. Reduction by the bladder is also celebrated in dislocations at this joint, and I have seen certain persons who, from ignorance, attempted to reduce both dislocations outward and backward therewith, not knowing that they were rather displacing than replacing the parts; it is clear, however, that he who first invented this method intended it for dislocation inward. It is proper, then, to know how the bladder should be used, if it is to be used, and it should be understood that many other methods are more powerful than it. The bladder should be placed between the thighs uninflated, so that it may be carried as far up the perineum as possible, and the thighs beginning at the patella are to be bound together with a swathe, as far up as the middle of the thigh, and then a brass pipe is to be introduced into one of the loose feet of the bladder, and air forced into it, the patient is to lie on his side with the injured limb uppermost. This, then, is the preparation; some, however,

do the thing worse than as I have described, for they do not bind the thighs together to any extent, but only at the knees, neither do they make extension, whereas extension should be made, and yet some people by having the good fortune to meet with a favorable case, have succeeded in making reduction. But it is not a convenient method of applying force, for the bladder, when inflated, does not present its most prominent part to the articular extremity of the femur, which is the place that ought to be more especially pressed outward, but its middle, which probably corresponds with the middle of the thigh, or still lower down, for the thighs are naturally curved, being fleshy, and in contact above, and becoming smaller downward, so that the natural configuration of the parts forces the bladder from the most proper place. And if a small bladder be introduced, its power will be small, and unable to overcome the resistance of the articular bone. But if the bladder must be used, the thighs are to be bound together to a considerable extent, and the bladder is to be inflated along with the extension of the body, and in this method of reduction both legs are to be bound together at their extremity.

78. The prime object of the physician in the whole art of medicine should be to cure that which is diseased; and if this can be accomplished in various ways, the least troublesome should be selected; for this is more becoming a good man, and one well skilled in the art, who does not covet popular coin of base alloy. With regard to the subject now on hand, the following are domestic means of making extension of the body, so that it is easy to choose from among the things at hand:—In the first place, when soft and supple thongs are not at hand for ligatures, either iron chains, or cords, or cables of ships, are to be wrapped round with scarfs or pieces of woolen rags, especially at the parts of them which are to be applied, and in this state they are to be used as bands. In the second place, the patient is to be comfortably laid on the strongest and largest couch that is at hand, and the feet of the couch, either those at the (*patient's?*) head, or those at the feet, are to be fastened to the threshold, either within or without, as is most suitable; and a square piece of wood is to be laid across, and extending from the one foot to the other; and if this piece of wood be slender, it should be bound to the feet of the couch, but, if it be thick, there will be no necessity for this; then the heads of the ligatures, both of those at the head and those at the feet, are to be fastened to a pestle, or some such piece of wood,

at either end; the ligatures should run along the line of the body, or be a little elevated above it, and it should be stretched proportionally to the pestles, so that, standing erect, the one may be fastened to the threshold, and the other to the transverse piece of wood. Extension is then to be made by bending back the ends of the pestles. A ladder, having strong steps, if laid below the bed, will serve the purpose of the threshold and the piece of wood laid along (*the foot of the couch?*), as the pestles can be fastened to the steps at either end, and when drawn back they thus make extension of the ligatures. Dislocation, inward or forward, may be reduced in the following manner: a ladder is to be fastened in the ground, and the man is to be seated upon it, and then the sound leg is to be gently stretched along and bound to it, wherever it is found convenient; and water is to be poured into an earthen vessel, or stones put into a hamper and slung from the injured leg, so as to effect the reduction. Another mode of reduction: a cross-beam is to be fastened between two pillars of moderate height; and at one part of the cross-beam there should be a protuberance proportionate to the size of the nates; and having bound a coverlet round the patient's breast, he is to be seated on the protuberant part of the cross-beam, and afterward the breast is to be fastened to the pillar by some broad ligature; then some one is to hold the sound leg so that he may not fall off, and from the injured limb is to be suspended some convenient weight, as formerly described.

79. It should be particularly known that the union of all bones is, for the most part, by a head and socket (*cotylé*); in some of these the place (*socket?*) is cotyloid and oblong, and in some the socket is glenoid (*shallow?*). In all dislocations reduction is to be effected, if possible, immediately, while still warm, but otherwise, as quickly as it can be done; for reduction will be a much easier and quicker process to the operator, and a much less painful one to the patient, if effected before swelling comes on. But all the joints when about to be reduced should be first softened, and gently moved about; for, thus they are more easily reduced. And, in all cases of reduction at joints, the patient must be put on a spare diet, but more especially in the case of the greatest joints, and those most difficult to reduce, and less so in those which are very small and easily reduced.

80. If any joint of the fingers is dislocated, whether the first, second, or the third, the same method of reduction is to be applied, but the largest joints are the most difficult to reduce. There are four modes of displacement—either upward, downward, or to either side; most commonly upward, and most rarely laterally, and in consequence of violent motion. On both sides of its articular cavity there is a sort of raised border. When the dislocation is upward or downward, owing to the articular cavity having smoother edges there than at the sides, if the joint of it be dislocated, it is more easily reduced. This is the mode of reduction:—The end of the finger is to be wrapped round with a fillet, or something such, that, when you lay hold of it and make extension, it will not slip; and when this is done, some person is to grasp the arm at the wrist, and another is to take hold of the finger which is wrapped in the fillet, and then each is to make considerable extension toward himself, and at the same time the projecting bone is to be pushed into its place. But, if the dislocation be lateral, the same mode of reduction is to be used; but when you think that the extremity of the bone has cleared the rim, at the same time that extension is made, the bone is to be pushed direct into its place, while another person on the other side of the finger is to take care and make counter-pressure, so that it may not again slip out there. The twisted nooses formed from palm-shoots are convenient for effecting reduction, if you will make extension and counter-extension by holding the twisted string in the one hand and the wrist in the other. When reduced, you must bind the part as quickly as possible with bandages; these are to be very slender and waxed with cerate, neither very soft nor very hard, but of middle consistence; for that which is hard drops off from the finger, while that which is soft and liquid is melted and lost by the increased heat of the finger. The bandage is to be loosed on the third or fourth day; but on the whole, if inflamed, it is to be the more frequently loosed, and if otherwise, more rarely; this I say respecting all the joints. The articulation of a finger is restored in fourteen days. The treatment of the fingers and of the toes is the same.

81. After all reductions of joints the patient should be confined to a restricted diet and abstinence until the seventh day; and if there be inflammation, the bandages are to be the more frequently loosed, but otherwise, less frequently, and the pained joint is to be kept constantly in a state of rest, and is to be laid in the most convenient position possible.

82. Accidents at the knee are more mild than at the elbow, from its being more compact, regu-

lar, and elegant in its construction; and, therefore, it is more readily dislocated and reduced. It is most frequently dislocated inward, but also outward and backward. The modes of reduction are these: by flexion at the knee, or by sudden calcitration, or having rolled a swathe into a ball, and fixed it in the ham, the patient's body is to be suddenly dropped on its bended knees. Dislocation backward, also, as in the case of the elbow, may be reduced by moderate extension, and to either side, either by flexion or calcitration, but also by moderate extension. The adjustment is the same in all cases. In dislocations backward which are not reduced, the patient cannot bend the joint, but neither can he, to any great extent, in the other varieties; the thigh and leg are wasted in front; but if inward the patients become bow-legged, and the external parts are wasted; but if outward they become more bandy-legged, but the impediment is less, for the body is supported on the larger of the bones, and the inner parts are wasted. When these accidents happen at birth or during adolescence, they follow the rule formerly stated.

83. Dislocations at the ankle-joints require strong extension, either with the hands or some such means; and adjustment, which at the same time effects both purposes, as is common in all cases.

84. Injuries of the foot are to be remedied like those of the hand.

85. The bones connected with the leg, and which are dislocated, either at birth or during adolescence, follow the same course as those in the hand.

86. When persons jumping from a height pitch on the heel, so as to occasion separation (*diastasis*) of the bones, ecchymosis of the veins, and contusion of the nerves; when these symptoms are very violent there is danger of sphacelus, and that the case may give trouble during life, for the bones are so constructed as to slip from one another, and the nerves communicate together. And, indeed, in cases of fracture, either from an injury in the leg or thigh, or in paralysis of the nerves (*tendons?*) connected with these parts, or from neglect during confinement to bed, when the heel gets blackened the most serious consequences result therefrom. Sometimes, in addition to the sphacelus, there come on acute fevers accompanied with hiccup, aberration of intellect, and speedy death, with lividities of the large blood-vessels. With regard to the symptoms attending exacerbations, if the ecchymosed and blackened parts and those around be somewhat hard and red, and if along with the hardness there be lividity, mortification is to be apprehended; but if the parts be slightly livid, or even very livid, and the swelling diffused, or if greenish and soft, these appearances, in such cases, are all favorable. The treatment, if no fever be present, consists in the administration of hellebore, but otherwise it is not to be given, but *oxyglyky* (*decoction of honeycombs and vinegar*) is to be given for drink, if required. Bandaging as in the other articulations: above all, more especially in contusions, the bandages should be numerous and softer than usual, but the compression should be less; most turns should be made around the heel. Position, like the bandaging, should be so regulated as not to determine to the heel. Splints are not to be used.

87. When the foot is dislocated, either alone or along with its epiphysis, the displacement is, for the most part, to the inside. If not reduced, in the course of time, the hip, the thigh, and the side of the leg opposite the dislocation, become atrophied. Reduction is the same as in the wrist, but the extension requires to be very powerful. Treatment, agreeably to the general rule for joints. Exacerbations do occur, but less frequently than in dislocations at the wrist, provided the parts get rest. While they remain at rest the diet should be restricted. Those which occur at birth, or during adolescence, follow the rule formerly stated.

Instruments of Reduction

WITH regard to the construction of bones, the bones and joints of the fingers are simple, the bones of the hand and foot are numerous, and articulated in various ways; the uppermost are the largest; the heel consists of one bone which is seen to project outward, and the back tendons are attached to it. The leg consists of two bones, united together above and below, but slightly separated in the middle; the external bone (*fibula*), where it comes into proximity with the little toe, is but slightly smaller than the other, more so where they are separated, and at the knee, the outer hamstring arises from it; these bones have a common epiphysis below, with which the foot is moved, and another epiphysis above,[1] in which is moved the articular extremity of the femur, which is simple and light in proportion to its length, in the form of a condyle, and having the patella (connected with it?), the femur itself bends outward and forward; its head is a round epiphysis which gives origin to ligament inserted in the acetabulum of the hip-joint. This bone is articulated somewhat obliquely, but less so than the humerus. The ischium is united to the great vertebra contiguous to the os sacrum by a cartilaginous ligament. The spine, from the os sacrum to the great vertebra, is curved backward; in this quarter are situated the bladder, the organs of generation, and the inclined portion of the rectum; from this to the diaphragm it proceeds in a straight line inclining forward, and the psoæ are situated there; from this point, to the great vertebra above the tops of the shoulders, it rises in a line that is curved backward, and the curvature appears greater than it is in reality, for the posterior processes of the spine are there highest; the articulation of the neck inclines forward. The vertebræ on the inside are regularly placed upon one another, but behind they are connected by a cartilaginous ligament; they are articulated in the form of synarthrosis at the back part of the spinal marrow; behind they have a sharp process having a cartilaginous epiphysis, whence proceeds the roots of nerves running downward, as also muscles extending from the neck to the loins, and filling the space between the ribs and the spine. The ribs are connected to all the intervertebral spaces on the inside, from the neck to the lumbar region, by a small ligament, and before to the sternum, their extremities being spongy and soft; their form is the most arched in man of all animals; for in this part, man is, of all animals, the narrowest in proportion to his bulk. The ribs are united to each vertebra by a small ligament at the place from which the short and broad lateral processes (transverse processes?) arise. The sternum is one continuous bone, having lateral pits for the insertion of the ribs; it is of a spongy and cartilaginous structure. The clavicles are rounded in front, having some slight movements at the sternum, but more free at the acromion. The acromion, in man, arises from the scapulæ differently from most other animals. The scapula is cartilaginous toward the spine, and spongy elsewhere, having an irregular figure externally; its neck and articular

[1] Epiphysis means a close union of the two bones by means of a ligament.

cavity cartilaginous; it does not interfere with the movements of the ribs, and is free of all connection with the other bones, except the humerus. The head of the humerus is articulated with its (glenoid?) cavity, by means of a small ligament, and it consists of a rounded epiphysis composed of spongy cartilage, the humerus itself is bent outward and forward, and it is articulated with its (glenoid?) cavity by its side, and not in a straight line. At the elbow it is broad, and has condyles and cavities, and is of a solid consistence; behind it is a cavity in which the coronoid process (olecranon?) of the ulna is lodged, when the arm is extended; here, too, is inserted the benumbling nerve, which arises from between the two bones of the forearm at their junction, and terminates there.

2. When the nose is fractured, the parts should be modeled instantly, if possible. If the fracture be in its cartilaginous part, introduce into the nostrils a tent formed of caddis, inclosed in the outer skin of a Carthaginian hide, or anything else which does not irritate; the skin is to be glued to the parts displaced, which are to be thus rectified. Bandaging in this case does mischief. The treatment is to consist of flour with manna, or of sulphur with cerate. You will immediately adjust the fragments, and afterward retain them in place with your fingers introduced into the nostrils, and turning the parts into place; then the Carthaginian skin is to be used. Callius forms even when there is a wound; and the same things are to be done, even when there is to be exfoliation of the bones, for this is not of a serious nature.

3. In fractures of the ears, neither bandages nor cataplasms should be used; or, if any bandage be used, it should be put on very tight; the cerate and sulphur should be applied to agglutinate the bandages. When matter forms in the ears, it is found to be more deeply seated than might be supposed, for all parts that are pulpy, and consist of juicy flesh, prove deceptious in such a case. But no harm will result from making an opening, for the parts are lean, watery, and full of mucus. No mention is here made of the places and circumstances which render it fatal to make an opening. The cure is soonest effected by transfixing the ear with a cautery; but the ear is maimed and diminished in size, if burned across. If opened, one of the gentle medicines for flesh wounds should be used as a dressing.

4. The jaw-bone is often slightly displaced (subluxated?), and is restored again; it is dislocated but rarely, especially in gaping; in fact,

the bone is never dislocated unless it slips while the mouth is opened wide. It slips, however, the more readily from its ligaments being oblique, supple, and of a yielding nature. The symptoms are: the lower jaw protrudes, it is distorted to the side opposite the dislocation, and the patient cannot shut his mouth; when both sides are dislocated, the jaw projects more, the mouth can be less shut, but there is no distortion; this is shown by the rows of the teeth in the upper and lower jaw corresponding with one another. If, then, both sides be dislocated, and not immediately reduced, the patient for the most part dies on the tenth day, with symptoms of continued fever, stupor, and coma, for the muscles there induce such effects; there is disorder of the bowels attended with scanty and unmixed dejection; and the vomitings, if any, are of the same character. The other variety is less troublesome. The method of reduction is the same in both:—The patient being laid down or seated, the physician is to take hold of his head, and grasping both sides of the jaw-bone with both hands, within and without, he must perform three manœuvres at once,—rectify the position of the jaw, push it backward, and shut the mouth. The treatment should consist of soothing applications, position, and applying a suitable bandage to support the jaw-bone, so as to co-operate with the reduction.

5. The bone of the shoulder is dislocated downward. I have never heard of any other mode. The parts put on the appearance of dislocation forward, when the flesh about the joint is wasted during consumption, as also seems to be the case with cattle when in a state of leanness after winter. Those persons are most liable to dislocations who are thin, slender, and have humidities about their joints without inflammation, for it knits the joints. Those who attempt to reduce and rectify dislocations in oxen, commit a blunder, as forgetting that the symptoms arise from the manner in which the ox uses the limb, and that the appearance is the same in a man who is in a similar condition, and forgetting also that Homer has said, that oxen are most lean at that season. In this dislocation, then, when not reduced, the patient cannot perform any of those acts which others do, by raising the arm from the side. I have thus stated who are the persons most subject to this dislocation, and how they are affected. In congenital dislocations the nearest bones are most shortened, as is the case with persons who are *weasel-armed;* the fore-arm less so, and the hand still less; the bones above are not affected.

And the parts (near the seat of the injury) are most wasted in flesh; and this happens more especially on the side of the arm opposite the dislocation, and that during adolescence, yet in a somewhat less degree than in congenital cases. The deep-seated suppurations occur most frequently to new-born infants about the joint of the shoulder, and these produce the same consequences as dislocations. In adults, the bones are not so diminished in size, and justly, seeing that the others will not increase as in the former case; but wasting of the flesh takes place, for it is increased, and is diminished every day, and at all ages. And attention should be paid to the force of habit, and to the symptom produced by the tearing away of the acromion, whereby a void is left, which makes people suppose that the humerus is dislocated. The head of the humerus is felt in the armpit, and the patient cannot raise his arm, nor swing it to this side and that, as formerly. The other shoulder shows the difference. Modes of reduction:— The patient himself having placed his fist in the arm pit, pushes up the head of the humerus with it, and brings the hand forward to the breast. Another:—Force it backward, so that you may turn it round. Another:—Apply your head to the acromion, and your hands to the armpit, separate the head of the humerus (*from the side?*), and push the elbow in the opposite direction; or, instead of your knees, another person may turn aside the elbow, as formerly directed. Or, place the patient on your shoulder, with the shoulder in his armpit. Or, with the heel, something being introduced to fill up the hollow of the armpit, and using the right foot to the right shoulder. Or, with a pestle. Or, with the step of a ladder. Or, by rotation made with piece of wood stretched below the arm. Treatment:—As to attitude, the arm placed by the side, the hand and shoulder raised; the bandaging and adjustment of the parts while in this attitude. If not reduced, the top of the shoulder becomes attenuated.

6. When the acromion is torn away, the appearance is the same as in dislocation of the shoulder; but there is no impediment, except that the bone does not return to its position. The figure should be the same as in dislocation, both as regards bandaging and suspending the limb. The bandaging according to rule.

7. When partial displacement (*sub-luxation?*) takes place at the elbow, either inside or outside, but the sharp point (*olecranon?*) remains in the cavity of the humerus, make extension in a straight line, and push the projecting parts

backward and to the sides.

8. In complete dislocations to either side, make extension while the arm is in the position it is put in to be bandaged for a fracture, for thus the rounded part of the elbow will not form an obstacle to it. Dislocation most commonly takes place inward. The parts are to be adjusted by separating the bones as much as possible, so that the end of the humerus may not come in contact with the olecranon, but it is to be carried up and turned round, and not forced in a straight line; at the same time the opposite sides are to be pushed together, and the bones reduced to their place. In these cases rotation of the elbow co-operates; that is to say, turning the arm into a state of supination and pronation; so much for the reduction. With regard to the attitude in which it is to be put,—the hand is to be placed somewhat higher than the elbow, and the arm by the side; this position suits with it when slung from the neck, is easily borne, is its natural position, and one adapted for ordinary purposes, unless callus form improperly: the callus soon forms. Treatment:—By bandages according to the common rule for articulations, and the point of the elbow is to be included in the bandage.

9. The elbow, when luxated, induces the most serious consequences, fevers, pain, nausea, vomiting of pure bile; and this especially in dislocations backward, from pressure on the nerve which occasions numbness; next to it is dislocation forward. The treatment is the same. The reduction of dislocation backward is by extension and adaptation: the symptom of this variety, loss of the power of extension; of dislocation forward, loss of the power of flexion. In it a hard ball is to be placed in the bend of the elbow, and the fore-arm is to be bent over this while sudden extension is made.

10. Diastasis of the bones may be recognized by examining the part where the vein which runs along the arm divides.

11. In these cases callus is speedily formed. In congenital dislocations, the bones below the seat of the injury are shorter than natural; in this case, the greatest shortening is in the nearest, namely, those of the fore-arm; second, those of the hand; third, those of the fingers. The arm and shoulders are stronger, owing to the nourishment which they receive, and the other arm, from the additional work it has to perform, is still more strong. The wasting of the flesh, if the dislocation was outward, is on the inside; or if otherwise, on the side opposite the dislocation.

12. In dislocation at the elbow, whether outward or inward, extension is to be made with the fore-arm at right angles to the arm; the arm is to be suspended by a shawl passed through the armpit, and a weight is to be attached to the extremity of the elbow; or force is to be applied with the hands. The articular extremity being properly raised, the parts are to be adjusted with the palms of the hands, as in dislocations of the hands. It is to be bandaged, suspended in a sling, and placed, while in this attitude.

13. Dislocations backward are to be rectified with the palms of the hands along with sudden extension. These two acts are to be performed together, as in other cases of the kind. In dislocation forward, the arm is to bend around a ball of cloth, of proper size, and at the same time replaced.

14. If the displacement be on the other side both these operations are to be performed in effecting the adjustment of the arm. With regard to the treatment,—the position and the bandaging are the same as in the other cases. For all these cases may be reduced by ordinary distention.

15. With regard to the modes of reduction, some act upon the principle of carrying the one piece of bone over the other, some by extension, and some by rotation: these last consist in rapidly turning the arm to this side and that.

16. The joint of the hand is dislocated inward or outward, but most frequently inward. The symptoms are easily recognized; if inward, the patient cannot at all bend his fingers, but if outward, he cannot extend them. Reduction: —By placing the fingers above a table, extension and counter-extension are to be made by assistance, while, with the palm of the hand or the heel on the projecting bone, one presses forward, and from behind, upon the other bone, and lays some soft substance on it; and, if the dislocation be above, the hand is to be turned into a state of pronation; or, if backward, into a state of supination. The treatment is to be conducted with bandages.

17. The whole hand is dislocated either inward, or outward, but especially inward, or to this side or that. Sometimes the epiphysis is displaced, and sometimes there is displacement (*diastasis*) of the one bone from the other. Powerful extension is to be made in this case; and the projecting part is to be pressed upon, and counter-pressure made on the opposite side: both modes being performed at the same time, both backward and laterally, either with the hands on a table, or with the heel. These ac-

cidents give rise to serious consequences and deformities; but in time the parts get so strong as to admit of being used. The treatment consists of bandages comprehending the hand and forearm, and splints are to be applied as far as the fingers; when put in splints, they are to be more frequently loosed than in fractures, and more copious affusions of water are to be used.

18. In congenital dislocations the hand becomes shortened, and the atrophy of the flesh is generally on the side opposite the dislocation. In the adult the bones remain of their proper size.

19. The symptoms of dislocation of the finger are obvious, and need not be described. This is the mode of reduction:—By stretching in a straight line, and making pressure on the projecting part, and counter-pressure, at the opposite side, on the other. The proper treatment consists in the application of bandages. When not reduced, the parts unite by callus outside of the joints. In congenital dislocations, and in those which occur during adolescence, the bones below the dislocation are shortened, and the flesh is wasted principally on the side opposite to the dislocation; in the adult the bones remain of their proper size.

20. Dislocation at the hip-joint occurs in four modes, inward most frequently, outward next, the others of equal frequency. The symptoms: —The common, a comparison with the sound leg. The peculiar symptoms of dislocations inward; the head of the bone is felt at the perineum; the patient cannot bend his leg as formerly; the limb appears elongated, and to a great extent, unless you bring both limbs into the middle space between them in making a comparison of them; and the foot and the knee are inclined outward. If the dislocation has taken place from birth, or during one's growth, the thigh is shortened, the leg less so, and the others according to the same rule; the fleshy parts are atrophied, especially on the outside. Such persons are afraid to stand erect, and crawl along on the sound limb; or, if compelled, they walk with one or two staves, and bear up the affected limb; and the smaller the limb so much the more easily do they walk. If the accident happens to adults the bones remain of their proper size, but the flesh is wasted, as formerly described; the patients walk in a wriggling manner, like oxen; they are bent toward the flank, and the buttock on the uninjured side is prominent; for the uninjured limb must necessarily come below that it may support the body, whilst the other must be carried out of the way, as it cannot support the body, like those who have

an ulcer in the foot. They poise the body by means of a staff on the sound side, and grasp the affected limb with the hand above the knee so as to carry the body in shifting from one place to another. If the parts below the hip-joint be used, the bones below are less atrophied, but the flesh more.

21. The symptoms and attitudes in dislocation outward are the opposite, and the knee and foot incline a little inward. When it is congenital, or occurs during adolescence, the bones do not grow properly; according to the same rule, the bone of the hip-joint is somewhat higher than natural, and does not grow proportionally. In those who have frequent dislocations outward, without inflammation, the limb is of a more humid (flabby?) temperament than natural, like the thumb, for it is the part most frequently dislocated, owing to its configuration; in what persons the dislocation is to a greater or less extent; and in what persons it is more difficultly or easily produced; in what there is reason to hope that it can be speedily reduced, and in what not; and the remedy for this; and in what cases the dislocation frequently happens, and treatment of this. In dislocation outward from birth, or during adolescence, or from disease, (and it happens most frequently from disease, in which case there is sometimes exfoliation of the bone, but even where there is no exfoliation), the patients experience the same symptoms, but to an inferior degree to those in dislocations inward, if properly managed so that in walking they can put the whole foot to the ground and lean to either side. The younger the patient is, the greater care should be bestowed on him; when neglected, the case gets worse; when attended to, it improves; and, although there be atrophy in all parts of the limb, it is to a less extent.

22. When there is a dislocation on both sides, the affections of the bones are the same; the flesh is well developed, except within, the nates protrude, the thighs are arched, unless there be sphacelus. If there be curvature of the spine above the hip-joint, the patients enjoy good health, but the body does not grow, with the exception of the head.

23. The symptoms of dislocation backward are:—The parts before more empty, behind they protrude, the foot straight, flexion impossible, except with pain, extension least of all: in these the limb is shortened. They can neither extend the limb at the ham, nor at the groin, unless it be much raised, nor can they bend it. The uppermost joint, in most cases, takes the lead: this

is common in joints, nerves, muscles, intestines, uteri, and other parts. There the bone of the hip-joint is carried backward to the nates, and on that account it is shortened, and because the patient cannot extend it. The flesh of the whole leg is wasted in all cases, in which most, and to what extent, has been already stated. Every part of the body which performs its functional work is strong, but, if inactive, it gets into a bad condition, unless its inactivity arise from fatigue, fever, or inflammation. And in dislocations outward, the limb is shortened, because the bone is lodged in flesh which yields; but, in dislocations inward, it is longer, because the bone is lodged on a projecting bone. Adults, then, who have this dislocation unreduced, are bent at the groins in walking, and the other ham is flexed; they scarcely reach the ground with the ball of the foot; they grasp the limb with the hand, and walk without a staff if they choose; if the staff be too long, their foot cannot reach the ground,—if they wish to reach the ground, they must use a short staff. There is wasting of the flesh in cases attended with pain; and the inclination of the leg is forward, and the sound leg in proportion. In congenital cases, or when in adolescence, or from disease, the bone is dislocated (under what circumstances will be explained afterward), the limb is particularly impaired, owing to the nerves and joints not being exercised, and the knee is impaired for the reasons stated. These persons, keeping the limb bent, walk with one staff or two. But the sound limb is in good flesh from usage.

24. In dislocations forward the symptoms are the opposite: a vacuity behind, a protuberance before; of all motions they can least perform flexion, and extension best; the foot is straight, the limb is of the proper length at the heel; at its extremity the foot a little turned up; they are especially pained at first: of all these dislocations retention of urine occurs most frequently in this variety, because the bone is lodged among important nerves. The fore parts are stretched, do not grow, are diseased, and are obnoxious to premature decay; the back parts are wrinkled. In the case of adults, they walk erect, resting merely on the heel, and this they do decidedly if they can take great steps; but they drag it along; the wasting is least of all in this variety of dislocation, owing to their being able to use the limb, but the wasting is most behind. The whole limb being straighter than natural they stand in need of a staff on the affected side. When the dislocation is congenital, or has occurred during adolescence, if properly managed, the patient has the use of the limb as well as adults (otherwise?) have of it. But, if neglected, it is shortened and extended, for in such cases the joint is generally ankylosed in a straight position. The diminution of the bones, and wasting of the fleshy parts, are analogous.

25. In reduction—the extension of the thigh is to be powerful, and the adjustment what is common in all such cases, with the hands, or a board, or a lever, which, in dislocations inward, should be round, and in dislocations outward, flat; but it is mostly applicable in dislocations outward. Dislocations inward are to be remedied by means of bladders, extending to the bare part of the thigh, along with extension and binding together of the limbs. The patient may be suspended, with his feet a little separated from one another, and then a person inserting his arm within the affected limb, is to suspend himself from it, and perform extension and readjustment at the same time; and this method is sufficient in dislocations forward and the others, but least of all in dislocations backward. A board fastened under the limb, like the board fastened below the arm in dislocations at the shoulder, answers in dislocations inward, but less so in the other varieties. Along with extension you will use pressure either with the foot, the hand, or a board, especially in dislocations forward and backward.

26. Dislocations at the knee are of a milder character than those of the elbow, owing to the compactness and regularity of the joint; and hence it is more readily dislocated and reduced. Dislocation generally takes place inward, but also outward and backward. The methods of reduction are—by circumflexion, or by rapid excalcitration, or by rolling a fillet into a ball, placing it in the ham, and then letting the patient's body suddenly drop down on his knees: this mode applies best in dislocations backward. Dislocations backward, like those of the elbows, may also be reduced by moderate extension. Lateral dislocations may be reduced by circumflexion or excalcitration, or by extension (but this is most applicable in dislocation backward), but also by moderate extension. The adjustment is what is common in all. If not reduced, in dislocations backward, they cannot bend the leg and thigh upon one another, but neither can they do this in the others except to a small extent; and the fore parts of the thigh and leg are wasted. In dislocations inward they are bandy-legged, and the external parts are atrophied. But, in dislocations outward, they incline more

outward, but are less lame, for the body is supported on the thicker bone, and the inner parts are wasted. The consequences of a congenital dislocation, or one occurring during adolescence, are analogous to the rule formerly laid down.

27. Dislocations at the ankle-joint require strong extension, either with the hands or some such means, and adjustment, which at the same time effects both acts; this is common in all cases.

28. Dislocations of the bones of the foot are to be treated like those of the hand.

29. Dislocations of the bones connected with the leg, if not reduced, whether occurring at birth or during adolescence, are of the same character as those in the hand.

30. Persons who, in jumping from a height, have pitched on the heel, so as to occasion diastasis (separation) of the bones, ecchymosis of the veins, and contusion of the nerves,—when these symptoms are very violent, there is danger that the parts may sphacelate, and give trouble to the patient during the remainder of his life; for these bones are so constructed as to slip past one another, and the nerves communicate together. And, likewise in cases of fracture, either from an injury in the leg or thigh, or in paralysis of the nerves connected with these parts, or, when in any other case of confinement to bed the heel, from neglect, becomes blackened, in all these cases serious effects result therefrom. Sometimes, in addition to the sphacelus, very acute fevers supervene, attended with hiccup, tumors, aberration of intellect, and speedy death, along with lividity of the large blood-vessels, and gangrene. The symptoms of the exacerbations are these: if the ecchymosis, the blackened parts, and those around them, be somewhat hard and red, and if lividity be combined with the hardness, there is danger of mortification; but, if the parts are sublivid, or even very livid and diffused, or greenish and soft, these symptoms, in all such cases, are favorable. The treatment consists in the administration of hellebore, if they be free from fever, but otherwise, they are to have *oxyglyky* for drink, if required. Bandaging,—agreeably to the rule in other joints; but this is to be attended to also,—the bandages should be numerous, and softer than usual; compression less; more water than usual to be used in the affusions; to be applied especially to the heel. The same object should be sought after in the position as in the bandaging, namely, that the humors may not be determined to the heel; the limb to be well laid should have the heel higher than the knee. Splints not to be used.

31. When the foot is dislocated, either alone, or with the epiphysis, the displacement is more apt to be inward. If not reduced, in the course of time the parts of the hips, thigh, and leg, opposite the dislocation, become attenuated. Reduction:—As in dislocation at the wrist; but the extension requires to be very powerful. Treatment:—Agreeably to the rule laid down for the other joints. Less apt to be followed by serious consequences than the wrist, if kept quiet. Diet restricted, as being in an inactive state. Those occurring at birth, or during adolescence, observe the rule formerly stated.

32. With regard to slight congenital dislocations, some of them can be rectified, especially club-foot. There is more than one variety of club-foot. The treatment consists in modeling the foot like a piece of wax; applying resinous cerate, and numerous bandages; or a sole, or a piece of lead is to be bound on, but not upon the bare skin; the adjustment and attitudes to correspond.

33. If the dislocated bones cause a wound in the skin, and protrude, it is better to let them alone, provided only they are not allowed to hang, nor are compressed. The treatment consists in applying pitched cerate, or compresses dipped in hot wine (for cold is bad in all such cases), and certain leaves; but in winter unwashed wool may be applied as a cover to the part; neither cataplasms nor bandaging; restricted diet. Cold, great weight, compression, violence, restricted position, all such are to be accounted as fatal measures. When treated moderately (they escape), maimed and deformed; for, if the dislocation be at the ankle, the foot is drawn upward, and, if elsewhere, according to the same rule. The bones do not readily exfoliate; for only small portions of them are denuded, and they heal by narrow cicatrices. The danger is greatest in the greatest joints, and those highest up. The only chance of recovery is, if they are not reduced, except at the fingers and hand, and in these cases the danger should be announced beforehand. Attempts at reduction to be made on the first or second day; or, if not accomplished then, on the tenth, by no means on the fourth. Reduction by levers. Treatment: —As in injuries of the bones of the head, and the part is to be kept hot; and it is better to give hellebore immediately after the parts have been reduced. With regard to the other bones, it should be well known, that, if replaced, death will be the consequence; the more surely and

expeditiously, the greater the articulation, and the more high its situation. Dislocation of the foot is attended with spasm (tetanus) and gangrene; and if, upon its being replaced, any of these symptoms come on, the chance of recovery, if there be any chance, is in displacing it anew; for spasms do not arise from relaxation, but from tension of the parts.

34. Excision, either of articular bones or of pieces of bones, when not high up in the body, but about the foot or the hand, is generally followed by recovery, unless the patient die at once from deliquium animi. Treatment:—As in injuries of the head; warmth.

35. Sphacelus of the fleshy parts is produced by the tight compression of bleeding wounds, and by pressure in the fractures of bones, and by blackening, arising from bandages. And in those cases in which a portion of the thigh or arm, both the bones and the flesh drop off, many recover, the case being less dangerous than many others. In cases, then, connected with fracture of the bones, the separation of the flesh quickly takes place, but the separation of the bone, at the boundary of its denuded part, is slower in taking place. But the parts below the seat of the injury, and the sound portion of the body, are to be previously taken away (for they die previously), taking care to avoid producing pain, for *deliquium animi* may occasion death. The bone of the thigh in such a case came away on the eightieth day, but the leg was removed on the twentieth day. The bones of the leg, in a certain case, came away at the middle of the sixtieth day. In these cases the separation is quick or slow, according to the compression applied by the physician. When the compression is gently applied the bones do not drop off at all, neither are they denuded of flesh, but the gangrene is confined in the more superficial parts. The treatment of such cases must be undertaken; for most of them are more formidable in appearance than in reality. The treatment should be mild, but, with a restricted diet; hemorrhages and cold are to be dreaded; the position, so as that the limb may be inclined upward, and afterward, on account of the purulent abscess, horizontally, or such as may suit with it. In such cases, and in mortifications, there are, usually, about the crisis, hemorrhages and violent diarrhœas, which, however, only last for a few days; the patients do not lose their appetite, neither are they feverish, nor should they be put upon a reduced diet.

36. Displacement of the spine, if inward, threatens immediate death, attended with retention of urine and loss of sensibility. Outward, the accident is free from most of these bad effects, much more so than where there is merely concussion without displacement; the effects in the former case being confined to the spot affected, whereas in the latter they are further communicated to the whole body, and are of a mortal character. In like manner, when the ribs are fractured, whether one or more, provided there be no splinters, there is rarely fever, spitting of blood, and sphacelus, and ordinary treatment without evacuation will suffice, provided there be no fever;—bandaging, according to rule; and the callus forms in twenty days, the bone being of a porous nature. But in cases of contusion, tubercles form, along with cough, suppurating sores, and sphacelus of the ribs, for nerves from all the parts run along each rib. In many of these cases hæmoptysis and empyema also take place. The management of this case consists in careful treatment, bandaging according to rule, diet at first restricted, but afterward more liberal, quiet, silence, position, bowels, and venereal matters regulated. Even when there is no spitting of blood, these contusions are more painful than fractures, and are more subject in time to relapses; and when any mucous collection is left in the part, it makes itself be felt in disorders of the body. Treatment:—burning, when the bone is affected, down to the bone, but not touching the bone itself; if in the intercostal space, the burning must not extend through it, nor be too superficial. In sphacelus of the ribs, tents are to be tried, all other particulars will be stated afterward: but they should be learned by sight rather than by words, namely, food, drink, heat, cold, attitude; medicines, dry, liquid, red, dark, white, sour, for the ulcers, and so with regard to the diet.

37. Displacements (*of the vertebræ*) from a fall rarely admit of being rectified, and those above the diaphragm are most difficult to rectify. When the accident happens to children, the body does not grow, with the exception of the legs, the arms, and head. Excurvation, in adults, speedily relieves the individual from the disease he is laboring under, but in time it renews its attack, with the same symptoms as in children, but of a less serious nature. Some individuals have borne this affection well, and have turned out to be brawny and fat. But few of them have lived to the age of sixty. Lateral curvatures also occur, the proximate cause of which is the attitudes in which these persons lie. These cases have their prognostics accordingly.

38. The rule for the reduction and adjustment:—The axle, the lever, the wedge, pressure above; the axle to separate, the lever to push aside. Reduction and adjustment are to be accomplished by forcible extension, the parts being placed in such a position as will facilitate the conveying of the displaced bone over the extremity of the bone from which it was displaced: this is to be accomplished either with the hands, or by suspension, or axles, or turned round something. With the hands this is to be effected properly, according to the structure of the parts. In the case of the wrist and elbow, the parts are to be forced asunder, at the wrist in the line of the elbow, and the elbow with the fore-arm at a right angle with the arm, as when it is suspended in a sling. When we want to separate the protruding bones, and force them into place, in the case of the fingers, the toes, or the wrist, the proper separation may be made by hands, while the projecting part is forced into its place by pressing down with the heel or the palm of the hand upon some resisting object, while something moderately soft is laid under the projecting part, but nothing such under the other, and then pressure is to be made backward and downward, whether the dislocation be inward or outward. In lateral displacement, pressure and counter-pressure must be made on the opposite sides. Displacements forward can be reduced neither by sneezing, nor coughing, nor by the injection of air, nor by the cupping-instrument; and if anything can do good in such a case, it is extension. People are deceived in fractures of the spinal processes, the pain of which causing the patient to stoop forward, the case is taken for dislocation inward; these fractures heal speedily and easily. Dislocation outward is to be remedied by succussion, when high up, toward the feet; and when situated low down, in the contrary direction; the part is to be pressed back into its place, either with the foot or a board. Dislocations to either side, if they admit of any remedy, are to be treated by extension, and suitable attitudes, with regimen. The whole apparatus should be broad, soft, and strong; or otherwise, they should be wrapped in rags; before being used, they should all be prepared proportionately to the length, height, and breadth. In applying extension to the thigh, for example, the bands should be fastened at the ankle and above the knee, these stretching in the same direction, another band to be passed by the loins, and around the armpits, and by the perineum and thigh, one end passing up the breast and the other along the back, these all stretching in the same direction and being fastened either to a piece of wood resembling a pestle or to an axle. When this is done on a couch, either of its feet is to be fastened to the threshold, and a strong block of wood is to be laid across the other, and the pieces of wood resembling a pestle are to be raised on these, to make extension and counter-extension; the naves of a wheel are to be fastened in the floor, or a ladder is to be adjusted, so that extension may be made in both directions. The thing commonly used is a bench six cubits long, two cubits broad, one fathom in thickness, having two low axles at this end and that, and having at its middle two moderate-sized pillars, to which is to be adjusted a transverse piece of wood like the step of a ladder, which is to receive the piece of wood tied below the limb, as is done in dislocation at the shoulder; and the bench is to have excavations like trays, smooth, four inches in breadth and depth, and at such an interval as to leave room for the lever used to reduce the limb. In the middle of the bench a square hole is to be scooped out to receive a small pillar, which, being adjusted to the perineum, will obviate the tendency of the body to slip downward, and being rather loose may act somewhat as a lever. In certain occasions a piece of wood is required, which is inserted into a hole scooped out of the wall; the other end of it is then to be pressed down, something moderately soft being placed under it.

39. In those cases where the bone of the palate has exfoliated, the nose sinks in its middle. In contusions of the head without a wound, either from a fall, a fracture, or pressure, in certain of these cases acrid humors descend from the head to the throat, and from the wound in the head to the liver and thigh.

40. The symptoms of subluxations and luxations, and where, and how, and how much these differ from one another. And the cases in which the articular cavity has been broke off, and in which the ligament has been torn, and in which the epiphysis has been broken off; and in which, and how, when the limb consists of two bones, one or both are broken: in consequence of these the dangers, chances in which bad, and when the injuries will result in death, and when in recovery. What cases are to be reduced or attempted, and when, and which, and when not; the hopes and dangers in these cases. Which and when congenital dislocations are to be undertaken: the parts in a state of growth, the parts fully grown, and why sooner, or slower: and why a part becomes maimed, and how, and how not: and why a certain part is atrophied, and where,

and how, and in what cases to a less extent. And why fractured parts unite sooner or slower, how distortions and callosities form, and the remedy for them. In what cases there are external wounds, either at first or afterwards: in what fractures the bones are shortened, and in what not: in what cases the fractured bones protrude, and when they protrude most: in what cases dislocated bones protrude. That physicians are deceived, and by what means, in what they see, and in what they devise, regarding affections, and regarding cures. Established rules with regard to bandaging: preparation, presentation of the part, extension, adjustment, friction, bandaging, suspension and placing of the limb, attitude, seasons, diet. The most porous parts heal fastest, and *vice versa*. Distortions, where the bones are crooked. Flesh and tendons wasted on the side of the dislocation. The force used in reduction to be applied at as great a distance as possible from the seat of the displacement. Of nerves (*ligaments?*), those which are in motion and in humidity (*flabby?*) are of a yielding nature; those that are not, less so. In every dislocation the most speedy reduction is best. Reduction not to be made while the patient is in a febrile state, nor on the fourth or fifth day; and least of all, in those of the elbow, and all cases which induce torpor; the soonest the best, provided the inflammatory stage be avoided. Parts torn asunder, whether nerves, or cartilages, or epiphyses, or parts separated at symphyses, cannot possibly be restored to their former state; but callus is quickly formed in most cases, yet the use of the limb is preserved. Of luxations, those nearest the extremities are least dangerous. Those joints which are most easily dislocated are the least subject to inflammation. Those which have been least inflamed, and have not been subjected to after-treatment, are most liable to be dislocated anew. Extension should be made in the position most calculated to enable the one bone to clear the extremity of the other, attention being paid to configuration and place. Adjustment to be made in the direction of the displacement; to push the displaced limb straight backward and sideways. Parts suddenly drawn aside are to be suddenly drawn back by a rotatory motion. Articulations which have been oftenest dislocated are the most easily reduced; the cause is the conformation of the nerves (*ligaments?*) or of the bones; of the ligaments that they are long and yielding; and of the bones, the shallowness of the articular cavity, and roundness of the head [of the bone that

enters it]. Usage, by its friction, forms a new socket. The cause—the disposition, and habit, and age. A part somewhat mucous is not subject to inflammation.

41. In those cases where there are wounds, either at first, or from protrusion of the bones; or afterward, from pruritus, or irritation; in the latter case you are immediately to unloose the bandages, and having applied pitched cerate to the wound, bandage the limb, placing the head of the roller upon the wound, and proceeding otherwise as if there were no wound in the case; for thus will the swelling be reduced as much as possible, and the wound will suppurate most quickly, and the diseased parts will separate, and when it becomes clean the wound will most quickly heal. Splints are not to be applied to the place, nor is it to be bound tight. Proceed thus when no large bones exfoliate, but not in the latter case, for then there is great suppuration, and the same treatment is not applicable, but the parts require to be exposed to the air on account of the abscesses. In such cases where the bones protrude, and whether reduced or not, bandaging is not befitting, but distention is to be practiced by means of rolls of cloth, made like those used upon shackles; one of these is to be placed at the ankle, and the other at the knee; they are to be flattened toward the leg, soft, strong, and having rings; and rods made of cornel, and of a proper length and thickness are to be adjusted to them, so as to keep the parts distended; and straps, attached to both extremities, are to be inserted into the rings, so that the extremities being fixed into the rolls, may effect distention. Treatment:—Pitched cerate, in a hot state; the attitudes, position of the foot and hip; regulated diet. The bones which have protruded through the skin are to be replaced the same day, or next; not on the fourth or fifth, but when the swelling has subsided. Reduction is to be performed with levers; when the bone does not present any place upon which the lever can rest, a portion of the part which prevents this is to be sawed off. But the denuded parts will drop off, and the limb become shortened.

42. Dislocations at the joints are to a greater and less extent. Those that are to a less extent are the most easily reduced; those that are to a greater extent occasion lesions of the bones, of the ligaments, of the joints, of the fleshy parts, and of the attitudes. The thigh and arm resemble one another very much in their dislocations.

Aphorisms

SECTION I

LIFE is short, and Art long; the crisis fleeting; experience perilous, and decision difficult. The physician must not only be prepared to do what is right himself, but also to make the patient, the attendants, and externals co-operate.

2. In disorders of the bowels and vomitings, occurring spontaneously, if the matters purged be such as ought to be purged, they do good, and are well borne; but if not, the contrary. And so artificial evacuations, if they consist of such matters as should be evacuated, do good, and are well borne; but if not, the contrary. One, then, ought to look to the country, the season, the age, and the diseases in which they are proper or not.

3. In the athletæ, embonpoint, if carried to its utmost limit, is dangerous, for they cannot remain in the same state nor be stationary; and since, then, they can neither remain stationary nor improve, it only remains for them to get worse; for these reasons the embonpoint should be reduced without delay, that the body may again have a commencement of reparation. Neither should the evacuations, in their case, be carried to an extreme, for this also is dangerous, but only to such a point as the person's constitution can endure. In like manner, medicinal evacuations, if carried to an extreme, are dangerous; and again, a restorative course, if in the extreme, is dangerous.

4. A slender and restricted diet is always dangerous in chronic diseases, and also in acute diseases, where it is not requisite. And again, a diet brought to the extreme point of attenuation is dangerous; and repletion, when in the extreme, is also dangerous.

5. In a restricted diet, patients who transgress are thereby more hurt (than in any other?); for every such transgression, whatever it may be, is followed by greater consequences than in a diet somewhat more generous. On this account, a very slender, regulated, and restricted diet is dangerous to persons in health, because they bear transgressions of it more difficultly. For this reason, a slender and restricted diet is generally more dangerous than one a little more liberal.

6. For extreme diseases, extreme methods of cure, as to restriction, are most suitable.

7. When the disease is very acute, it is attended with extremely severe symptoms in its first stage; and therefore an extremely attenuating diet must be used. When this is not the case, but it is allowable to give a more generous diet, we may depart as far from the severity of regimen as the disease, by its mildness, is removed from the extreme.

8. When the disease is at its height, it will then be necessary to use the most slender diet.

9. We must form a particular judgment of the patient, whether he will support the diet until the acme of the disease, and whether he will sink previously and not support the diet, or the disease will give way previously, and become less acute.

10. In those cases, then, which attain their acme speedily, a restricted diet should be enjoined at first; but in those cases which reach their acme later, we must retrench at that period or a little before it; but previously we must allow a more generous diet to support the patient.

11. We must retrench during paroxysms, for to exhibit food would be injurious. And in all diseases having periodical paroxysms, we must restrict during the paroxysms.

12. The exacerbations and remissions will be indicated by the diseases, the seasons of the year, the reciprocation of the periods, whether they occur every day, every alternate day, or after a longer period, and by the supervening symptoms; as, for example, in pleuritic cases, expectoration, if it occur at the commencement, shortens the attack, but if it appear later, it prolongs the same; and in the same manner the urine, and alvine discharges, and sweats, according as they appear along with favorable or unfavorable symptoms, indicate diseases of a short or long duration.

13. Old persons endure fasting most easily; next, adults; young persons not nearly so well; and most especially infants, and of them such as are of a particularly lively spirit.

14. Growing bodies have the most innate heat; they therefore require the most food, for otherwise their bodies are wasted. In old persons the heat is feeble, and therefore they require little fuel, as it were, to the flame, for it would be extinguished by much. On this account, also, fevers in old persons are not equally acute, because their bodies are cold.

15. In winter and spring the bowels are naturally the hottest, and the sleep most prolonged; at these seasons, then, the most sustenance is to be administered; for as the belly has then most

innate heat, it stands in need of most food. The well-known facts with regard to young persons and the athletæ prove this.

16. A humid regimen is befitting in all febrile diseases, and particularly in children, and others accustomed to live on such a diet.

17. We must consider, also, in which cases food is to be given once or twice a day, and in greater or smaller quantities, and at intervals. Something must be conceded to habit, to season, to country, and to age.

18. Invalids bear food worst during summer and autumn, most easily in winter, and next in spring.

19. Neither give nor enjoin anything to persons during periodical paroxysms, but abstract from the accustomed allowance before the crisis.

20. When things are at the crisis, or when they have just passed it, neither move the bowels, nor make any innovation in the treatment, either as regards purgatives or any other such stimulants, but let things alone.

21. Those things which require to be evacuated should be evacuated, wherever they most tend, by the proper outlets.

22. We must purge and move such humors as are concocted, not such as are unconcocted, unless they are struggling to get out, which is mostly not the case.

23. The evacuations are to be judged of not by their quantity, but whether they be such as they should be, and how they are borne. And when proper to carry the evacuation to *deliquium animi,* this also should be done, provided the patient can support it.

24. Use purgative medicines sparingly in acute diseases, and at the commencement, and not without proper circumspection.

25. If the matters which are purged be such as should be purged, the evacuation is beneficial, and easily borne; but, if otherwise, with difficulty.

SECTION II

1. In whatever disease sleep is laborious, it is a deadly symptom; but if sleep does good, it is not deadly.

2. When sleep puts an end to delirium, it is a good symptom.

3. Both sleep and insomnolency, when immoderate, are bad.

4. Neither repletion, nor fasting, nor anything else, is good when more than natural.

5. Spontaneous lassitude indicates disease.

6. Persons who have a painful affection in any part of the body, and are in a great measure insensible of the pain, are disordered in intellect.

7. Those bodies which have been slowly emaciated should be slowly recruited; and those which have been quickly emaciated should be quickly recruited.

8. When a person after a disease takes food, but does not improve in strength, it indicates that the body uses more food than is proper; but if this happen when he does not take food, it is to be understood that evacuation is required.

9. When one wishes to purge, he should put the body into a fluent state.

10. Bodies not properly cleansed, the more you nourish the more you injure.

11. It is easier to fill up with drink than with food.

12. What remains in diseases after the crisis is apt to produce relapses.

13. Persons in whom a crisis takes place pass the night preceding the paroxysm uncomfortably, but the succeeding night generally more comfortably.

14. In fluxes of the bowels, a change of the dejections does good, unless the change be of a bad character.

15. When the throat is diseased, or tubercles (*phymata*) form on the body, attention must be paid to the secretions; for if they be bilious, the disease affects the general system; but if they resemble those of a healthy person, it is safe to give nourishing food.

16. When in a state of hunger, one ought not to undertake labor.

17. When more food than is proper has been taken, it occasions disease; this is shown by the treatment.

18. From food which proves nourishing to the body either immediately or shortly, the dejections also are immediate.

19. In acute diseases it is not quite safe to prognosticate either death or recovery.

20. Those who have watery discharges from their bowels when young have dry when they are old; and those who have dry discharges when they are young will have watery when they are old.

21. Drinking strong wine cures hunger.

22. Diseases which arise from repletion are cured by depletion; and those that arise from depletion are cured by repletion; and in general, diseases are cured by their contraries.

23. Acute disease come to a crisis in fourteen days.

24. The fourth day is indicative of the seventh; the eighth is the commencement of the

second week; and hence, the eleventh being the fourth of the second week, is also indicative; and again, the seventeenth is indicative, as being the fourth from the fourteenth, and the seventh from the eleventh.

25. The summer quartans are, for the most part, of short duration; but the autumnal are protracted, especially those occurring near the approach of winter.

26. It is better that a fever succeed to a convulsion, than a convulsion to a fever.

27. We should not trust ameliorations in diseases when they are not regular, nor be much afraid of bad symptoms which occur in an irregular form; for such are commonly inconstant, and do not usually continue, nor have any duration.

28. In fevers which are not altogether slight, it is a bad symptom for the body to remain without any diminution of bulk, or to be wasted beyond measure; for the one state indicates a protracted disease, and the other weakness of body.

29. If it appear that evacuations are required, they should be made at the commencement of diseases; at the acme it is better to be quiet.

30. Toward the commencement and end of diseases all the symptoms are weaker, and toward the acme they are stronger.

31. When a person who is recovering from a disease has a good appetite, but his body does not improve in condition, it is a bad symptom.

32. For the most part, all persons in ill health, who have a good appetite at the commencement, but do not improve, have a bad appetite again toward the end; whereas, those who have a very bad appetite at the commencement, and afterward acquire a good appetite, get better off.

33. In every disease it is a good sign when the patient's intellect is sound, and he is disposed to take whatever food is offered to him; but the contrary is bad.

34. In diseases, there is less danger when the disease is one to which the patient's constitution, habit, age, and the season are allied, than when it is one to which they are not allied.

35. In all diseases it is better that the umbilical and hypogastric regions preserve their fullness; and it is a bad sign when they are very slender and emaciated; in the latter case it is dangerous to administer purgatives.

36. Persons in good health quickly lose their strength by taking purgative medicines, or using bad food.

37. Purgative medicines agree ill with persons in good health.

38. An article of food or drink which is slightly worse, but more palatable, is to be preferred to such as are better but less palatable.

39. Old people, on the whole, have fewer complaints than young; but those chronic diseases which do befall them generally never leave them.

40. Catarrhs and coryza in very old people are not concocted.

41. Persons who have had frequent and severe attacks of swooning, without any manifest cause, die suddenly.

42. It is impossible to remove a strong attack of apoplexy, and not easy to remove a weak attack.

43. Of persons who have been suspended by the neck, and are in a state of insensibility, but not quite dead, those do not recover who have foam at the mouth.

44. Persons who are naturally very fat are apt to die earlier than those who are slender.

45. Epilepsy in young persons is most frequently removed by changes of air, of country, and of modes of life.

46. Of two pains occurring together, not in the same part of the body, the stronger weakens the other.

47. Pains and fevers occur rather at the formation of pus than when it is already formed.

48. In every movement of the body, whenever one begins to endure pain, it will be relieved by rest.

49. Those who are accustomed to endure habitual labors, although they be weak or old, bear them better than strong and young persons who have not been so accustomed.

50. Those things which one has been accustomed to for a long time, although worse than things which one is not accustomed to, usually give less disturbance; but a change must sometimes be made to things one is not accustomed to.

51. To evacuate, fill up, heat, cool, or otherwise, move the body in any way much and suddenly, is dangerous; and whatever is excessive is inimical to nature; but whatever is done by little and little is safe, more especially when a transition is made from one thing to another.

52. When doing everything according to indications, although things may not turn out agreeably to indication, we should not change to another while the original appearances remain.

53. Those persons who have watery discharges from the bowels when they are young, come off better than those who have dry; but in old age they come off worse, for the bowels in aged persons are usually dried up.

54. Largeness of person in youth is noble and not unbecoming; but in old age it is inconvenient, and worse than a smaller structure.

SECTION III

1. The changes of the season mostly engender diseases, and in the seasons great changes either of heat or of cold, and the rest agreeably to the same rule.

2. Of natures (*temperaments?*), some are well- or ill-adapted for summer, and some for winter.

3. Of diseases and ages, certain of them are well- or ill-adapted to different seasons, places, and kinds of diet.

4. In the seasons, when during the same day there is at one time heat and at another time cold, the diseases of autumn may be expected.

5. South winds induce dullness of hearing, dimness of visions, heaviness of the head, torpor, and languor; when these prevail, such symptoms occur in diseases. But if the north wind prevail, coughs, affections of the throat, hardness of the bowels, dysuria attended with rigors, and pains of the sides and breast occur. When this wind prevails, all such symptoms may be expected in diseases.

6. When summer is like spring, much sweating may be expected in fevers.

7. Acute diseases occur in droughts; and if the summer be particularly such, according to the constitution which it has given to the year, for the most part such diseases may be expected.

8. In seasons which are regular, and furnish the productions of the season at the seasonable time, the diseases are regular, and come readily to a crisis; but in inconstant seasons, the diseases are irregular, and come to a crisis with difficulty.

9. In autumn, diseases are most acute, and most mortal, on the whole. The spring is most healthy, and least mortal.

10. Autumn is a bad season for persons in consumption.

11. With regard to the seasons, if the winter be of a dry and northerly character, and the spring rainy and southerly, in summer there will necessarily be acute fevers, ophthalmies, and dysenteries, especially in women, and in men of a humid temperament.

12. If the winter be southerly, rainy, and calm, but the spring dry and northerly, women whose term of delivery should be in spring, have abortions from any slight cause; and those who reach their full time, bring forth children who are feeble, and diseased, so that they either die

presently, or, if they live, are puny and unhealthy. Other people are subject to dysenteries and ophthalmies, and old men to catarrhs, which quickly cut them off.

13. If the summer be dry and northerly and the autumn rainy and southerly, headaches occur in winter, with coughs, hoarsenesses, coryzæ, and in some cases consumptions.

14. But if the autumn be northerly and dry, it agrees well with persons of a humid temperament, and with women; but others will be subject to dry ophthalmies, acute fevers, coryzæ, and in some cases melancholy.

15. Of the constitutions of the year, the dry, upon the whole, are more healthy than the rainy, and attended with less mortality.

16. The diseases which occur most frequently in rainy seasons are, protracted fevers, fluxes of the bowels, mortifications, epilepsies, apoplexies, and quinsies; and in dry, consumptive diseases, ophthalmies, arthritic diseases, stranguries, and dysenteries.

17. With regard to the states of the weather which continue but for a day, that which is northerly, braces the body, giving it tone, agility, and color, improves the sense of hearing, dries up the bowels, pinches the eyes, and aggravates any previous pain which may have been seated in the chest. But the southerly relaxes the body, and renders it humid, brings on dullness of hearing, heaviness of the head, and vertigo, impairs the movements of the eyes and the whole body, and renders the alvine discharges watery.

18. With regard to the seasons, in spring and in the commencement of summer, children and those next to them in age are most comfortable, and enjoy best health; in summer and during a certain portion of autumn, old people; during the remainder of the autumn and in winter, those of the intermediate ages.

19. All diseases occur at all seasons of the year, but certain of them are more apt to occur and be exacerbated at certain seasons.

20. The diseases of spring are, maniacal, melancholic, and epileptic disorders, bloody flux, quinsy, coryza, hoarseness, cough, leprosy, lichen alphos, exanthemata mostly ending in ulcerations, tubercles, and arthritic diseases.

21. Of summer, certain of these, and continued, ardent, and tertian fevers, most especially vomiting, diarrhœa, ophthalmy, pains of the ears, ulcerations of the mouth, mortifications of the privy parts, and the sudamina.

22. Of autumn, most of the summer, quartan, and irregular fevers, enlarged spleen, dropsy, phthisis, strangury, lientery, dysentery, sciat-

ica, quinsy, asthma, ileus, epilepsy, maniacal and melancholic disorders.

23. Of winter, pleurisy, pneumonia, coryza, hoarseness, cough, pains of the chest, pains of the ribs and loins, headache, vertigo, and apoplexy.

24. In the different ages the following complaints occur: to little and new-born children, aphthæ, vomiting, coughs, sleeplessness, frights, inflammation of the navel, watery discharges from the ears.

25. At the approach of dentition, pruritus of the gums, fevers, convulsions, diarrhœa, especially when cutting the canine teeth, and in those who are particularly fat, and have constipated bowels.

26. To persons somewhat older, affections of the tonsils, incurvation of the spine at the vertebra next the occiput, asthma, calculus, round worms, ascarides, acrochordon, satyriasmus, struma, and other tubercles (*phymata*), but especially the aforesaid.

27. To persons of a more advanced age, and now on the verge of manhood, the most of these diseases, and, moreover, more chronic fevers, and epistaxis.

28. Young people for the most part have a crisis in their complaints, some in forty days, some in seven months, some in seven years, some at the approach to puberty; and such complaints of children as remain, and do not pass away about puberty, or in females about the commencement of menstruation, usually become chronic.

29. To persons past boyhood, hæmoptysis, phthisis, acute fevers, epilepsy, and other diseases, but especially the aforementioned.

30. To persons beyond that age, asthma, pleurisy, pneumonia, lethargy, phrenitis, ardent fevers, chronic diarrhea, cholera, dysentery, lientery, hemorrhoids.

31. To old people dyspnœa, catarrhs accompanied with coughs, dysuria, pains of the joints, nephritis, vertigo, apoplexy, cachexia, pruritus of the whole body, insomnolency, defluxions of the bowels, of the eyes, and of the nose, dimness of sight, cataract (glaucoma), and dullness of hearing.

SECTION IV

1. We must purge pregnant women, if matters be turgid (in a state of orgasm?), from the fourth to the seventh month, but less freely in the latter; in the first and last stages of pregnancy it should be avoided.

2. In purging we should bring away such matters from the body as it would be advantageous had they come away spontaneously; but those of an opposite character should be stopped.

3. If the matters which are purged be such as should be purged, it is beneficial and well borne; but if the contrary, with difficulty.

4. We should rather purge upward in summer, and downward in winter.

5. About the time of the dog-days, and before it, the administration of purgatives is unsuitable.

6. Lean persons who are easily made to vomit should be purged upward, avoiding the winter season.

7. Persons who are difficult to vomit, and are moderately fat, should be purged downward, avoiding the summer season.

8. We must be guarded in purging phthisical persons upward.

9. And from the same mode of reasoning, applying the opposite rule to melancholic persons, we must purge them freely downward.

10. In very acute diseases, if matters be in a state of orgasm, we may purge on the first day, for it is a bad thing to procrastinate in such cases.

11. Those cases in which there are tormina, pains about the umbilicus, and pains about the loins, not removed either by purgative medicines or otherwise, usually terminate in dry dropsy.

12. It is a bad thing to purge upward in winter persons whose bowels are in a state of lientery.

13. Persons who are not easily purged upward by the hellebores, should have their bodies moistened by plenty of food and rest before taking the draught.

14. When one takes a draught of hellebore, one should be made to move more about, and indulge less in sleep and repose. Sailing on the sea shows that motion disorders the body.

15. When you wish the hellebore to act more, move the body, and when to stop, let the patient get sleep and rest.

16. Hellebore is dangerous to persons whose flesh is sound, for it induces convulsion.

17. Anorexia, heartburn, vertigo, and a bitter taste of the mouth, in a person free from fever, indicate the want of purging upward.

18. Pains seated above the diaphragm indicate purging upward, and those below it, downward.

19. Persons who have no thirst while under the action of a purgative medicine, do not cease from being purged until they become thirsty.

20. If persons free from fever be seized with

tormina, heaviness of the knees, and pains of the loins, this indicates that purging downward is required.

21. Alvine dejections which are black, like blood, taking place spontaneously, either with or without fever, are very bad; and the more numerous and unfavorable the colors, so much the worse; when with medicine it is better, and a variety of colors in this case is not bad.

22. When black bile is evacuated in the beginning of any disease whatever, either upward or downward, it is a mortal symptom.

23. In persons attenuated from any disease, whether acute or chronic, or from wounds, or any other cause, if there be a discharge either of black bile, or resembling black blood, they die on the following day.

24. Dysentery, if it commence with black bile, is mortal.

25. Blood discharged upward, whatever be its character, is a bad symptom, but downward it is (more?) favorable, and so also black dejections.

26. If in a person ill of dysentery, substances resembling flesh be discharged from the bowels, it is a mortal symptom.

27. In whatever cases of fever there is a copious hemorrhage from whatever channel, the bowels are in a loose state during convalescence.

28. In all cases whatever, bilious discharges cease if deafness supervenes, and in all cases deafness ceases when bilious discharges supervene.

29. Rigors which occur on the sixth day have a difficult crisis.

30. Diseases attended with paroxysms, if at the same hour that the fever leaves it return again next day, are of difficult crisis.

31. In febrile diseases attended with a sense of lassitude, deposits form about the joints, and especially those of the jaws.

32. In convalescents from diseases, if any part be pained, there deposits are formed.

33. But if any part be in a painful state previous to the illness, there the disease fixes.

34. If a person laboring under a fever, without any swelling in the fauces, be seized with a sense of suffocation suddenly, it is a mortal symptom.

35. If in a person affected with fever, the neck become suddenly distorted, and he cannot swallow unless with difficulty, although no swelling be present, it is a mortal symptom.

36. Sweats, in febrile diseases, are favorable, if they set in on the third, fifth, seventh, ninth, eleventh, fourteenth, seventeenth, twenty-first, twenty-seventh, and thirty-fourth day, for these sweats prove a crisis to the disease; but sweats not occurring thus, indicate pain, a protracted disease, and relapses.

37. Cold sweats occurring along with an acute fever, indicate death; and along with a milder one, a protracted disease.

38. And in whatever part of the body there is a sweat, it shows that the disease is seated there.

39. And in whatever part of the body heat or cold is seated, there is disease.

40. And wherever there are changes in the whole body, and if the body be alternately cold and hot, or if one color succeed another, this indicates a protracted disease.

41. A copious sweat after sleep occurring without any manifest cause, indicates that the body is using too much food. But if it occur when one is not taking food, it indicates that evacuation is required.

42. A copious sweat, whether hot or cold, flowing continuously, indicates, the cold a greater, and the hot a lesser disease.

43. Fevers, not of the intermittent type, which are exacerbated on the third day, are dangerous; but if they intermit in any form, this indicates that they are not dangerous.

44. In cases attended with protracted fevers, tubercles (*phymata*) or pains occur about the joints.

45. When tubercles (*phymata*) or pains attack the joints after fevers, such persons are using too much food.

46. If in a fever not of the intermittent type a rigor seize a person already much debilitated, it is mortal.

47. In fevers not of the intermittent type, expectorations which are livid bloody, fetid and bilious, are all bad; but if evacuated properly, they are favorable. So it is with the alvine evacuations and the urine. But if none of the proper excretions take place by these channels, it is bad.

48. In fevers not of the intermittent type, if the external parts be cold, but the internal be burnt up, and if there be thirst, it is a mortal symptom.

49. In a fever not of the intermittent type, if a lip, an eye-brow, an eye, or the nose, be distorted; or if there be loss of sight or of hearing, and the patient be in a weak state—whatever of these symptoms occur, death is at hand.

50. Apostemes in fevers which are not resolved at the first crisis, indicate a protracted disease.

51. When in a fever not of the intermittent type dyspnœa and delirium come on, the case is mortal.

52. When persons in fevers, or in other illnesses, shed tears voluntarily, it is nothing out of place; but when they shed tears involuntarily, it is more so.

53. In whatever cases of fever very viscid concretions form about the teeth, the fevers turn out to be particularly strong.

54. In whatever case of ardent fever dry coughs of a tickling nature with slight expectoration are long protracted, there is usually not much thirst.

55. All fevers complicated with buboes are bad, except ephemerals.

56. Sweat supervening in a case of fever without the fever ceasing, is bad, for the disease is protracted, and it indicates more copious humors.

57. Fever supervening in a case of confirmed spasm, or of tetanus, removes the disease.

58. A rigor supervening in a case of ardent fever, produces resolution of it.

59. A true tertian comes to a crisis in seven periods at furthest.

60. When in fevers there is deafness, if blood run from the nostrils, or the bowels become disordered, it carries off the disease.

61. In a febrile complaint, if the fever do not leave on the odd days, it relapses.

62. When jaundice supervenes in fevers before the seventh day, it a bad symptom, unless there be watery discharges from the bowels.

63. In whatever cases of fever rigors occur during the day, the fevers come to a resolution during the day.

64. When in cases of fever jaundice occurs on the seventh, the ninth, the eleventh, or the fourteenth day, it is a good symptom, provided the hypochondriac region be not hard. Otherwise it is not a good symptom.

65. A strong heat about the stomach and cardialgia are bad symptoms in fevers.

66. In acute fevers, spasms, and strong pains about the bowels are bad symptoms.

67. In fevers, frights after sleep, or convulsions, are a bad symptom.

68. In fevers, a stoppage of the respiration is a bad symptom, for it indicates convulsions.

69. When the urine is thick, grumoss, and scanty in cases not free from fever a copious discharge of thinner urine proves beneficial. Such a discharge more commonly takes place when the urine has had a sediment from the first, or soon after the commencement.

70. When in fevers the urine is turbid, like that of a beast of burden, in such a case there either is or will be headache.

71. In cases which come to a crisis on the seventh day, the urine has a red nubecula on the fourth day, and the other symptoms accordingly.

72. When the urine is transparent and white, it is bad; it appears principally in cases of phrenitis.

73. When the hypochondriac region is affected with meteorism and borborygmi, should pain of the loins supervene, the bowels get into a loose and watery state, unless there be an eruption of flatus or a copious evacuation of urine. These things occur in fevers.

74. When there is reason to expect that an abscess will form in joints, the abscess is carried off by a copious discharge of urine, which is thick, and becomes white, like what begins to form in certain cases of quartan fever, attended with a sense of lassitude. It is also speedily carried off by a hemorrhage from the nose.

75. Blood or pus in the urine indicates ulceration either of the kidneys or of the bladder.

76. When small fleshy substances like hairs are discharged along with thick urine, these substances come from the kidneys.

77. In those cases where there are furfuraceous particles discharged along with thick urine, there is scabies of the bladder.

78. In those cases where there is a spontaneous discharge of bloody urine, it indicates rupture of a small vein in the kidneys.

79. In those cases where there is a sandy sediment in the urine, there is calculus in the bladder (or kidneys).

80. If a patient pass blood and clots in his urine, and have strangury, and if a pain seize the hypogastric region and perineum, the parts about the bladder are affected.

81. If a patient pass blood, pus, and scales, in the urine, and if it have a heavy smell, ulceration of the bladder is indicated.

82. When tubercles form in the urethra, if these suppurate and burst, there is relief.

83. When much urine is passed during the night, it indicates that the alvine evacuations are scanty.

SECTION V

1. A spasm from taking hellebore is of a fatal nature.

2. Spasm supervening on a wound is fatal.

3. A convulsion, or hiccup, supervening on a copious discharge of blood is bad.

4. A convulsion, or hiccup, supervening upon hypercatharsis is bad.

5. If a drunken person suddenly lose his speech, he will die convulsed, unless fever come on, or he recover his speech at the time when the consequences of a debauch pass off.

6. Such persons as are seized with tetanus die within four days, or if they pass these they recover.

7. Those cases of epilepsy which come on before puberty may undergo a change; but those which come on after twenty-five years of age, for the most part terminate in death.

8. In pleuritic affections, when the disease is not purged off in fourteen days, it usually terminates in empyema.

9. Phthisis most commonly occurs between the ages of eighteen and thirty-five years.

10. Persons who escape an attack of quinsy, and when the disease is turned upon the lungs, die in seven days; or if they pass these they become affected with empyema.

11. In persons affected with phthisis, if the sputa which they cough up have a heavy smell when poured upon coals, and if the hairs of the head fall off, the case will prove fatal.

12. Phthisical persons, the hairs of whose head fall off, die if diarrhœa set in.

13. In persons who cough up frothy blood, the discharge of it comes from the lungs.

14. Diarrhœa attacking a person affected with phthisis is a mortal symptom.

15. Persons who become affected with empyema after pleurisy, if they get clear of it in forty days from the breaking of it, escape the disease; but if not, it passes into phthisis.

16. Heat produces the following bad effects on those who use it frequently: enervation of the fleshy parts, impotence of the nerves, torpor of the understanding, hemorrhages, deliquia, and, along with these, death.

17. Cold induces convulsions, tetanus, mortification, and febrile rigors.

18. Cold is inimical to the bones, the teeth, the nerves, the brain, and the spinal marrow, but heat is beneficial.

19. Such parts as have been congealed should be heated, except where there either is a hemorrhage, or one is expected.

20. Cold pinches ulcers, hardens the skin, occasions pain which does not end in suppuration, blackens, produces febrile rigors, convulsions, and tetanus.

21. In the case of a muscular youth having tetanus without a wound, during the midst of summer, it sometimes happens that the affusion of a large quantity of cold water recalls the heat. Heat relieves these diseases.

22. Heat is suppurative, but not in all kinds of sores, but when it is, it furnishes the greatest test of their being free from danger. It softens the skin, makes it thin, removes pain, soothes rigor, convulsions, and tetanus. It removes affections of the head, and heaviness of it. It is particularly efficacious in fractures of the bones, especially of those which have been exposed, and most especially in wounds of the head, and in mortifications and ulcers from cold; in herpes exedens, of the anus, the privy parts, the womb, the bladder, in all these cases heat is agreeable, and brings matters to a crisis; but cold is prejudicial, and does mischief.

23. Cold water is to be applied in the following cases; when there is a hemorrhage, or when it is expected, but not applied *to* the spot, but *around* the spot whence the blood flows; and in inflammations and inflammatory affections, inclining to a red and subsaguineous color, and consisting of fresh blood, in these cases it is to be applied but it occasions mortification in old cases; and in erysipelas not attended with ulceration, as it proves injurious to erysipelas when ulcerated.

24. Cold things, such as snow and ice, are inimical to the chest, being provocative of coughs, of discharges of blood, and of catarrhs.

25. Swellings and pains in the joints, without ulceration, those of a gouty nature, and sprains, are generally improved by a copious affusion of cold water, which reduces the swelling, and removes the pain; for a moderate degree of numbness removes pain.

26. The lightest water is that which is quickly heated and quickly cooled.

27. When persons have intense thirst, it is a good thing if they can sleep off the desire of drinking.

28. Fumigation with aromatics promotes menstruation, and would be useful in many other cases, if it did not occasion heaviness of the head.

29. Women in a state of pregnancy may be purged, if there be any urgent necessity (*or,* if the humors be in a state of orgasm?), from the fourth to the seventh month, but less so in the latter case. In the first and last periods it must be avoided.

30. It proves fatal to a woman in a state of pregnancy, if she be seized with any of the acute diseases.

31. If a woman with child be bled, she will have an abortion, and this will be the more likely to happen, the larger the fœtus.

32. Hæmoptysis in a woman is removed by

an eruption of the menses.

33. In a woman when there is a stoppage of the menses, a discharge of blood from the nose is good.

34. When a pregnant woman has a violent diarrhœa, there is danger of her miscarrying.

35. Sneezing occurring to a woman affected with hysterics, and in difficult labor, is a good symptom.

36. When the menstrual discharge is of a bad color and irregular, it indicates that the woman stands in need of purging.

37. In a pregnant woman, if the breasts suddenly lose their fullness, she has a miscarriage.

38. If, in a woman pregnant with twins, either of her breasts lose its fullness, she will part with one of her children; and if it be the right breast which becomes slender, it will be the male child, or if the left, the female.

39. If a woman who is not with child, nor has brought forth, have milk, her menses are obstructed.

40. In women, blood collected in the breasts indicates madness.

41. If you wish to ascertain if a woman be with child, give her hydromel to drink when she is going to sleep, and has not taken supper, and if she be seized with tormina in the belly, she is with child, but otherwise she is not pregnant.

42. A woman with child, if it be a male, has a good color, but if a female, she has a bad color.

43. If erysipelas of the womb seize a woman with child, it will probably prove fatal.

44. Women who are very lean, have miscarriages when they prove with child, until they get into better condition.

45. When women, in a moderate condition of body, miscarry in the second or third month, without any obvious cause, their cotyledones are filled with mucosity, and cannot support the weight of the fœtus, but are broken asunder.

46. Such women as are immoderately fat, and do not prove with child, in them it is because the epiploon (*fat?*) blocks up the mouth of the womb, and until it be reduced, they do not conceive.

47. If the portion of the uterus seated near the hip-joint suppurate, it gets into a state requiring to be treated with tents.

48. The male fœtus is usually seated in the right, and the female in the left side.

49. To procure the expulsion of the secundines, apply a sternutatory, and shut the nostrils and mouth.

50. If you wish to stop the menses in a wom-

an, apply as large a cupping instrument as possible to the breasts.

51. When women are with child, the mouth of their womb is closed.

52. If in a woman with child, much milk flow from the breasts, it indicates that the fœtus is weak; but if the breasts be firm, it indicates that the fœtus is in a more healthy state.

53. In women that are about to miscarry, the breasts become slender; but if again they become hard, there will be pain, either in the breasts, or in the hip-joints, or in the eyes, or in the knees, and they will not miscarry.

54. When the mouth of the uterus is hard, it is also necessarily shut.

55. Women with child who are seized with fevers, and who are greatly emaciated, without any (other?) obvious cause, have difficult and dangerous labors, and if they miscarry, they are in danger.

56. In the female flux (*immoderate menstruation?*), if convulsion and deliquium come on, it is bad.

57. When the menses are excessive, diseases take place, and when the menses are stopped, diseases from the uterus take place.

58. Strangury supervenes upon inflammation of the rectum, and of the womb, and strangury supervenes upon suppuration of the kidney, and hiccup upon inflammation of the liver.

59. If a woman do not conceive, and wish to ascertain whether she can conceive, having wrapped her up in blankets, fumigate below, and if it appear that the scent passes through the body to the nostrils and mouth, know that of herself she is not unfruitful.

60. If woman with a child have her courses, it is impossible that the child can be healthy.

61. If a woman's courses be suppressed, and neither rigor nor fever has followed, but she has been affected with nausea, you may reckon her to be with child.

62. Women who have the uterus cold and dense (*compact?*) do not conceive; and those also who have the uterus humid, do not conceive, for the semen is extinguished, and in women whose uterus is very dry, and very hot, the semen is lost from the want of food; but women whose uterus is in an intermediate state between these temperaments prove fertile.

63. And in like manner with respect to males; for either, owing to the laxity of the body, the pneuma is dissipated outwardly, so as not to propel the semen, or, owing to its density, the fluid (*semen?*) does not pass outwardly; or, owing to coldness, it is not heated so as to col-

lect in its proper place (*seminal vessels?*), or, owing to its heat, the very same thing happens.

64. It is a bad thing to give milk to persons having headache, and it is also bad to give it in fevers, and to persons whose hypochondria are swelled up, and troubled with borborygmi, and to thirsty persons; it is bad also, when given to those who have bilious discharges in acute fevers, and to those who have copious discharges of blood; but it is suitable in phthisical cases, when not attended with very much fever; it is also to be given in fevers of a chronic and weak nature, when none of the aforementioned symptoms are present, and the patients are excessively emaciated.

65. When swellings appear on wounds, such cases are not likely to be attacked either with convulsions, or delirium, but when these disappear suddenly, if situated behind, spasms and tetanus supervene, and if before, mania, acute pains of the sides, or suppurations, or dysentery, if the swellings be rather red.

66. When no swelling appears on severe and bad wounds, it is a great evil.

67. In such cases, the soft are favorable; and crude, unfavorable.

68. When a person is pained in the back part of the head, he is benefited by having the straight vein in the forehead opened.

69. Rigors commence in women, especially at the loins, and spread by the back to the head; and in men also, rather in the posterior than the anterior side of the body, as from the arms and thighs; the skin there is rare, as is obvious from the growth of hair on them.

70. Persons attacked with quartans are not readily attacked with convulsions, or if previously attacked with convulsions, they cease if a quartan supervene.

71. In those persons in whom the skin is stretched, and parched and hard, the disease terminates without sweats; but in those in whom the skin is loose and rare, it terminates with sweats.

72. Persons disposed to jaundice are not very subject to flatulence.

SECTION VI

1. In cases of chronic lientery, acid eructations supervening when there were none previously, is a good symptom.

2. Persons whose noses are naturally watery, and their seed watery, have rather a deranged state of health; but those in the opposite state, a more favorable.

3. In protracted cases of dysentery, loathing of food is a bad symptom, and still worse, if along with fever.

4. Ulcers, attended with a falling off of the hair, are *mali moris*.

5. It deserves to be considered whether the pains in the sides, and in the breasts, and in the other parts, differ much from one another.

6. Diseases about the kidneys and bladder are cured with difficulty in old men.

7. Pains occurring about the stomach, the more superficial they are, the more slight are they; and the less superficial, the more severe.

8. In dropsical persons, ulcers forming on the body are not easily healed.

9. Broad exanthemata are not very itchy.

10. In a person having a painful spot in the head, with intense cephalalgia, pus or water running from the nose, or by the mouth, or at the ears, removes the disease.

11. Hemorrhoids appearing in melancholic and nephritic affections are favorable.

12. When a person has been cured of chronic hemorrhoids, unless one be left, there is danger of dropsy or phthisis supervening.

13. Sneezing coming on, in the case of a person afflicted with hiccup, removes the hiccup.

14. In a case of dropsy, when the water runs by the veins into the belly, it removes the disease.

15. In confirmed diarrhœa, vomiting, when it comes on spontaneously, removes the diarrhœa.

16. A diarrhœa supervening in a confirmed case of pleurisy or pneumonia is bad.

17. It is a good thing in ophthalmy for the patient to be seized with diarrhœa.

18. A severe wound of the bladder, of the brain, of the heart, of the diaphragm, of the small intestines, of the stomach, and of the liver, is deadly.

19. When a bone, cartilage, nerve, the slender part of the jaw, or prepuce, are cut out, the part is neither restored, nor does it unite.

20. If blood be poured out preternaturally into a cavity, it must necessarily become corrupted.

21. In maniacal affections, if varices or hemorrhoids come on, they remove the mania.

22. Those ruptures in the back which spread down to the elbows are removed by venesection.

23. If a fright or despondency lasts for a long time, it is a melancholic affection.

24. If any of the small intestines be transfixed, it does not unite.

25. It is not a good sign for an erysipelas

spreading outwardly to be determined inward; but for it to be determined outward from within is good.

26. In whatever cases of ardent fever tremors occur, they are carried off by a delirium.

27. Those cases of empyema or dropsy which are treated by incision or the cautery, if the water or pus flow rapidly all at once, certainly prove fatal.

28. Eunuchs do not take the gout, nor become bald.

29. A woman does not take the gout, unless her menses be stopped.

30. A young man does not take the gout until he indulges in coition.

31. Pains of the eyes are removed by drinking pure wine, or the bath, or a fomentation, or venesection, or purging.

32. Persons whose speech has become impaired are likely to be seized with chronic diarrhœa.

33. Persons having acid eructations are not very apt to be seized with pleurisy.

34. Persons who have become bald are not subject to large varices; but should varices supervene upon persons who are bald, their hair again grows thick.

35. Hiccup supervening in dropsical cases is bad.

36. Venesection cures dysuria; open the internal veins of the arm.

37. It is a good symptom when swelling on the outside of the neck seizes a person very ill of quinsy, for the disease is turned outwardly.

38. It is better not to apply any treatment in cases of occult cancer; for, if treated, the patients die quickly; but if not treated, they hold out for a long time.

39. Convulsions take place either from repletion or depletion; and so it is with hiccup.

40. When pains, without inflammation, occur about the hypochondria, in such cases, fever supervening removes the pain.

41. When pus formed anywhere in the body does not point, this is owing to the thickness of the part.

42. In cases of jaundice, it is a bad symptom when the liver becomes indurated.

43. When persons having large spleens are seized with dysentery, and if the dysentery pass into a chronic state, either dropsy or lientery supervenes, and they die.

44. When ileus comes on in a case of strangury, they prove fatal in seven days, unless, fever supervening, there be a copious discharge of urine.

45. When ulcers continue open for a year or upward, there must necessarily be exfoliation of bone, and the cicatrices are hollow.

46. Such persons as become hump-backed from asthma or cough before puberty, die.

47. Persons who are benefited by venesection or purging, should be bled or purged in spring.

48. In enlargement of the spleen, it is a good symptom when dysentery comes on.

49. In gouty affections, the inflammation subsides in the course of forty days.

50. When the brain is severely wounded, fever and vomiting of bile necessarily supervene.

51. When persons in good health are suddenly seized with pains in the head, and straightway are laid down speechless, and breathe with stertor, they die in seven days, unless fever come on.

52. We must attend to the appearances of the eyes in sleep, as presented from below; for if a portion of the white be seen between the closed eyelids, and if this be not connected with diarrhœa or severe purging, it is a very bad and mortal symptom.

53. Delirium attended with laughter is less dangerous than delirium attended with a serious mood.

54. In acute diseases, complicated with fever, a moaning respiration is bad.

55. For the most part, gouty affections rankle in spring and in autumn.

56. In melancholic affections, determinations of the humor which occasions them produce the following diseases; either apoplexy of the whole body, or convulsion, or madness, or blindness.

57. Persons are most subject to apoplexy between the ages of forty and sixty.

58. If the omentum protrude, it necessarily mortifies and drops off.

59. In chronic diseases of the hip-joint, if the bone protrude and return again into its socket, there is mucosity in the place.

60. In persons affected with chronic disease of the hip-joint, if the bone protrude from its socket, the limb becomes wasted and maimed, unless the part be cauterized.

SECTION VII

1. In acute diseases, coldness of the extremities is bad.

2. Livid flesh on a diseased bone is bad.

3. Hiccup and redness of the eyes, when they supervene on vomiting, are bad.

4. A chill supervening on a sweat is not good.

5. Dysentery, or dropsy, or ecstacy coming on madness is good.

6. In a very protracted disease, loss of appetite

and unmixed discharges from the bowels are bad symptoms.

7. A rigor and delirium from excessive drinking are bad.

8. From the rupture of an internal abscess, prostration of strength, vomiting, and deliquium animi result.

9. Delirium or convulsion from a flow of blood is bad.

10. Vomiting, or hiccup, or convulsion, or delirium, in ileus, is bad.

11. Pneumonia coming on pleurisy is bad.

12. Phrenitis along with pneumonia is bad.

13. Convulsion or tetanus, coming upon severe burning, is bad.

14. Stupor or delirium from a blow on the head is bad.

15. From a spitting of blood there is a spitting of pus.

16. From spitting of pus arise phthisis and a flux; and when the sputa are stopped, they die.

17. Hiccup in inflammation of the liver is bad.

18. Convulsion or delirium supervening upon insomnolency is bad.

18a. Trembling upon lethargus is bad.

19. Erysipelas upon exposure of a bone (is bad?).

20. Mortification or suppuration upon erysipelas is bad.

21. Hemorrhage upon a strong pulsation in wounds is bad.

22. Suppuration upon a protracted pain of the parts about the bowels is bad.

23. Dysentery upon unmixed alvine discharges is bad.

24. Delirium upon division of the cranium, if it penetrate into the cavity of the head, is bad.

25. Convulsion upon severe purging is mortal.

26. Upon severe pain of the parts about the bowels, coldness of the extremities coming on is bad.

27. Tenesmus coming on in a case of pregnancy causes abortion.

28. Whatever piece of bone, cartilage, or nerve (tendon?) is cut off, it neither grows nor unites.

29. When strong diarrhœa supervenes in a case of leucophlegmatia, it removes the disease.

30. In those cases in which frothy discharges occur in diarrhœa there are defluxions from the head.

31. When there is a farinaceous sediment in the urine during fever, it indicates a protracted illness.

32. In those cases in which the urine is thin at first, and the sediments become bilious, an acute disease is indicated.

33. In those cases in which the urine becomes divided there is great disorder in the body.

34. When bubbles settle on the surface of the urine, they indicate disease of the kidneys, and that the complaint will be protracted.

35. When the scum on the surface is fatty and copious, it indicates acute diseases of the kidneys.

36. Whenever the aforementioned symptoms occur in nephritic diseases, and along with them acute pains about the muscles of the back, provided these be seated about the external parts, you may expect that there will be an abscess; but if the pains be rather about the internal parts, you may also rather expect that the abscess will be seated internally.

37. Hæmatemesis, without fever, does not prove fatal, but with fever it is bad; it is to be treated with refrigerant and styptic things.

38. Defluxions into the cavity of the chest suppurate in twenty days.

39. When a patient passes blood and clots, and is seized with strangury and pain in the perineum and pubes, disease about the bladder is indicated.

40. If the tongue suddenly lose its powers, or a part of the body become apoplectic, the affection is of a melancholic nature.

41. In hypercatharsis, of old persons, hiccup supervening is not a good symptom.

42. In a fever, which is not of a bilious nature, a copious affusion of hot water upon the head removes the fever.

43. A woman does not become ambidexterous.

44. When empyema is treated either by the cautery or incision, if pure and white pus flow from the wound, the patients recover; but if mixed with blood, slimy and fetid, they die.

45. When abscess of the liver is treated by the cautery or incision, if the pus which is discharged be pure and white, the patients recover, (for in this case it is situated in the coats of the liver;) but if it resemble the lees of oil as it flows, they die.

46. Pains of the eyes are removed by drinking undiluted wine, plenteous bathing with hot water, and venesection.

47. If a dropsical patient be seized with hiccup the case is hopeless.

48. Strangury and dysuria are cured by drinking pure wine, and venesection; open the vein on the inside.

49. It is a good sign when swelling and redness on the breast seize a person very ill of

quinsy, for in this case the disease is diverted outwardly.

50. When the brain is attacked with sphacelus, the patients die in three days; or if they escape these, they recover.

51. Sneezing arises from the head, owing to the brain being heated, or the cavity (*ventricle*) in the head being filled with humors; the air confined in it then is discharged, and makes a noise, because it comes through a narrow passage.

52. Fever supervening on painful affections of the liver removes the pain.

53. Those persons to whom it is beneficial to have blood taken from their veins, should have it done in spring.

54. In those cases where phlegm is collected between the diaphragm and the stomach, and occasions pain, as not finding a passage into either of the cavities, the disease will be carried off if the phlegm be diverted to the bladder by the veins.

55. When the liver is filled with water and bursts into the epiploon, in this case the belly is filled with water and the patient dies.

56. Anxiety, yawning, rigor,—wine drunk with an equal proportion of water, removes these complaints.

57. When tubercles (*phymata*) form in the urethra, if they suppurate and burst, the pain is carried off.

58. In cases of concussion of the brain produced by any cause, the patients necessarily lose their speech.

59. In a person affected with fever, when there is no swelling in the fauces, should suffocation suddenly come on, and the patient not be able to swallow, except with difficulty, it is a mortal symptom.

59a. In the case of a person oppressed by fever, if the neck be turned aside, and the patient cannot swallow, while there is no swelling in the neck, it is a mortal sign.

60. Fasting should be prescribed for those persons who have humid flesh; for fasting dries bodies.

61. When there are changes in the whole body, and the body becomes sometimes cold and sometimes hot, and the color changes, a protracted disease is indicated.

62. A copious sweat, hot or cold, constantly flowing, indicates a superabundance of humidity; we must evacuate then, in a strong person upward, and in a weak, downward.

63. Fevers, not of the intermittent type, if they become exacerbated every third day are

dangerous; but if they intermit in any form whatever, this shows that they are not dangerous.

64. In cases of protracted fever, either chronic abscesses or pains in the joints come on.

65. When chronic abscesses (*phymata*) or pains in the joints take place after fevers, the patients are using too much food.

66. If one give to a person in fever the same food which is given to a person in good health, what is strength to the one is disease to the other.

67. We must look to the urinary evacuations, whether they resemble those of persons in health; if not at all so, they are particularly morbid, but if they are like those of healthy persons, they are not at all morbid.

68. When the dejections are allowed to stand and not shaken, and a sediment is formed like scrapings (of the bowels), in such a case it is proper to purge the bowels; and if you give ptisans before purging, the more you give the more harm you will do.

69. Crude dejections are the product of black bile; if abundant, of more copious, and if deficient, of less copious collections of it.

70. The sputa in fevers, not of an intermittent type, which are livid, streaked with blood, and fetid, are all bad, it is favorable when this evacuation, like the urinary and alvine, passes freely; and whenever any discharge is suppressed and not purged off it is bad.

71. When you wish to purge the body, you must bring it into a state favorable to evacuations; and if you wish to dispose it to evacuations upward, you must bind the belly; and if you wish to dispose it to evacuations downward, you must moisten the belly.

72. Sleep and watchfulness, both of them, when immoderate, constitute disease.

73. In fevers which do not intermit, if the external parts be cold, and the internal burning hot, and fever prevail, it is a mortal sign.

74. In a fever which does not intermit, if a lip, the nose, or an eye be distorted, if the patient lose his sense of sight or of hearing, while now in a weak state,—whatever of these symptoms occurs it is mortal.

75. Upon leucophlegmatia dropsy supervenes.

76. Upon diarrhœa dysentery.

77. Upon dysentery lientery.

78. Upon sphacelus exfoliation of the bone.

79 and 80. Upon vomiting of blood consumption, and a purging of pus upward; upon consumption a defluxion from the head; upon a defluxion diarrhœa; upon diarrhœa a stoppage of

the purging upward; upon the stoppage of it death.

81. In the discharges by the bladder, the belly, and the flesh (*the skin?*) if the body has departed slightly from its natural condition, the disease is slight; if much, it is great; if very much, it is mortal.

82. Persons above forty years of age who are affected with frenzy, do not readily recover; the danger is less when the disease is cognate to the constitution and age.

83. In whatever diseases the eyes weep voluntarily, it is a good symptom, but when involuntarily, it is a bad.

84. When in quartan fevers blood flows from the nostrils it is a bad symptom.

85. Sweats are dangerous when they do not occur on critical days, when they are strong, and quickly forced out of the forehead, either in the form of drops or in streams, and if excessively cold and copious; for such a sweat must proceed from violence, excess of pain, and prolonged squeezing (*affliction?*).

86. In a chronic disease an excessive flux from the bowels is bad.

87. Those diseases which medicines do not cure, iron (*the knife?*) cures; those which iron cannot cure, fire cures; and those which fire cannot cure, are to be reckoned wholly incurable.

The Law

MEDICINE is of all the Arts the most noble; but, owing to the ignorance of those who practice it, and of those who, inconsiderately, form a judgment of them, it is at present far behind all the other arts. Their mistake appears to me to arise principally from this, that in the cities there is no punishment connected with the practice of medicine (and with it alone) except disgrace, and that does not hurt those who are familiar with it. Such persons are like the figures which are introduced in tragedies, for as they have the shape, and dress, and personal appearance of an actor, but are not actors, so also physicians are many in title but very few in reality.

2. Whoever is to acquire a competent knowledge of medicine, ought to be possessed of the following advantages: a natural disposition; instruction; a favorable position for the study; early tuition; love of labor; leisure. First of all, a natural talent is required; for, when Nature opposes, everything else is in vain; but when Nature leads the way to what is most excellent, instruction in the art takes place, which the student must try to appropriate to himself by reflection, becoming an early pupil in a place well adapted for instruction. He must also bring to the task a love of labor and perseverance, so that the instruction taking root may bring forth proper and abundant fruits.

3. Instruction in medicine is like the culture of the productions of the earth. For our natural disposition is, as it were, the soil; the tenets of our teacher are, as it were, the seed; instruction in youth is like the planting of the seed in the ground at the proper season; the place where the instruction is communicated is like the food imparted to vegetables by the atmosphere; diligent study is like the cultivation of the fields; and it is time which imparts strength to all things and brings them to maturity.

4. Having brought all these requisites to the study of medicine, and having acquired a true knowledge of it, we shall thus, in traveling through the cities, be esteemed physicians not only in name but in reality. But inexperience is a bad treasure, and a bad fund to those who possess it, whether in opinion or reality, being devoid of self-reliance and contentedness, and the nurse both of timidity and audacity. For timidity betrays a want of powers, and audacity a want of skill. There are, indeed, two things, knowledge and opinion, of which the one makes its possessor really to know, the other to be ignorant.

5. Those things which are sacred, are to be imparted only to sacred persons; and it is not lawful to import them to the profane until they have been initiated in the mysteries of the science.

On Ulcers

WE MUST avoid wetting all sorts of ulcers except with wine, unless the ulcer be situated in a joint. For, the dry is nearer to the sound, and the wet to the unsound, since an ulcer is wet, but a sound part is dry. And it is better to leave the part without a bandage unless a cataplasm be applied. Neither do certain ulcers admit of cataplasms, and this is the case with the recent rather than the old, and with those situated in joints. A spare diet and water agree with all ulcers, and with the more recent rather than the older; and with an ulcer which either is inflamed or is about to be so; and where there is danger of gangrene; and with the ulcers an inflammation in joints; and where there is danger of convulsion; and in wounds of the belly; but most especially in fractures of the head and thigh, or any other member in which a fracture may have occurred. In the case of an ulcer, it is not expedient to stand; more especially if the ulcer be situated in the leg; but neither, also, is it proper to sit or walk. But quiet and rest are particularly expedient. Recent ulcers, both the ulcers themselves and the surrounding parts, will be least exposed to inflammation, if one shall bring them to a suppuration as expeditiously as possible, and if the matter is not prevented from escaping by the mouth of the sore; or, if one should restrain the suppuration, so that only a small and necessary quantity of pus may be formed, and the sore may be kept dry by a medicine which does not create irritation. For the part becomes inflamed when rigor and throbbing supervene; for ulcers then get inflamed when suppuration is about to form. A sore suppurates when the blood is changed and becomes heated; so that becoming putrid, it constitutes the pus of such ulcers. When you seem to require a cataplasm, it is not the ulcer itself to which you must apply the cataplasm, but to the surrounding parts, so that the pus may escape and the hardened parts may become soft. Ulcers formed either from the parts having been cut through by a sharp instrument, or excised, admit of medicaments for bloody wounds ('έναιμα), and which will prevent suppuration by being desiccant to a certain degree. But, when the flesh has been contused and roughly cut by the weapon, it is to be so treated that it may suppurate as quickly as possible; for thus the inflammation is less, and it is necessary that the pieces of flesh which are bruised and cut should melt away by becoming putrid,

being converted into pus, and that new flesh should then grow up. In every recent ulcer, except in the belly, it is expedient to cause blood to flow from it abundantly, and as may seem seasonable; for thus will the wound and the adjacent parts be less attacked with inflammation. And, in like manner, from old ulcers, especially if situated in the leg, in a toe or finger, more than in any other part of the body. For when the blood flows they become drier and less in size, as being thus dried up. It is this (the blood?) especially which prevents such ulcers from healing, by getting into a state of putrefaction and corruption. But, it is expedient, after the flow of the blood, to bind over the ulcer a thick and soft piece of sponge, rather dry than wet, and to place above the sponge some slender leaves. Oil, and all things of an emollient and oily nature, disagree with such ulcers, unless they are getting nearly well. Neither does oil agree with wounds which have been recently inflicted, nor yet do medicines formed with oil or suet, more especially if the ulcer stands in need of more cleansing. And, in a word, it is in summer and in winter that we are to smear with oil these sores that require such medicines.

2. Gentle purging of the bowels agrees with most ulcers, and in wounds of the head, belly, or joints, where there is danger of gangrene, in such as require sutures, in phagedænic, spreading and in otherwise inveterate ulcers. And when you want to apply a bandage, no plasters are to be used until you have rendered the sore dry, and then indeed you may apply them. The ulcer is to be frequently cleaned with a sponge, and then a dry and clean piece of cloth is to be frequently applied to it, and in this way the medicine which it is supposed will agree with it is to be applied, either with or without a bandage. The hot season agrees better than winter with most ulcers, except those situated in the head and belly; but the equinoctial season agrees still better with them. Ulcers which have been properly cleansed and dried as they should be, do not usually get into a fungated state. When a bone has exfoliated, or has been burned, or sawed, or removed in any other way, the cicatrices of such ulcers become deeper than usual. Ulcers which are not cleansed, are not disposed to unite if brought together, nor do the lips thereof approximate of their own accord. When the points adjoining to an ulcer are inflamed,

the ulcer is not disposed to heal until the in-flammation subside, nor when the surrounding parts are blackened by mortification, nor when a varix occasions an overflow of blood in the part, is the ulcer disposed to heal, unless you bring the surrounding parts into a healthy con-dition.

3. Circular ulcers, if somewhat hollow, you must scarify all along their edges, or to the ex-tent of half the circle, according to the natural stature of the man. When erysipelas supervenes upon any sore, you must purge the body, in the way most suitable to the ulcer, either upward or downward. When swelling arises around an ulcer, and if the ulcer remain free from inflam-mation, there will be a deposit of matter in proc-ess of time. And whatever ulcer gets swelled along with inflammation and does not subside as the other parts subside which became in-flamed and swelled at the same time, there is a danger that such an ulcer may not unite. When from a fall, or in any other way, a part has been torn or bruised, and the parts surrounding the ulcer have become swelled, and, having sup-purated, matter flows from the swelling by the ulcer, if in such cases a cataplasm be required, it should not be applied to the sore itself, but to the surrounding parts, so that the pus may have free exit, and the indurated parts may be sof-tened. But when the parts are softened as the in-flammation ceases, then the parts which are sep-arated are to be brought toward one another, binding on sponges and applying them, begin-ning from the sound parts and advancing to the ulcer by degrees. But plenty of leaves are to be bound above the sponge. When the parts are prevented from coming together by a piece of flesh full of humors, it is to be removed. When the ulcer is deep seated in the flesh, it is swelled up, both from the bandaging and the compres-sion. Such an ulcer should be cut up upon a di-rector (specillum) if possible, at the proper time, so as to admit a free discharge of the mat-ter, and then the proper treatment is to be ap-plied as may be needed. For the most part, in every hollow ulcer which can be seen into di-rect without any swelling being present, if there be putrefaction in it, or if the flesh be flabby and putrid, such an ulcer, and the parts which surround it, will be seen to be black and some-what livid. And of corroding ulcers, those which are phagedænic, spread and corrode most pow-erfully, and, in this case, the parts surrounding the sore will have a black and sub-livid appear-ance.

4. Cataplasms for swellings and inflamma-tion in the surrounding parts. Boiled mullein, the raw leaves of the trefoil, and the boiled leaves of the epipetrum, and the poley, and if the ulcer stand in need of cleansing, all these things also cleanse; and likewise the leaves of the fig-tree, and of the olive, and the horehound, all these are to be boiled; and more especially the chaste-tree, and the fig, and the olive, and the leaves of the pomegranate are to be boiled in like manner. These are to be used raw: and the leaves of the mallow pounded with wine, and the leaves of rue, and those of the green origany. With all these, linseed is to be boiled up and mixed by pounding it as a very fine powder. When there is danger of erysipelas seizing the ulcers, the leaves of woad are to be pounded and applied raw in a cataplasm along with linseed, or the linseed is to be moistened with the juice of strychnos or of woad, and ap-plied as a cataplasm. When the ulcer is clean, but both it and the surrounding parts are in-flamed, lentil is to be boiled in wine and finely triturated, and, being mixed with a little oil, it is to be applied as a cataplasm; and the leaves of the hip-tree are to be boiled in water and pounded in a fine powder and made into a cataplasm; and apply below a thin, clean piece of cloth wetted in wine and oil; and when you wish to produce contraction, prepare the leaves of the hip-tree like the lentil, and the cress; wine and finely-powdered linseed are to be mixed to-gether. And this is proper: linseed, and raw chaste-tree, and Melian alum, all these things being macerated in vinegar.

5. Having pounded the white unripe grape in a mortar of red bronze, and passed it through the strainer, expose it to the sun during the day, but remove it during the night, that it may not suffer from the dew; rub it constantly during the day, so that it may dry equally, and may contract as much virtue as possible from the bronze: let it be exposed to the sun for as great a length of time as till it acquire the thickness of honey; then put it into a bronze pot with the fresh honey and sweet wine, in which turpen-tine resin has been previously boiled, boil the resin in the wine until it become hard like boiled honey; then take out the resin and pour off the wine: there should be the greatest pro-portion of the juice of unripe grape, next of the wine, and third of the honey and myrrh, either the liquid (stacte) or otherwise. The finest kind is to be levigated and moistened by having a small quantity of the same wine poured on it; and then the myrrh is to be boiled by itself, stirring it in the wine; and when it appears to

have attained the proper degree of thickness, it is to be poured into the juice of the unripe grape; and the finest natron is to be toasted, and gently added to the medicine, along with a smaller quantity of the flowers of copper (*flos æris*) than of the natron. When you have mixed these things, boil for not less than three days, on a gentle fire made with fuel of the fig-tree or with coals, lest it catch fire. The applications should all be free from moisture, and the sores should not be wetted when this medicine is applied in the form of liniment. This medicine is to be used for old ulcers, and also for recent wounds of the glans penis, and ulcers on the head and ears. Another medicine for the same ulcers:—The dried gall of an ox, the finest honey, white wine, in which the shavings of the lotus have been boiled, frankincense, of myrrh an equal part, of saffron an equal part, the flowers of copper, in like manner of liquids, the greatest proportion of wine, next of honey, and least of the gall. Another:—Wine, a little cedar honey, of dried things, the flowers of copper, myrrh, dried pomegranate rind. Another: —Of the roasted flower of copper half a drachm, of myrrh two half-drachms, of saffron three drachms, of honey a small quantity, to be boiled with wine. Another:—Of frankincense a drachm, of gall a drachm, of saffron three drachms; let each of these be dried and finely levigated, then, having mixed, triturate in a very strong sun, pouring in the juice of an unripe grape, until it become of a gelatinous consistence, for three days; then let them be allowed to macerate in an austere, dark-colored, fragrant wine, which is gradually poured upon them. Another:—Boil the roots of the holm-oak in sweet white wine; and when it appears to be properly done, having poured off two parts of the wine, and of the lees of wine as free of water as possible one part; then boil, stirring it, so that it may not be burnt, at a gentle fire, until it appear to have attained the proper consistence. Another:—The other things are to be the same; but, instead of the wine, use the strongest white vinegar, and dip into it wool as greasy as can be procured, and then, moistening it with the lees of oil, boil, and pour in the juice of the wild fig-tree, and add Melian alum, and natron, and the flowers of copper, both toasted. This cleanses the ulcers better than the former, but the other is no less desiccant. Another:—Dip the wool in a very little water; and then, having added a third part of wine, boil until it attain the proper consistence. By these, recent ulcers are most speedily prevented

from getting into a state of suppuration.

6. Another:—Sprinkle on it dried wakerobin, and add the green bark of the fig-tree, pounding it in the juice: do this with or without wine, and along with honey. Another:—Boiling the shavings of lotus with vinegar (the *vinegar* should be white); then mix the lees of oil and raw tar-water, and use it as a liniment or wash, and bandage above. These things in powder prevent recent wounds from suppurating, or they may be used for cleansing the sore along with vinegar, or for sponging with wine.

7. Another:—Sprinkle (*on the sore?*) lead finely triturated with the recrement of copper; and sprinkle on it, also, the shavings of lotus, and the scales of copper, and alum, and chalcitis, with copper, both alone, and with the shavings of lotus. And otherwise, when it is wanted to use these in a dry state, do it with the Illyrian spodos triturated with the shavings, and with the shavings alone. And the flowers of silver alone, in the finest powder; and birthwort, when scraped and finely pounded, may be sprinkled on the part. Another, for bloody sores myrrh, frankincense, galls, verdigris the roasted flower of copper, Egyptian alum roasted, vine flowers, grease of wool, plumbago, each of these things is to be diluted, in equal proportions, with wine like the former. And there is another preparation of the same:—The strongest vinegar of a white color, honey, Egyptian alum, the finest natron; having toasted these things gently, pour in a little gall; this cleanses fungous ulcers, renders them hollow, and is not pungent. Another:—The herb with the small leaves, which gets the name of Parthenium parviflorum, and is used for removing thymia (*warts?*) from the glans penis, alum, chalcitis, a little crude Melian alum (?); sprinkle a little dried elaterium, and a little dried pomegranate rind in like manner.

8. The herb which has got the name of lagopyrus, fills up hollow and clean ulcers; (when dried it resembles wheat; it has a small leaf like that of the olive, and more long;) and the leaf of horehound, with oil. Another:—The internal fatty part, resembling honey, of a fig much dried, of water two parts, of linseed not much toasted and finely levigated, one part. Another: —Of the dried fig, of the flower of copper levigated a little, and the juice of the fig. The preparation from dried fig:—The black chamæleon, the dried gall of an ox, the other things the same. Of the powders:—Of the slender cress in a raw state, of horehound, of each equal parts; of the dried fig, two parts; of linseed, two parts;

the juice of the fig. When you use any of these medicines, apply above it compresses wetted in vinegar, apply a sponge about the compresses and make a little more pressure. If the surrounding parts be in an inflamed state, apply to them any medicine which may appear suitable.

9. If you wish to use a liquid application, the medicine called *caricum* may be rubbed in, and the bandages may be applied as formerly described upon the same principle. The medicine is prepared of the following ingredients:—Of black hellebore, of sandarach, of the flakes of copper, of lead washed, with much sulphur, arsenic, and cantharides. This may be compounded so as may be judged most proper, and it is to be diluted with oil of juniper. When enough has been rubbed in, lay aside the medicine, and apply boiled wakerobin in a soft state, either rubbing it in dry, or moistening it with honey. But if you use the caricum in a dry state, you must abstain from these things, and sprinkle the medicine on the sore. The powder from hellebore and sandarach alone answers. Another liquid medicine:—The herb, the leaf of which resembles the arum (wakerobin) in nature, but is white, downy, of the size of the ivy-leaf: this herb is applied with wine, or the substance which forms upon the branches of the ilex, when pounded with wine, is to be applied. Another:—The juice of the unripe grape, the strongest vinegar, the flower of copper, natron, the juice of the wild fig-tree. Alum, the most finely levigated, is to be put into the juice of the wild grape, and it is to be put into a red bronze mortar and stirred in the sun, and removed when it appears to have attained its proper consistence.

10. These are other powders:—Black hellebore, as finely levigated as possible, is to be sprinkled on the sore while any humidity remains about it, and while it continues to spread. The bandaging is the same as when plasters are used. Another, in like manner:—The driest lumps of salt are to be put into a copper, or earthen pot, of equal size, as much as possible, and not large, and the finest honey, of double the size of the salt, as far as can be guessed, is to be poured upon the lumps of salt, then the vessel is to be put upon coals and allowed to sit there until the whole is consumed. Then, having sponged the ulcer and cleansed it, bandage it as before, and compress it a little more. Next day, wherever the medicine has not been taken in, sprinkle it on, press it down, and bandage. But when you wish to remove the medicine, pour in hot vinegar until it separate, and

again do the same things, sponging it away, if necessary. Another corrosive powder:—Of the most finely-levigated misy, sprinkle upon the moist and gangrenous parts, and a little of the flower of copper, not altogether levigated. Another powder equally corrosive:—Having sponged the ulcer, burn the most greasy wool upon a shell placed on the fire until the whole be consumed; having reduced this to a fine powder, and sprinkled it on the sore, apply the bandage in the same manner. Another powder for the same ulcers:—The black chamæleon, when prepared with the juice of the fig. It is to be prepared roasted, and alkanet mixed with it. Or, pimpernel, and Egyptian alum roasted, and sprinkle on them the Orchomenian powder. For spreading ulcers:—Alum, both the Egyptian roasted, and the Melian; but the part is to be first cleansed with roasted natron and sponged; and the species of alum called chalcitis roasted. It is to be roasted until it catch fire.

11. For old ulcers which occur on the fore part of the legs; they become bloody and black: —Having pounded the flower of the melilot and mixed it with honey, use as a plaster. For nerves (*tendons?*) which have been cut asunder:—Having pounded, sifted, and mixed with oil the roots of the wild myrtle, bind on the part; and the herb cinquefoil (it is white and downy, and more raised above the ground than the black cinquefoil), having pounded this herb in oil bind it on the part, and then remove it on the third day.

12. *Emollients* (?):—These medicines are to be used in winter rather than in summer. Emollient medicines which make the cicatrices fair: —Pound the inner mucous part of the squill and pitch, with fresh swine's seam, and a little oil, and a little resin, and ceruse. And the grease of a goose, fresh swine's seam, and squill, and a little oil. The whitest wax, fresh clean grease, or squill and white oil, and a little resin. Wax, swine's seam (old and fresh), and oil, and verdigris, and squill and resin. Let there be two parts of the old grease to the fresh, and of the other things, q. s. Having melted the grease that is fresh, pour it into another pot; having levigated plumbago finely and sifted it, and mixed them together, boil and stir at first; boil until when poured upon the ground it concretes; then taking it off the fire, pour it all into another vessel, with the exception of the stony sediment, and add resin and stir, and mix a little oil of juniper, and what has been taken off. In all the emollient medicines to which you add the resin,

when you remove the medicine from the fire, pour in and mix the resin while it is still warm. Another:—Old swine's seam, wax, and oil, the dried shavings of the lotus, frankincense, plumbago,—namely, of the frankincense one part, and of the other one part, and of the shavings of the lotus one part; but let there be two parts of the old grease, one of wax, and of fresh swine's seam one part. Another:—Or old swine's seam along with the fresh grease of a goat; when cleaned, let it retain as little as possible of its membrane: having triturated or pounded it smooth, pour in oil, and sprinkle the lead with the spodium and half the shavings of the lotus. Another:—Swine's seam, spodium, blue chalcitis, oil.

13. *For Burns:*—You must boil the tender roots of the ilex, and if their bark be very thick and green, it must be cut into small parts, and having poured in white wine, boil upon a gentle fire, until it appear to you to be of the proper consistence, so as to be used for a liniment. And it may be prepared in water after the same manner. Another, not corrosive:—Old swine's seam is to be rubbed in by itself, and it is to be melted along with squill, the root of which is to be divided and applied with a bandage. Next day it is to be fomented; and having melted old swine's seam and wax, and mixed with them oil, frankincense, and the shavings of lotus and vermilion, this is to be used as a liniment. Having boiled the leaves of the wakerobin in wine and oil, apply a bandage. Another:—When you have smeared the parts with old swine's seam let the roots of asphodel be pounded in wine and triturated, and rubbed in. Another:—Having melted old swine's seam, and mixed with resin and bitumen, and having spread it on a piece of cloth and warmed it at the fire, apply a bandage. When an ulcer has formed on the back from stripes or otherwise, let squill, twice boiled, be pounded and spread upon a linen cloth and bound on the place. Afterward the grease of a goat, and fresh swine's seam, spodium, oil, and frankincense are to be rubbed in.

14. Swellings which arise on the feet, either spontaneously or otherwise, when neither the swellings nor the inflammation subside under the use of cataplasms, and although sponges or wool, or anything else be bound upon the sound part; but the swelling and inflammation return of themselves again, an influx of blood into the veins is the cause, when not occasioned by a bruise. And the same story applies if this happen in any other part of the body. But blood is to be abstracted, especially from the veins, which

are the seat of the influx, if they be conspicuous; but if not, deeper and more numerous scarifications are to be made in the swellings; and whatever part you scarify, this is to be done with the sharpest and most slender instruments of iron. When you have removed the blood, you must not press hard upon the part with the specillum, lest you produce contusion. Bathe with vinegar, and do not allow a clot of blood to remain between the lips of the wounds, and having spread greasy wool with a medicine for bloody wounds, and having carded the woof and made it soft, bind it on, having wetted it with wine and oil. And let the scarified part be so placed that the determination of the blood may be upward and not downward; and do not wet the part at all, and let the patient be put upon a restricted diet and drink water. If upon loosing the bandages you find the scarifications inflamed, apply a cataplasm of the fruit of the chaste-tree and linseed. But if the scarifications become ulcerated and break into one another, we must be regulated by circumstances, and otherwise apply whatever else appears to be proper.

15. When a varix is on the fore part of the leg, and is very superficial, or below the flesh, and the leg is black, and seems to stand in need of having the blood evacuated from it, such swellings are not, by any means, to be cut open; for, generally, large ulcers are the consequence of the incisions, owing to the influx from the varix. But the varix itself is to be punctured in many places, as circumstances may indicate.

16. When you have opened a vein and abstracted blood, and although the fillet be loosed the bleeding does not stop, the member, whether the arm or leg, is to be put into the reverse position to that from which the blood flows; so that the blood may flow backward, and it is to be allowed to remain in this position for a greater or less space of time. Then bind up the part while matters are so, no clots of blood being allowed to remain in the opening. Then having applied a double compress, and wetted it with wine, apply above it clean wool which has been smeared with oil. For, although the flow of blood be violent, it will be stopped in this way. If a thrombus be formed in the opening, it will inflame and suppurate. Venesection is to be practiced when the person has dined more or less freely and drunk, and when somewhat heated, and rather in hot weather than in cold.

17. When in cupping, the blood continues to flow after the cupping-instrument has been

removed, and if the flow of blood, or serum be copious, the instrument is to be applied again before the part is healed up, so as to abstract what is left behind. Otherwise coagula of blood will be retained in the incisions and inflammatory ulcers will arise from them. In all such cases the parts are to be bathed with vinegar, after which they are not to be wetted; neither must the person lie upon the scarifications, but they are to be anointed with some of the medicines for bloody wounds. When the cupping-instrument is to be applied below the knee, or at the knee, it should be done, if possible, while the man stands erect.

On Fistulæ

FISTULÆ are produced by contusions and tubercles, and they are also occasioned by rowing, or riding on horseback, when blood accumulates in the nates near the anus. For, having become putrid, it spreads to the soft parts (the breech being of a humid nature, and the flesh in which it spreads being soft), until the tubercle break and corrupt below at the anus. When this happens, a fistula is formed, having an ichorous discharge, and fæces pass by it, with flatus and much abomination. It is produced, then, by contusions when any of the parts about the anus are bruised by a blow, or a fall, or a wound, or by riding, or rowing, or any such cause. For blood is collected, and it, becoming corrupted, suppurates; and from the suppuration the same accidents happen, as have been described in the case of tubercles.

2. In the first place, then, when you see any such tubercle formed, you must cut it open while still unripe, before it suppurate and burst into the rectum. But if a fistula be already formed when you undertake the case, take a stalk of fresh garlic, and having laid the man on his back, and separated his thighs on both sides, push down the stalk as far as it will go, and thereby measure the depth of the fistula. Then, having bruised the root of seseli to a very fine powder, and poured in some water, let it macerate for four days, and, mixing the water with honey, let the patient drink it, fasting, to the amount of three cyathi, and at the same time purge away the ascarides. Those who are left without treatment die.

3. In the next place, having moistened the strip of cotton cloth, with the juice of the great tithymallus, and sprinkling on it the flos æris, roasted and triturated, and having made it into a tent equal in length to the fistula, and having passed a thread through the ends of the tent and again through the stalk, and having placed the patient in a reclining position, and having examined the ulcerated parts of the rectum with a speculum, pass the stalk by it, and when it reaches the rectum, take hold of it and draw it out until the tent be pushed through, and be brought on a level above and below. When it (the tent?) has been pushed inward, introduce a ball of horn into the rectum (the rectum having been previously smeared with Cimolian chalk), and leave it there, and when the patient wants to go to stool, let it be taken out and again replaced, and let this practice be continued for five days. On the sixth day let it be removed, and drawing the tent out of the flesh, and afterwards pounding alum and filling the ball (pessary) and introducing it into the rectum, leave it until the alum melts. Anoint the rectum with myrrh until the parts appear to be united.

4. Another method of cure:—Taking a very slender thread of raw lint, and uniting it into five folds of the length of a span, and wrapping them round with a horse hair; then having made a director (specillum) of tin, with an eye at its extremity, and having passed through it the end of raw lint wrapped round as above described, introduce the director into the fistula, and, at the same time, introduce the index finger of the left hand per anum; and when the director touches the finger, bring it out with the finger, bending the extremity of the director and the end of the threads in it, and the director is to be withdrawn, but the ends of the threads are to be knotted twice or thrice, and the rest of the raw threads is to be twisted around and fastened into a knot. Then the patient is to be told that he may go and attend to his matters. The rest of the treatment:—Whenever any part of the thread gets loose owing to the fistula becoming putrid, it is to be tightened and twisted every day; and should the raw thread rot before the fistula is eaten through, you must attach another piece of raw thread to the hair, pass it through, and tie it, for it was for this purpose that the hair was rolled round the raw lint, as it is not liable to rot. When the fistula has sloughed through, a soft sponge is to be cut into very slender pieces and applied, and then the flowers

of copper, roasted, are to be frequently applied with a director; and the sponge smeared with honey is to be introduced with the index finger of the left hand, and pushed forward; and another bit of sponge being added, it is to be bound on in the same manner as in the operation for hemorrhoids. Next day, having loosed the bandages, the fistula is to be washed with hot water, and cleansed, as far as possible, with the finger of the left hand by means of the sponge, and again the flos æris is to be applied. This is to be done for seven days, for generally the coat of the fistula takes that time to slough through. The same mode of bandaging is to be persevered in afterwards, until the cure be completed. For in this way, the fistula being forcibly expanded by the sponge will not fill up and heal unequally, but it will all become whole together. During the treatment, the part should be bathed with plenty of warm water, and the patient kept on a spare diet.

5. When the fistula does not get eaten through, having first examined it with a sound, cut down as far as it passes, and sprinkle with the flos æris, and let it remain for five days. Then pour warm water upon it, and above lay flour mixed with water, and bind on it the leaves of beet. When the flos æris comes away, and the fistulous sore becomes clean, cure it as before described. But if the fistula be in a part which does not admit of this treatment, and if it be deep, syringe it with the flowers of copper, and myrrh, and natron, diluted with urine, and introduce a piece of lead into the orifice of the fistula so that it may not close. Syringe the fistula by means of a quill attached to a bladder, so that the injection may distend the fistula. But it does not heal unless it be cut open.

6. If the anus gets inflamed, and there is pain, fever, a frequent desire of going to stool without passing anything, and the anus appears to protrude, owing to the inflammation, and if at times strangury come on, this disease is formed, when phlegm, collected from the whole body, is determined to the rectum. Warm things are beneficial in this case; for these, when applied, can attenuate and dissolve the phlegm, and dilute the acrid and salt particles, so that the heat subsides, and the irritation in the rectum is removed. Wherefore it is to be treated thus:— The patient is to be put into a hip-bath of hot water, and sixty grains of the grana gnidia are to be pounded and infused in a hemina of wine, with half a hemina of oil, and injected. This brings away phlegm and fæces. When the patient does not take the hip-bath, boil eggs in dark-colored fragrant wine, and apply to the anus, and spread something warm below, either a bladder filled with warm water, or linseed toasted and ground, and its meal stirred up and mixed equally with dark, fragrant wine, and oil, and this applied very warm as a cataplasm; or, having mixed barley and Egyptian alum pulverized, form into an oblong ball (*suppository?*) and warming it gently at the fire, make it into a cataplasm, foment, form it into shape with the fingers, and then making it quite tepid, introduce it into the anus. The external parts are to be anointed with cerate, and a cataplasm of boiled garlic, with dark wine diluted, is to be applied. But if you remove these things, let him take the hip-bath of hot water, and having mixed together the juice of srychnos, the grease of a goose, swine's seam, chrysocolla, resin, and white wax, and then having melted in the same and mixed together, anoint with these things, and while the inflammation lasts, use the cataplasm of boiled garlic. And if by these means he be freed from the pain, it is enough; but if not, give him the white meconium (*Euphorbia peplus?*), or, if not it, any other phlegmagogue medicine. While the inflammation lasts, the diet should be light.

7. The strangury comes on in this way:—The bladder being heated from the rectum, phlegm is attracted by the heat, and by the phlegm (*inflammation?*) the strangury is occasioned. If, then, as is frequently the case, it cease with the disease, well; but, if not, give any of the medicines for strangury.

8. If procidentia ani take place, having fomented the part with a soft sponge, and anointed it with a snail, bind the man's hands together, and suspend him for a short time, and the gut will return. But if it still prolapse, and will not remain up, fasten a girdle round his loins and attach a shawl behind, and having pushed up the anus, apply to it a soft sponge, moistened with hot water in which the shavings of lotus have been boiled; pour of this decoction upon the anus by squeezing the sponge; then, bringing the shawl below between the legs, fasten it at the navel. But if he wish to evacuate the bowels, let him do so upon a very narrow night-stool. Or, if the patient be a child, let him be placed on the feet of a woman, with his back reclined to her knees, and when the bowels are evacuated, let the legs be extended. In this way the anus will be the least disposed to fall out. When a watery and ichorous discharge flows from the rectum, wash it out with burnt lees of wine, and water from myrtle, and

having dried maiden-hair, pound and sift it, and apply as a cataplasm. But if there be a discharge of blood, having washed with the same, and pounded chalcitis, and the shavings of cypress, or of juniper, or of stone-pine, or of turpentine, the latter in equal proportions with the chalcitis, apply as a cataplasm. Anoint the external parts with thick cerate.

9. When the gut protrudes and will not remain in its place, scrape the finest and most compact silphium (*assafœtida?*) into small pieces and apply as a cataplasm, and apply a sternutatory medicine to the nose and provoke sneezing, and having moistened pomegranate rind with hot water, and having powdered alum in white wine, pour it on the gut, then apply rags, bind the thighs together for three days, and let the patient fast, only he may drink sweet wine. If even thus matters do not proceed properly, having mixed vermillion with honey, anoint.

10. If procidentia ani be attended with a discharge of blood, pare off the rind of the root of wakerobin, then pound and mix flour with it, and apply it warm as a cataplasm. Another:—Having scraped off the rind of the most tender roots of the wild vine, which some call *psilothrion,* boil in a dark austere wine undiluted; then having pounded, apply as a tepid cataplasm; but mix also flour and stir it up with white wine and oil in a tepid state. Another:—Having pounded the seed of hemlock, pour on it a fragrant white wine, and then apply in a tepid state as a cataplasm.

11. But if it be inflamed, having boiled in water the root of the ivy, finely powdered, and mixing the finest flour, and stirring it up with white wine, apply as a cataplasm, and mix up some fat with these things. Another:—Take the root of the mandrake, especially the green (fresh) root, but otherwise the dried, and having cleaned the green root and cut it down, boil in diluted wine, and apply as a cataplasm; but the dry may be pounded and applied as a cataplasm in like manner. Another:—Having bruised the inner part of a ripe cucumber to a soft state, apply as a cataplasm.

12. If there be pain without inflammation, having roasted red natron, and pounded it to a fine powder, and added alum and roasted salts, finely triturated, mix together in equal proportions; then having mixed it up with the best pitch and spread upon a rag, apply, and bind. Another:—Having pounded the green leaves of capers, put into a bag and bind on the part; and when it appears to burn, take it away and apply it afterward; or, if you have not the leaves of capers, pound the rind of its roots, and having mixed it up with dark-colored wine, bind on the part in the same manner. This is a good application also for pains of the spleen. Of these poultices, those which are cooling, stop the discharge; those which are emollient and heating, discuss; and those which are attractive, dry up and attenuate. This disease is formed when bile and phlegm become seated in the parts. When the anus is inflamed, it should be anointed with the ointment, the ingredients of which are resin, oil, wax, plumbago, and suet, these being all melted and applied quite hot as a cataplasm.

On Hemorrhoids

THE disease of the hemorrhoids is formed in this way: if bile or phlegm be determined to the veins in the rectum, it heats the blood in the veins; and these veins becoming heated attract blood from the nearest veins, and being gorged the inside of the gut swells outwardly, and the heads of the veins are raised up, and being at the same time bruised by the fæces passing out, and injured by the blood collected in them, they squirt out blood, most frequently along with the fæces, but sometimes without fæces. It is to be cured thus:

2. In the first place it should be known in what sort of a place they are formed. For cutting, excising, sewing, binding, applying putrefacient means to the anus,—all these appear to be very formidable things, and yet, after all, they are not attended with mischief. I recommend seven or eight small pieces of iron to be prepared, a fathom in size, in thickness like a thick specillum, and bent at the extremity, and a broad piece should be on the extremity, like a small obolus. Having on the preceding day first purged the man with medicine, on the day of the operation apply the cautery. Having laid him on his back, and placed a pillow below the breech, force out the anus as much as possible with the fingers, and make the irons red-hot, and burn the pile until it be dried up, and so as that no part may be left behind. And burn so as to leave none of the hemorrhoids unburnt, for you should burn them all up. You will rec-

ognize the hemorrhoids without difficulty, for they project on the inside of the gut like dark-colored grapes, and when the anus is forced out they spurt blood. When the cautery is applied the patient's head and hands should be held so that he may not stir, but he himself should cry out, for this will make the rectum project the more. When you have performed the burning, boil lentils and tares, finely triturated in water, and apply as a cataplasm for five or six days. But on the seventh, cut a soft sponge into a very slender slice, its width should be about six inches square. Then a thin smooth piece of cloth, of the same size as the sponge, is to be smeared with honey and applied; and with the index finger of the left hand the middle of the sponge is to be pushed as far up as possible; and afterward wool is to be placed upon the sponge so that it may remain in the anus. And having girded the patient about the loins and fastened a shawl to the girdle, bring up this band from behind between the legs and attach it to the girdle at the navel. Then let the medicine which I formerly said is calculated to render the skin thick and strong, be bound on. These things should be kept on for not less than twenty days. The patient should once a day take a draught from flour or millet, or bran, and drink water. When the patient goes to stool the part should be washed with hot water. Every third day he should take the bath.

3. Another method of cure:—Having got the anus to protrude as much as possible, foment with hot water, and then cut off the extremities of the hemorrhoids. But this medicine should be prepared beforehand, as an application to the wound:—Having put urine into a bronze vessel, sprinkle upon the urine the flower of bronze calcined and finely triturated; then, when it is moistened, shake the vessel and dry in the sun. When it becomes dry, let it be scraped down and levigated, and apply with the finger to the part, and having oiled compresses, apply them, and bind a sponge above.

4. Another method:—There grows upon the bleeding condy—loma, a protuberance like the fruit of the mulberry, and if the condyloma be far without, an envelope of flesh is adherent to it. Having placed the man over two round stones upon his knees, examine, for you will find the parts near the anus between the buttocks inflated, and blood proceeding from within. If, then, the condyloma below the cover be of a soft nature, bring it away with the finger, for there is no more difficulty in this than in skinning a sheep, to pass the finger between the

hide and the flesh. And this should be accomplished without the patient's knowledge, while he is kept in conversation. When the condyloma is taken off, streaks of blood necessarily flow from the whole of the torn part. It must be speedily washed with a decoction of galls, in a dry wine, and the bleeding vein will disappear along with the condyloma, and its cover will be replaced. The older it is, the more easy the cure.

5. But if the condyloma be higher up, you must examine it with the speculum, and you should take care not to be deceived by the speculum; for when expanded, it renders the condyloma level with the surrounding parts, but when contracted, it shows the tumor right again. It is to be removed by smearing it with black hellebore on the finger. Then, on the third day, wash it out with a dry wine. You need not be surprised that there is no discharge of blood when you remove the condyloma, for neither, if you cut off the hands or legs at the articulations will there be any flow of blood; but if you cut them off above or below the joints, you will find there hollow veins which pour out blood, and you will have difficulty in stopping the bleeding. In the same manner, the bleeding vein in the anus, if you cut it above or below the point of separation of the condyloma, will pour forth blood; but if you take away the condyloma at its junction (*with the natural parts?*) there will be no flow of blood. If matters then be thus put to rights, it will be well; but otherwise burn it, taking care not to touch the place with the iron, but bringing it close so as to dry it up, and apply the flos æris in the urine.

6. Another method of curing hemorrhoids:—You must prepare a cautery like the *arundo phragmites,* and an iron that exactly fits is to be adapted to it; then the tube being introduced into the anus, the iron, red hot, is to be passed down it, and frequently drawn out, so that the part may bear the more heat, and no sore may result from the heating, and the dried veins may heal up. But if you are neither disposed to burn nor excise, having first fomented with plenty of hot water and turned out the anus, levigate myrrh, and having burnt galls and Egyptian alum, in the proportion of one and a half to the other things, and as much of melanteria; these things are all to be used in a dry state. The hemorrhoid will separate under the use of these medicines, like a piece of burnt hide. You are to proceed thus until the whole are removed, and a half part of burnt chalcitis does the same thing. But if you wish to effect the cure by suppositories, take the shell of the cuttle fish, a third

part of plumbago, bitumen, alum, a little of the flos æris, galls, a little verdigris; having poured a small quantity of boiled honey on these, and formed an oblong suppository, apply until you remove them.

7. An hemorrhoid in a woman may be thus cured. Having fomented with plenty of hot water, boil in the water certain of the fragrant medicines, add pounded tamarisk, roasted litharge and galls, and pour on them white wine, and oil, and the grease of a goose, pounding all together. Give to use after fomenting. In fomenting the anus is to be made to protrude as much as possible.

On the Sacred Disease

IT IS thus with regard to the disease called Sacred: it appears to me to be nowise more divine nor more sacred than other diseases, but has a natural cause from which it originates like other affections. Men regard its nature and cause as divine from ignorance and wonder, because it is not at all like to other diseases. And this notion of its divinity is kept up by their inability to comprehend it, and the simplicity of the mode by which it is cured, for men are freed from it by purifications and incantations. But if it is reckoned divine because it is wonderful, instead of one there are many diseases which would be sacred; for, as I will show, there are others no less wonderful and prodigious, which nobody imagines to be sacred. The quotidian, tertian, and quartan fevers, seem to me no less sacred and divine in their origin than this disease, although they are not reckoned so wonderful. And I see men become mad and demented from no manifest cause, and at the same time doing many things out of place; and I have known many persons in sleep groaning and crying out, some in a state of suffocation, some jumping up and fleeing out of doors, and deprived of their reason until they awaken, and afterward becoming well and rational as before, although they be pale and weak; and this will happen not once but frequently. And there are many and various things of the like kind, which it would be tedious to state particularly.

They who first referred this malady to the gods appear to me to have been just such persons as the conjurors, purificators, mountebanks, and charlatans now are, who give themselves out for being excessively religious, and as knowing more than other people. Such persons, then, using the divinity as a pretext and screen of their own inability to afford any assistance, have given out that the disease is sacred, adding suitable reasons for this opinion, they have instituted a mode of treatment which is safe for themselves, namely, by applying purifications and incantations, and enforcing abstinence from baths and many articles of food which are unwholesome to men in diseases. Of sea substances, the surmullet, the blacktail, the mullet, and the eel; for these are the fishes most to be guarded against. And of fleshes, those of the goat, the stag, the sow, and the dog: for these are the kinds of flesh which are aptest to disorder the bowels. Of fowls, the cock, the turtle, and the bustard, and such others as are reckoned to be particularly strong. And of potherbs, mint, garlic, and onions; for what is acrid does not agree with a weak person. And they forbid to have a black robe, because black is expressive of death; and to sleep on a goat's skin, or to wear it, and to put one foot upon another, or one hand upon another; for all these things are held to be hindrances to the cure. All these they enjoin with reference to its divinity, as if possessed of more knowledge, and announcing beforehand other causes so that if the person should recover, theirs would be the honor and credit; and if he should die, they would have a certain defense, as if the gods, and not they, were to blame, seeing they had administered nothing either to eat or drink as medicines, nor had overheated him with baths, so as to prove the cause of what had happened. But I am of opinion that (if this were true) none of the Libyans, who live in the interior, would be free from this disease, since they all sleep on goats' skins, and live upon goats' flesh; neither have they couch, robe, nor shoe that is not made of goat's skin, for they have no other herds but goats and oxen. But if these things, when administered in food, aggravate the disease, and if it be cured by abstinence from them, godhead is not the cause at all; nor will purifications be of any avail, but it is the food which is beneficial and prejudicial, and the influence of the divinity vanishes.

Thus, they who try to cure these maladies in this way, appear to me neither to reckon them sacred nor divine. For when they are removed by such purifications, and this method of cure, what is to prevent them from being brought upon men and induced by other devices similar to these? So that the cause is no longer divine, but human. For whoever is able, by purifications and conjurations, to drive away such an affection, will be able, by other practices, to excite it; and, according to this view, its divine nature is entirely done away with. By such sayings and doings, they profess to be possessed of superior knowledge, and deceive mankind by enjoining lustrations and purifications upon them, while their discourse turns upon the divinity and the godhead. And yet it would appear to me that their discourse savors not of piety, as they suppose, but rather of impiety, and as if there were no gods, and that what they hold to be holy and divine, were impious and unholy. This I will now explain.

For, if they profess to know how to bring down the moon, darken the sun, induce storms and fine weather, and rains and droughts, and make the sea and land unproductive, and so forth, whether they arrogate this power as being derived from mysteries or any other knowledge or consideration, they appear to me to practice impiety, and either to fancy that there are no gods, or, if there are, that they have no ability to ward off any of the greatest evils. How, then, are they not enemies to the gods? For if a man by magical arts and sacrifices will bring down the moon, and darken the sun, and induce storms, or fine weather, I should not believe that there was anything divine, but human, in these things, provided the power of the divine were overpowered by human knowledge and subjected to it. But perhaps it will be said, these things are not so, but, men being in want of the means of life, invent many and various things, and devise many contrivances for all other things, and for this disease, in every phase of the disease, assigning the cause to a god. Nor do they remember the same things once, but frequently. For, if they imitate a goat, or grind their teeth, or if their right side be convulsed, they say that the mother of the gods is the cause. But if they speak in a sharper and more intense tone, they resemble this state to a horse, and say that Poseidon is the cause. Or if any excrement be passed, which is often the case, owing to the violence of the disease, the appellation of Enodia is adhibited; or, if it be passed in smaller and denser masses, like bird's, it is said to be from Apollo Nomius. But if foam be emitted by the mouth, and the patient kick with his feet, Ares then gets the blame. But terrors which happen during the night, and fevers, and delirium, and jumpings

out of bed, and frightful apparitions, and fleeing away,—all these they hold to be the plots of Hecate, and the invasions of the Heroes, and use purifications and incantations, and, as appears to me, make the divinity to be most wicked and most impious. For they purify those laboring under this disease, with the same sorts of blood and the other means that are used in the case of those who are stained with crimes, and of malefactors, or who have been enchanted by men, or who have done any wicked act; who ought to do the very reverse, namely, sacrifice and pray, and, bringing gifts to the temples, supplicate the gods. But now they do none of these things, but purify; and some of the purifications they conceal in the earth, and some they throw into the sea, and some they carry to the mountains where no one can touch or tread upon them. But these they ought to take to the temples and present to the god, if a god be the cause of the disease. Neither truly do I count it a worthy opinion to hold that the body of man is polluted by god, the most impure by the most holy; for were it defiled, or did it suffer from any other thing, it would be like to be purified and sanctified rather than polluted by god. For it is the divinity which purifies and sanctifies the greatest of offenses and the most wicked, and which proves our protection from them. And we mark out the boundaries of the temples and the groves of the gods, so that no one may pass them unless he be pure, and when we enter them we are sprinkled with holy water, not as being polluted, but as laying aside any other pollution which we formerly had. And thus it appears to me to hold, with regard to purifications.

But this disease seems to me to be no more divine than others; but it has its nature such as other diseases have, and a cause whence it originates, and its nature and cause are divine only just as much as all others are, and it is curable no less than the others, unless when, from length of time, it is confirmed, and has became stronger than the remedies applied. Its origin is hereditary, like that of other diseases. For if a phlegmatic person be born of a phlegmatic, and a bilious of a bilious, and a phthisical of a phthisical, and one having spleen disease, of another having disease of the spleen, what is to hinder it from happening that where the father and mother were subject to this disease, certain of their offspring should be so affected also? As the semen comes from all parts of the body, healthy particles will come from healthy parts, and unhealthy from unhealthy parts. And another great proof that it is in nothing more divine than other diseases is, that it occurs in those who are of a phlegmatic constitution, but does not attack the bilious. Yet, if it were more divine than the others, this disease ought to befall all alike, and make no distinction between the bilious and phlegmatic.

But the brain is the cause of this affection, as it is of other very great diseases, and in what manner and from what cause it is formed, I will now plainly declare. The brain of man, as in all other animals, is double, and a thin membrane divides it through the middle, and therefore the pain is not always in the same part of the head; for sometimes it is situated on either side, and sometimes the whole is affected; and veins run toward it from all parts of the body, many of which are small, but two are thick,— the one from the liver, and the other from the spleen. And it is thus with regard to the one from the liver: a portion of it runs downward through the parts on the right side, near the kidneys and the psoas muscles, to the inner part of the thigh, and extends to the foot. It is called vena cava. The other runs upward by the right veins and the lungs, and divides into branches for the heart and the right arm. The remaining part of it rises upward across the clavicle to the right side of the neck, and is superficial so as to be seen; near the ear it is concealed, and there it divides; its thickest, largest, and most hollow part ends in the brain; another small vein goes to the right ear, another to the right eye, and another to the nostril. Such are the distributions of the hepatic vein. And a vein from the spleen is distributed on the left side, upward and downward, like that from the liver, but more slender and feeble.

By these veins we draw in much breath, since they are the spiracles of our bodies inhaling air to themselves and distributing it to the rest of the body, and to the smaller veins, and they cool and afterwards exhale it. For the breath cannot be stationary, but it passes upward and downward, for if stopped and intercepted, the part where it is stopped becomes powerless. In proof of this, when, in sitting or lying, the small veins are compressed, so that the breath from the larger vein does not pass into them, the part is immediately seized with numbness; and it is so likewise with regard to the other veins.

This malady, then, affects phlegmatic people, but not bilious. It begins to be formed while the fœtus is still *in utero*. For the brain, like the other organs, is depurated and grows before birth. If, then, in this purgation it be properly and moderately depurated, and neither more nor less than what is proper be secreted from it, the head is thus in the most healthy condition. If the secretion (melting) from the whole brain be greater than natural, the person, when he grows up, will have his head diseased, and full of noises, and will neither be able to endure the sun nor cold. Or, if the melting take place from any one part, either from the eye or ear, or if a vein has become slender, that part will be deranged in proportion to the melting. Or, should depuration not take place, but congestion accumulate in the brain, it necessarily becomes phlegmatic. And such children as have an eruption of ulcers on the head, on the ears, and along the rest of the body, with copious discharges of saliva and mucus,—these, in after life, enjoy best health; for in this way the phlegm which ought to have been purged off in the womb, is discharged and cleared away, and persons so purged, for the most part, are not subject to attacks of this disease. But such as have had their skin free from eruptions, and have had no discharge of saliva or mucus, nor have undergone the proper purgation in the womb, these persons run the risk of being seized with this disease.

But should the defluxion make its way to the heart, the person is seized with palpitation and asthma, the chest becomes diseased, and some also have curvature of the spine. For when a defluxion of cold phlegm takes place on the lungs and heart, the blood is chilled, and the veins, being violently chilled, palpitate in the lungs and heart, and the heart palpitates, so that from this necessity asthma and orthopnœa supervene. For it does not receive the spirits as much breath as he needs until the defluxion of phlegm be mastered, and being heated is distributed to the veins, then it ceases from its palpitation and difficulty of breathing, and this takes place as soon as it obtains an abundant supply; and this will be more slowly, provided the defluxion be more abundant, or if it be less, more quickly. And if the defluxions be more condensed, the epileptic attacks will be more frequent, but otherwise if it be rarer. Such are the symptoms when the defluxion is upon the lungs and heart; but if it be upon the bowels, the person is attacked with diarrhœa.

And if, being shut out from all these outlets, its defluxion be determined to the veins I have formerly mentioned, the patient loses his speech, and chokes, and foam issues by the mouth, the teeth are fixed, the hands are contracted, the eyes distorted, he becomes insensible, and in some cases the bowels are evacuated. And these symptoms occur sometimes on the left side, sometimes on the right, and sometimes in both. The cause of every one of these symptoms I will now explain. The man becomes speechless when the phlegm, suddenly descending into the veins, shuts out the air, and does not admit it either to the brain or to the vena cava, or to the ventricles, but interrupts the inspiration. For when a person draws in air by the mouth and nostrils, the breath goes first to the brain, then the greater part of it to the internal cavity, and part to the lungs, and part to the veins, and from them it is distributed to the other parts of the body along the veins; and whatever passes to the stomach cools, and does nothing more; and so also with regard to the lungs. But the air which enters the veins is of use (to the body) by entering the brain and its ventricles, and thus it imparts sensibility and motion to all the members, so that when the veins are excluded from the air by the phlegm and do not receive it, the man loses his speech and intellect, and the hands become powerless, and are contracted, the blood stopping and not being diffused, as it was wont; and the eyes are distorted owing to the veins being excluded from the air; and they palpitate; and froth from the lungs issues by the mouth. For when the breath does not find entrance to him, he foams and sputters like a dying person. And the bowels are evacuated in consequence of the violent suffocation; and the suffocation is produced when the liver and stomach ascend to the diaphragm, and the mouth of the stomach is shut up; this takes place when the breath does not enter by the mouth, as it is wont. The patient kicks with his feet when the air is shut up in the lungs and cannot find an outlet, owing to the phlegm; and rushing by the blood upward and downward, it occasions convulsions and pain, and therefore he kicks with his feet. All these symptoms he endures when the cold phlegm passes into the warm blood, for it congeals and stops the blood. And if the deflexion be copious and thick, it immediately proves fatal to him, for by its cold it prevails over the blood and congeals it; or, if it be less, it in the first place obtains the mastery, and stops the respiration; and then in the course of time, when it is diffused along the veins and mixed with much warm blood, it is thus overpowered, the veins receive the air, and the patient recovers his senses.

Of little children who are seized with this disease, the greater part die, provided the defluxion be copious and humid, for the veins being slender cannot admit the phlegm, owing to its thickness and abundance; but the blood is cooled and congealed, and the child immediately dies. But if the phlegm be in small quantity, and make a defluxion into both the veins, or to those on either side, the children survive, but exhibit notable marks of the disorder; for either the mouth is drawn aside, or an eye, the neck, or a hand, wherever a vein being filled with phlegm loses its tone, and is attenuated, and the part of the body connected with this vein is necessarily rendered weaker and defective. But for the most it affords relief for a longer interval; for the child is no longer seized with these attacks, if once it has contracted this impress of the disease, in consequence of which the other veins are necessarily affected, and to a certain degree attenuated, so as just to admit the air, but no longer to permit the influx of phlegm. However, the parts are proportionally enfeebled whenever the veins are in an unhealthy state. When in striplings the defluxion is small and to the right side, they recover without leaving any marks of the disease, but there is danger of its becoming habitual, and even increasing if not treated by suitable remedies. Thus, or very nearly so, is the case when it attacks children.

To persons of a more advanced age, it neither proves fatal, nor produces distortions. For their veins are capacious and are filled with hot blood; and therefore the phlegm can neither prevail nor cool the blood, so as to coagulate it, but it is quickly overpowered and mixed with the blood, and thus the veins receive the air, and sensibility remains; and, owing to their strength, the aforesaid symptoms are less likely to seize them. But when this disease attacks very old people, it therefore proves fatal, or induces paraplegia, because the veins are empty, and the blood scanty, thin, and watery. When, therefore, the defluxion is copious, and the season winter, it proves fatal; for it chokes up the exhalents, and coagulates the blood if the defluxion be to both sides; but if to either, it merely induces paraplegia. For the blood being thin, cold, and scanty, cannot prevail over the phlegm, but being itself overpowered, it is coagulated, so that those parts in which the blood is corrupted, lose their strength.

The flux is to the right rather than to the left because the veins there are more capacious and numerous than on the left side, for on the one side they spring from the liver, and on the other from the spleen. The defluxion and melting down take place most especially in the case of children in whom the head is heated either by the sun or by fire, or if the brain suddenly contract a rigor, and then the phlegm is excreted. For it is melted down by the heat and diffusion of the brain, but it is excreted by the congealing and contracting of it, and thus a defluxion takes place. And in some this is the cause of the disease, and in others, when the south wind quickly succeeds to northern breezes, it suddenly unbinds and relaxes the brain, which is contracted and weak, so that there is an inundation of phlegm, and thus the defluxion takes place. The defluxion also takes place in consequence of fear, from any hidden cause, if we are frightened at any person's calling aloud, or while crying, when one cannot quickly recover one's breath, such as often happens to children. When any of these things occur, the body immediately shivers, the person becoming speechless cannot draw his breath, but the breath (*pneuma*) stops, the brain is contracted, the blood stands still, and thus the excretion and defluxion of the phlegm take place. In children, these are the causes of the attack at first. But to old persons winter is most inimical. For when the head and brain have been heated at a great fire, and then the person is brought into cold and has a rigor, or when from cold he comes into warmth, and sits at the fire, he is apt to suffer in the same way, and thus he is seized in the manner described above. And there is much danger of the same thing occurring, if in spring his head be exposed to the sun, but less so in summer, as the changes are not sudden. When a person has passed the twentieth year of his life, this disease is not apt to seize him, unless it has become habitual from childhood, or at least this is rarely or never the case. For the veins are filled with blood, and the brain consistent and firm, so that it does not run down into the veins, or if it do, it does not master the blood, which is copious and hot.

But when it has gained strength from one's childhood, and become habitual, such a person usually suffers attacks, and is seized with them in changes of the winds, especially in south winds, and it is difficult of removal. For the brain becomes more humid than natural, and is inundated with phlegm, so that the defluxions become more frequent, and the phlegm can no longer be excreted, nor the brain be dried up, but it becomes wet and humid. This you may ascertain in particular, from beasts of the flock which are seized with this disease, and more especially goats, for they are most frequently attacked with it. If you will cut open the head, you will find the brain humid, full of sweat, and having a bad smell. And in this way truly you may see that it is not a god that injures the body, but disease. And so it is with man. For when the disease has prevailed for a length of time, it is no longer curable, as the brain is corroded by the phlegm, and melted, and what is melted down becomes water, and surrounds the brain externally, and overflows it; wherefore they are more frequently and readily seized with the disease. And therefore the disease is protracted, because the influx is thin, owing to its quantity, and is immediately overpowered by the blood and heated all through.

But such persons as are habituated to the disease know beforehand when they are about to be seized and flee from men; if their own house be at hand, they run home, but if not, to a deserted place, where as few persons as possible will see them falling, and they immediately cover themselves up. This they do from shame of the affection, and not from fear of the divinity, as many suppose. And little children at first fall down wherever they may happen to be, from inexperience. But when they have been often seized, and feel its approach beforehand, they flee to their mothers, or to any other person they are acquainted with, from terror and dread of the affection, for being still infants they do not know yet what it is to be ashamed.

Therefore, they are attacked during changes of the winds, and especially south winds, then also with north winds, and afterwards also with the others. These are the strongest winds, and the most opposed to one another, both as to direction and power. For, the north wind condenses the air, and separates from it whatever is muddy and nebulous, and renders it clearer and brighter, and so in like manner also, all the winds which arise from the sea and other waters; for they extract the humidity and nebulosity from all objects, and from men themselves, and therefore it (the north wind) is the most wholesome of the winds. But the effects of the south are the very reverse. For in the first place it begins by melting and diffusing the condensed air, and therefore it does not blow strong at first, but is gentle at the commencement, because it is not able at once to overcome the dense and compacted air, which yet in a while it dissolves. It produces the same effects upon the land, the sea, the rivers, the fountains, the wells, and on every production which contains humidity, and this, there is in all things, some more, some less. For all these feel the effects of this wind, and from clear they become cloudy, from cold, hot; from dry, moist; and whatever earthen vessels are placed upon the ground, filled with wine or any other fluid, are affected with the south wind, and undergo a change. And the sun, the moon, and the stars it renders blunter in appearance than they naturally are. When, then, it possesses such powers over things so great and strong, and the body is made to feel and undergo changes in the changes of the winds, it necessarily follows that the brain should be dissolved and overpowered with moisture, and that the veins should become more relaxed by the south winds, and that by the north the healthiest portion of the brain should become contracted, while the most morbid and humid is secreted, and overflows externally, and that catarrhs should thus take place in the changes of these winds. Thus is this disease formed and prevails from those things which enter into and go out of the body, and it is not more difficult to understand or to cure than the others, neither is it more divine than other diseases.

Men ought to know that from nothing else but the brain come joys, delights, laughter and sports, and sorrows, griefs, despondency, and lamentations. And by this, in an especial manner, we acquire wisdom and knowledge, and see and hear, and know what are foul and what are fair, what are bad and what are good, what are sweet, and what unsavory; some we discriminate by habit, and some we perceive by their utility. By this we distinguish objects of relish and disrelish, according to the seasons; and the same things do not always please us. And by the same organ we become mad and delirious, and fears and terrors assail us, some by night, and some by day, and dreams and untimely wanderings, and cares that are not suitable, and ignorance of present circumstances, desuetude, and unskilfulness. All these things we endure from the brain, when it is not healthy, but is more hot, more cold, more moist, or more dry than natural, or when it suffers any other preternatural and unusual affection. And we become mad from its humidity. For when it is more moist than natural, it is necessarily put into motion, and the affection being moved, neither the sight nor hearing can be at rest, and the tongue speaks in accordance with the sight and hearing.

As long as the brain is at rest, the man enjoys his reason, but the depravement of the brain arises from phlegm and bile, either of which you may recognize in this manner: Those who are mad from phlegm are quiet, and do not cry out nor make a noise; but those from bile are vociferous, malignant, and will not be quiet, but are always doing something im-

proper. If the madness be constant, these are the causes thereof. But if terrors and fears assail, they are connected with derangement of the brain, and derangement is owing to its being heated. And it is heated by bile when it is determined to the brain along the bloodvessels running from the trunk; and fear is present until it returns again to the veins and trunk, when it ceases. He is grieved and troubled when the brain is unseasonably cooled and contracted beyond its wont. This it suffers from phlegm, and from the same affection the patient becomes oblivious. He calls out and screams at night when the brain is suddenly heated. The bilious endure this. But the phlegmatic are not heated, except when much blood goes to the brain, and creates an ebullition. Much blood passes along the aforesaid veins. But when the man happens to see a frightful dream and is in fear as if awake, then his face is in a greater glow, and the eyes are red when the patient is in fear. And the understanding meditates doing some mischief, and thus it is affected in sleep. But if, when awakened, he returns to himself, and the blood is again distributed along the veins, it ceases.

In these ways I am of the opinion that the brain exercises the greatest power in the man. This is the interpreter to us of those things which emanate from the air, when the brain happens to be in a sound state. But the air supplies sense to it. And the eyes, the ears, the tongue and the feet, administer such things as the brain cogitates. For inasmuch as it is supplied with air, does it impart sense to the body. It is the brain which is the messenger to the understanding. For when the man draws the breath into himself, it passes first to the brain, and thus the air is distributed to the rest of the body, leaving in the brain its acme, and whatever has sense and understanding. For if it passed first to the body and last to the brain, then having left in the flesh and veins the judgment, when it reached the brain it would be hot, and not at all pure, but mixed with the humidity from flesh and blood, so as to be no longer pure.

Wherefore, I say, that it is the brain which interprets the understanding. But the diaphragm has obtained its name (φρένες) from accident and usage, and not from reality or nature, for I know no power which it possesses, either as to sense or understanding, except that when the man is affected with unexpected joy or sorrow, it throbs and produces palpitations, owing to its thinness, and as having no belly to receive anything good or bad that may present themselves to it, but it is thrown into commotion by both these, from its natural weakness. It then perceives beforehand none of those things which occur in the body, but has received its name vaguely and without any proper reason, like the parts about the heart, which are called auricles, but which contribute nothing towards hearing. Some say that we think with the heart, and that this is the part which is grieved, and experiences care. But it is not so; only it contracts like the diaphragm, and still more so for the same causes. For veins from all parts of the body run to it, and it has valves, so as to perceive if any pain or pleasurable emotion befall the man. For when grieved the body necessarily shudders, and is contracted, and from excessive joy it is affected in like manner. Wherefore the heart and the diaphragm are particularly sensitive, they have nothing to do, however, with the operations of the understanding, but of all these the brain is the cause. Since, then, the brain, as being the primary seat of sense and of the spirits, perceives whatever occurs in the body, if any change more powerful than usual take place in the air, owing to the seasons, the brain becomes changed by the state of the air. For, on this account, the brain first perceives, because, I say, all the most acute, most powerful, and most deadly diseases, and those which are most difficult to be understood by the inexperienced, fall upon the brain.

And the disease called the Sacred arises from causes as the others, namely, those things which enter and quit the body, such as cold, the sun, and the winds, which are ever changing and are never at rest. And these things are divine, so that there is no necessity for making a distinction, and holding this disease to be more divine than the others, but all are divine, and all human. And each has its own peculiar nature and power, and none is of an ambiguous nature, or irremediable. And the most of them are curable by the same means as those by which they were produced. For any other thing is food to one, and injurious to another. Thus, then, the physician should understand and distinguish the season of each, so that at one time he may attend to the nourishment and increase, and at another to abstraction and diminution. And in this disease as in all others, he must strive not to feed the disease, but endeavor to wear it out by administering whatever is most opposed to each disease, and not that which favors and is allied to it. For by that which is allied to it, it gains vigor and increase, but it wears out and disappears under the use of that which is opposed to it. But whoever is acquainted with such a change in men, and can render a man humid and dry, hot and cold by regimen, could also cure this disease, if he recognizes the proper season for administering his remedies, without minding purifications, spells, and all other illiberal practices of a like kind.

GALEN
ON THE NATURAL FACULTIES

BIOGRAPHICAL NOTE

GALEN, *c.* A.D. 130–*c.* 200

GALEN the physician was born at Pergamum, the capital of Mysia in Asia Minor, which had once been a center of art and learning and which still possessed at the time of Galen's birth the second greatest library in the ancient world and a temple of Æsculapius. His father was an architect or engineer, "amiable, just, worthy, and benevolent"; his mother "had a very bad temper, at times used to bite her serving-maids, and was forever shouting at my father and quarrelling with him—worse than Xanthippe with Socrates." "When I compared the excellence of my father's disposition with the disgraceful passions of my mother," Galen wrote, "I resolved to love and imitate the former qualities and to hate and avoid the latter."

The father provided a liberal education for his son, and by the age of seventeen or eighteen Galen was familiar with the Platonic, Aristotelian, Stoic, and Epicurean philosophies. About this time, in obedience to a dream of his father, he began the study of medicine in his native city. When he fell ill from overwork, he kept a careful record of his symptoms. After his father's death, he left Pergamum for Smyrna in order to study with Pelops the physician and Albinus the peripatetic. In search of more knowledge he roamed through Greece, Cilicia, Phoenicia, Palestine, Crete, Cyprus, and finally visited the famous medical school at Alexandria, which was still the best place to learn anatomy, although the dissection of the human body was no longer allowed.

On his return to Pergamum in 157-158, Galen was appointed physician and surgeon to the gladiators; he supervised their diet and treated their wounds. He also had a private practice, continued the study of philosophy, and wrote the first of his many treatises.

In the first years of the reign of Marcus Aurelius, Galen went to Rome, where he soon acquired fame as a physician and as a philosopher. He healed the celebrated Aristotelian, Eudemus, and other persons of distinction, and by his learning attracted to his lectures many of the most eminent people of Rome, including the consul Flavius Boethus. His success earned for him the titles of "Paradoxologus," the wonder-speaker, and "Paradoxopoeus," the wonder-worker.

Despite his name, meaning "gentle" or "peaceful," and his disapproval of his mother's temper, Galen was an incessant critic of the contemporary medical sects then flourishing in Rome. He opposed all fads and cults, the tyranny of theory and the contempt of theory, and every doctor who lost sight of what he held to be the Hippocratic teaching on the unity of the living organism and the force of "what nature does." The enmities he incurred by polemical activity may have caused his sudden departure from Rome in 168 and retirement to Pergamum. He was soon recalled by imperial command. Marcus Aurelius, who was one of his patients, desired his attendance for the campaigns against the Germans. But Galen did not wish to go and in the end was allowed to remain at Rome as physician to Commodus, the young heir to the throne.

Little is known of Galen after this appointment. He certainly devoted much of his time to writing. He left five hundred treatises written in clear Attic Greek. One of them argued "That the best Physician is also a Philosopher," and many of his own works dealt with philosophical problems. In his *De Libris propriis* he mentions one hundred and twenty-four philosophical treatises, which include commentaries on the *Categories* and *Analytics* of Aristotle, and on the *Timæus* and *Philebus* of Plato. He also wrote five treatises on Ancient Comedy. Only fragments remain of his non-medical writings. Of the surviving medical works some eighty or ninety are believed to have been written by him; sixty-five are of doubtful authorship or certainly spurious. Fifteen of his commentaries on the Hippocratic works are extant.

Galen was apparently in Rome during the fire of 191, when his library burned, and he was still lecturing and practising during the reign of Pertinax. He may have spent his last years as physician-in-ordinary to the emperor. He died at the turn of the century.

Contents

GALEN
ON THE NATURAL FACULTIES

Book One

1. Since feeling and voluntary motion are peculiar to animals, whilst growth and nutrition are common to plants as well, we may look on the former as effects of the soul and the latter as effects of the nature. And if there be anyone who allows a share in soul to plants as well, and separates the two kinds of soul, naming the kind in question vegetative, and the other sensory, this person is not saying anything else, although his language is somewhat unusual. We, however, for our part, are convinced that the chief merit of language is clearness, and we know that nothing detracts so much from this as do unfamiliar terms; accordingly we employ those terms which the bulk of people are accustomed to use, and we say that animals are governed at once by their soul and by their nature, and plants by their nature alone, and that growth and nutrition are the effects of nature, not of soul.

2. Thus we shall enquire, in the course of this treatise, from what faculties these effects themselves, as well as any other effects of nature which there may be, take their origin.

First, however, we must distinguish and explain clearly the various terms which we are going to use in this treatise, and to what things we apply them; and this will prove to be not merely an explanation of terms but at the same time a demonstration of the effects of nature.

When, therefore, such and such a body undergoes no change from its existing state, we say that it is at rest; but, if it departs from this in any respect we then say that in this respect it undergoes motion. Accordingly, when it departs in various ways from its pre-existing state, it will be said to undergo various kinds of motion. Thus, if that which is white becomes black, or what is black becomes white, it undergoes motion in respect to colour; or if what was previously sweet now becomes bitter, or, conversely, from being bitter now becomes sweet, it will be said to undergo motion in respect to flavour; to both of these instances, as well as to

those previously mentioned, we shall apply the term qualitative motion. And further, it is not only things which are altered in regard to colour and flavour which, we say, undergo motion; when a warm thing becomes cold, and a cold warm, here too we speak of its undergoing motion; similarly also when anything moist becomes dry, or dry moist. Now, the common term which we apply to all these cases is alteration.

This is one kind of motion. But there is another kind which occurs in bodies which change their position, or as we say, pass from one place to another; the name of this is transference.

These two kinds of motion, then, are simple and primary, while compounded from them we have growth and decay, as when a small thing becomes bigger, or a big thing smaller, each retaining at the same time its particular form. And two other kinds of motion are genesis and destruction, genesis being a coming into existence, and destruction being the opposite.

Now, common to all kinds of motion is change from the pre-existing state, while common to all conditions of rest is retention of the pre-existing state. The Sophists, however, while allowing that bread in turning into blood becomes changed as regards sight, taste, and touch, will not agree that this change occurs in reality. Thus some of them hold that all such phenomena are tricks and illusions of our senses; the senses, they say, are affected now in one way, now in another, whereas the underlying susbtance does not admit of any of these changes to which the names are given. Others (such as Anaxagoras) will have it that the qualities do exist in it, but that they are unchangeable and immutable from eternity to eternity, and that these apparent alterations are brought about by separation and combination.

Now, if I were to go out of my way to confute these people, my subsidiary task would be greater than my main one. Thus, if they do not know all that has been written, "On Complete

Alteration of Substance" by Aristotle, and after him by Chrysippus, I must beg of them to make themselves familiar with these men's writings. If, however, they know these, and yet willingly prefer the worse views to the better, they will doubtless consider my arguments foolish also. I have shown elsewhere that these opinions were shared by Hippocrates, who lived much earlier than Aristotle. In fact, of all those known to us who have been both physicians and philosophers Hippocrates was the first who took in hand to demonstrate that there are, in all, four mutually interacting qualities, and that to the operation of these is due the genesis and destruction of all things that come into and pass out of being. Nay, more; Hippocrates was also the first to recognise that all these qualities undergo an intimate mingling with one another; and at least the beginnings of the proofs to which Aristotle later set his hand are to be found first in the writings of Hipprocates.

As to whether we are to suppose that the substances as well as their qualities undergo this intimate mingling, as Zeno of Citium afterwards declared, I do not think it necessary to go further into this question in the present treatise; for immediate purposes we only need to recognize the complete alteration of substance. In this way, nobody will suppose that bread represents a kind of meeting-place for bone, flesh, nerve, and all the other parts, and that each of these subsequently becomes separated in the body and goes to join its own kind; before any separation takes place, the whole of the bread obviously becomes blood; (at any rate, if a man takes no other food for a prolonged period, he will have blood enclosed in his veins all the same). And clearly this disproves the view of those who consider the elements unchangeable, as also, for that matter, does the oil which is entirely used up in the flame of the lamp, or the faggots which, in a somewhat longer time, turn into fire.

I said, however, that I was not going to enter into an argument with these people, and it was only because the example was drawn from the subject-matter of medicine, and because I need it for the present treatise, that I have mentioned it. We shall then, as I said, renounce our controversy with them, since those who wish may get a good grasp of the views of the ancients from our own personal investigations into these matters.

The discussion which follows we shall devote entirely, as we originally proposed, to an enquiry into the number and character of the faculties of Nature, and what is the effect which each naturally produces. Now, of course, I mean by an effect that which has already come into existence and has been completed by the activity of these faculties—for example, blood, flesh, or nerve. And activity is the name I give to the active change or motion, and the cause of this I call a faculty. Thus, when food turns into blood, the motion of the food is passive, and that of the vein active. Similarly, when the limbs have their position altered, it is the muscle which produces, and the bones which undergo the motion. In these cases I call the motion of the vein and of the muscle an activity, and that of the food and the bones a symptom or affection, since the first group undergoes alteration and the second group is merely transported. One might, therefore, also speak of the activity as an effect of Nature—for example, digestion, absorption, blood-production; one could not, however, in every case call the effect an activity; thus flesh is an effect of Nature, but it is, of course, not an activity. It is, therefore, clear that one of these terms is used in two senses, but not the other.

3. It appears to me, then, that the vein, as well as each of the other parts, functions in such and such a way according to the manner in which the four qualities are mixed. There are, however, a considerable number of not undistinguished men—philosophers and physicians —who refer action to the Warm and the Cold, and who subordinate to these, as passive, the Dry and the Moist; Aristotle, in fact, was the first who attempted to bring back the causes of the various special activities to these principles, and he was followed later by the Stoic school. These latter, of course, could logically make active principles of the Warm and Cold, since they refer the change of the elements themselves into one another to certain diffusions and condensations. This does not hold of Aristotle, however; seeing that he employed the four qualities to explain the genesis of the elements, he ought properly to have also referred the causes of all the special activities to these. How is it that he uses the four qualities in his book "On Genesis and Destruction," whilst in his "Meteorology," his "Problems," and many other works he uses the two only? Of course, if anyone were to maintain that in the case of animals and plants the Warm and Cold are more active, the Dry and Moist less so, he might perhaps have even Hippocrates on his side; but if he were to say that this happens in all cases, he would, I imagine, lack support, not merely from Hippocrates, but even from Aristotle himself—if, at least, Aris-

totle chose to remember what he himself taught us in his work "On Genesis and Destruction," not as a matter of simple statement, but with an accompanying demonstration. I have, however, also investigated these questions, in so far as they are of value to a physician, in my work "On Temperaments."

4. The so-called blood-making faculty in the veins, then, as well as all the other faculties, fall within the category of relative concepts; primarily because the faculty is the cause of the activity, but also, accidentally, because it is the cause of the effect. But, if the cause is relative to something—for it is the cause of what results from it, and of nothing else—it is obvious that the faculty also falls into the category of the relative; and so long as we are ignorant of the true essence of the cause which is operating, we call it a faculty. Thus we say that there exists in the veins a blood-making faculty, as also a digestive faculty in the stomach, a pulsatile faculty in the heart, and in each of the other parts a special faculty corresponding to the function or activity of that part. If, therefore, we are to investigate methodically the number and kinds of faculties, we must begin with the effects; for each of these effects comes from a certain activity, and each of these again is preceded by a cause.

5. The effects of Nature, then, while the animal is still being formed in the womb, are all the different parts of its body; and after it has been born, an effect in which all parts share is the progress of each to its full size, and thereafter its maintenance of itself as long as possible.

The activities corresponding to the three effects mentioned are necessarily three—one to each—namely, Genesis, Growth, and Nutrition. Genesis, however, is not a simple activity of Nature, but is compounded of alteration and of shaping. That is to say, in order that bone, nerve, veins, and all other [tissues] may come into existence, the underlying substance from which the animal springs must be altered; and in order that the substance so altered may acquire its appropriate shape and position, its cavities, outgrowths, attachments, and so forth, it has to undergo a shaping or formative process. One would be justified in calling this substance which undergoes alteration the material of the animal, just as wood is the material of a ship, and wax of an image.

Growth is an increase and expansion in length, breadth, and thickness of the solid parts of the animal (those which have been subjected to the moulding or shaping process). Nutrition is an addition to these, without expansion.

6. Let us speak then, in the first place, of Genesis, which, as we have said, results from alteration together with shaping.

The seed having been cast into the womb or into the earth (for there is no difference), then, after a certain definite period, a great number of parts become constituted in the substance which is being generated; these differ as regards moisture, dryness, coldness and warmth, and in all the other qualities which naturally derive therefrom. These derivative qualities, you are acquainted with, if you have given any sort of scientific consideration to the question of genesis and destruction. For, first and foremost after the qualities mentioned come the other so-called tangible distinctions, and after them those which appeal to taste, smell, and sight. Now, tangible distinctions are hardness and softness, viscosity, friability, lightness, heaviness, density, rarity, smoothness, roughness, thickness and thinness; all of these have been duly mentioned by Aristotle. And of course you know those which appeal to taste, smell, and sight. Therefore, if you wish to know which alterative faculties are primary and elementary, they are moisture, dryness, coldness, and warmth, and if you wish to know which ones arise from the combination of these, they will be found to be in each animal of a number corresponding to its sensible elements. The name sensible elements is given to all the homogeneous parts of the body, and these are to be detected not by any system, but by personal observation of dissections.

Now Nature constructs bone, cartilage, nerve, membrane, ligament, vein, and so forth, at the first stage of the animal's genesis, employing at this task a faculty which is, in general terms, generative and alterative, and, in more detail, warming, chilling, drying, or moistening; or such as spring from the blending of these, for example, the bone-producing, nerve-producing, and cartilage-producing faculties (since for the sake of clearness these names must be used as well).

Now the peculiar flesh of the liver is of this kind as well, also that of the spleen, that of the kidneys, that of the lungs, and that of the heart; so also the proper substance of the brain, stomach, gullet, intestines, and uterus is a sensible element, of similar parts all through, simple, and uncompounded. That is to say, if you remove from each of the organs mentioned its arteries, veins, and nerves, the substance remaining in each organ is, from the point of view of the senses, simple and elementary. As regards those organs consisting of two dissimilar coats, of which each is simple, of these organs the coats are the elements—for example, the coats of the stomach, oesophagus, intestines, and arteries; each of these two coats has an alterative faculty peculiar to it, which has engendered it from the menstrual blood of the mother. Thus the special alterative faculties in each animal are of the same number as the elementary parts; and further, the activities must necessarily correspond each to one of the special parts, just as each part has its special use—for example, those ducts which extend from the kidneys into the bladder, and which are called ureters; for these are not arteries, since they do not pulsate nor do they consist of two coats; and they are not veins, since they neither contain blood, nor do their coats in any way resemble those of veins; from nerves they differ still more than from the structures mentioned.

"What, then, are they?" someone asks—as though every part must necessarily be either an artery, a vein, a nerve, or a complex of these, and as though the truth were not what I am now stating, namely, that every one of the various organs has its own particular substance. For in fact the two bladders—that which receives the urine, and that which receives the yellow bile—not only differ from all other organs, but also from one another. Further, the ducts which spring out like kinds of conduits from the gall-bladder and which pass into the liver have no resemblance either to arteries, veins or nerves. But these parts have been treated at a greater length in my work "On the Anatomy of Hippocrates," as well as elsewhere.

As for the actual substance of the coats of the stomach, intestine, and uterus, each of these has been rendered what it is by a special alterative faculty of Nature; while the bringing of these together, the combination therewith of the structures which are inserted into them, the outgrowth into the intestine,* the shape of the inner cavities, and the like, have all been determined by a faculty which we call the shaping or formative faculty; this faculty we also state to be artistic—nay, the best and highest art—doing everything for some purpose, so that there is nothing ineffective or superfluous, or capable of being better disposed. This, how-

* By this is meant the duodenum, considered as an outgrowth or prolongation of the stomach towards the intestines.

ever, I shall demonstrate in my work "On the Use of Parts."

7. Passing now to the faculty of Growth let us first mention that this, too, is present in the foetus in utero as is also the nutritive faculty, but that at that stage these two faculties are, as it were, handmaids to those already mentioned, and do not possess in themselves supreme authority. When, however, the animal has attained its complete size, then, during the whole period following its birth and until the acme is reached, the faculty of growth is predominant, while the alterative and nutritive faculties are accessory—in fact, act as its handmaids. What, then, is the property of this faculty of growth? To extend in every direction—that is to say, the solid parts of the body, the arteries, veins, nerves, bones, cartilages, membranes, ligaments, and the various coats which we have just called elementary, homogeneous, and simple. And I shall state in what way they gain this extension in every direction, first giving an illustration for the sake of clearness.

Children take the bladders of pigs, fill them with air, and then rub them on ashes near the fire, so as to warm, but not to injure them. This is a common game in the district of Ionia, and among not a few other nations. As they rub, they sing songs, to a certain measure, time, and rhythm, and all their words are an exhortation to the bladder to increase in size. When it appears to them fairly well distended, they again blow air into it and expand it further; then they rub it again. This they do several times, until the bladder seems to them to have become large enough. Now, clearly, in these doings of the children, the more the interior cavity of the bladder increases in size, the thinner, necessarily, does its substance become. But, if the children were able to bring nourishment to this thin part, then they would make the bladder big in the same way that Nature does. As it is, however, they cannot do what Nature does, for to imitate this is beyond the power not only of children, but of any one soever; it is a property of Nature alone.

It will now, therefore, be clear to you that nutrition is a necessity for growing things. For if such bodies were distended, but not at the same time nourished, they would take on a false appearance of growth, not a true growth. And further, to be distended in all directions belongs only to bodies whose growth is directed by Nature; for those which are distended by us undergo this distension in one direction but grow less in the others; it is impossible to find a body which will remain entire and not be torn through whilst we stretch it in the three dimensions. Thus Nature alone has the power to expand a body in all directions so that it remains unruptured and preserves completely its previous form.

Such then is growth, and it cannot occur without the nutriment which flows to the part and is worked up into it.

8. We have, then, it seems, arrived at the subject of Nutrition, which is the third and remaining consideration which we proposed at the outset. For, when the matter which flows to each part of the body in the form of nutriment is being worked up into it, this activity is nutrition, and its cause is the nutritive faculty. Of course, the kind of activity here involved is also an alteration, but not an alteration like that occurring at the stage of genesis. For in the latter case something comes into existence which did not exist previously, while in nutrition the inflowing material becomes assimilated to that which has already come into existence. Therefore, the former kind of alteration has with reason been termed genesis, and the latter, assimilation.

9. Now, since the three faculties of Nature have been exhaustively dealt with, and the animal would appear not to need any others (being possessed of the means for growing, for attaining completion, and for maintaining itself as long a time as possible), this treatise might seem to be already complete, and to constitute an exposition of all the faculties of Nature. If, however, one considers that it has not yet touched upon any of the parts of the animal (I mean the stomach, intestines, liver, and the like), and that it has not dealt with the faculties resident in these, it will seem as though merely a kind of introduction had been given to the practical parts of our teaching. For the whole matter is as follows: Genesis, growth, and nutrition are the first, and, so to say, the principal effects of Nature; similarly also the faculties which produce these effects—the first faculties—are three in number, and are the most dominating of all. But as has already been shown, these need the service both of each other, and of yet different faculties. Now, these which the faculties of generation and growth require have been stated. I shall now say what ones the nutritive faculty requires.

10. For I believe that I shall prove that the organs which have to do with the disposal of the nutriment, as also their faculties, exist for the sake of this nutritive faculty. For since the action of this faculty is assimilation, and it is impossible for anything to be assimilated by, and to change into anything else unless they already possess a certain community and affinity in their qualities, therefore, in the first place, any animal cannot naturally derive nourishment from any kind of food, and secondly, even in the case of those from which it can do so, it cannot do this at once. Therefore, by reason of this law, every animal needs several organs for altering the nutriment. For in order that the yellow may become red, and the red yellow, one simple process of alteration is required, but in order that the white may become black, and the black white, all the intermediate stages are needed. So also, a thing which is very soft cannot all at once become very hard, nor vice versa; nor, similarly can anything which has a very bad smell suddenly become quite fragrant, nor again, can the converse happen.

How, then, could blood ever turn into bone, without having first become, as far as possible, thickened and white? And how could bread turn into blood without having gradually parted with its whiteness and gradually acquired redness? Thus it is quite easy for blood to become flesh; for, if Nature thicken it to such an extent that it acquires a certain consistency and ceases to be fluid, it thus becomes original newly-formed flesh; but in order that blood may turn into bone, much time is needed and much elaboration and transformation of the blood. Further, it is quite clear that bread, and, more particularly lettuce, beet, and the like, require a great deal of alteration in order to become blood.

This, then, is one reason why there are so many organs concerned in the alteration of food. A second reason is the nature of the superfluities. For, as we are unable to draw any nourishment from grass, although this is possible for cattle, similarly we can derive nourishment from radishes, albeit not to the same extent as from meat; for almost the whole of the latter is mastered by our natures; it is transformed and altered and constituted useful blood; but, in the radish, what is appropriate and capable of being altered (and that only with difficulty, and with much labour) is the very smallest part; almost the whole of it is surplus matter, and passes through the digestive organs, only a very little being taken up into the veins as blood—nor is this itself entirely utilisable blood. Nature, therefore, had need of a second process of separation for the su-

perfluities in the veins. Moreover, these superfluities need, on the one hand, certain fresh
routes to conduct them to the outlets, so that
they may not spoil the useful substances, and
they also need certain reservoirs, as it were, in
which they are collected till they reach a sufficient quantity, and are then discharged.

Thus, then, you have discovered bodily parts
of a second kind, consecrated in this case to the
[removal of the] superfluities of the food.
There is, however, also a third kind, for carrying the pabulum in every direction; these are
like a number of roads intersecting the whole
body.

Thus there is one entrance—that through
the mouth—for all the various articles of food.
What receives nourishment, however, is not
one single part, but a great many parts, and
these widely separated; do not be surprised,
therefore, at the abundance of organs which
Nature has created for the purpose of nutrition.
For those of them which have to do with alteration prepare the nutriment suitable for each
part; others separate out the superfluities; some
pass these along, others store them up, others
excrete them; some, again, are paths for the
transit in all directions of the utilisable juices.
So, if you wish to gain a thorough acquaintance
with all the faculties of Nature, you will have
to consider each one of these organs.

Now in giving an account of these we must
begin with those effects of Nature, together
with their corresponding parts and faculties,
which are closely connected with the purpose
to be achieved.

11. Let us once more, then, recall the actual
purpose for which Nature has constructed all
these parts. Its name, as previously stated, is
nutrition, and the definition corresponding to
the name is: an assimilation of that which nourishes to that which receives nourishment. And
in order that this may come about, we must
assume a preliminary process of adhesion, and
for that, again, one of presentation. For whenever the juice which is destined to nourish any
of the parts of the animal is emitted from the
vessels, it is in the first place dispersed all
through this part, next it is presented, and next
it adheres, and becomes completely assimilated.

The so-called white [leprosy] shows the difference between assimilation and adhesion, in
the same way that the kind of dropsy which
some people call *anasarca* clearly distinguishes
presentation from adhesion. For, of course, the
genesis of such a dropsy does not come about

as do some of the conditions of atrophy and
wasting, from an insufficient supply of moisture; the flesh is obviously moist enough,—in
fact it is thoroughly saturated,—and each of
the solid parts of the body is in a similar condition. While, however, the nutriment conveyed
to the part does undergo presentation, it is still
too watery, and is not properly transformed
into a juice, nor has it acquired that viscous and
agglutinative quality which results from the
operation of innate heat; therefore, adhesion
cannot come about, since, owing to this abundance of thin, crude liquid, the pabulum runs off
and easily slips away from the solid parts of the
body. In white [leprosy], again, there is adhesion of the nutriment but no real assimilation.
From this it is clear that what I have just said
is correct, namely, that in that part which is to
be nourished there must first occur presentation, next adhesion, and finally assimilation
proper.

Strictly speaking, then, nutriment is that
which is actually nourishing, while the quasi-
nutriment which is not yet nourishing (e.g.
matter which is undergoing adhesion or presentation) is not, strictly speaking, nutriment, but
is so called only by an equivocation. Also, that
which is still contained in the veins, and still
more, that which is in the stomach, from the
fact that it is destined to nourish if properly
elaborated, has been called "nutriment." Similarly we call the various kinds of food "nutriment," not because they are already nourishing
the animal, nor because they exist in the same
state as the material which actually is nourishing it, but because they are able and destined
to nourish it if they be properly elaborated.

This was also what Hippocrates said, viz.,
"Nutriment is what is engaged in nourishing,
as also is quasi-nutriment, and what is destined
to be nutriment." For to that which is already
being assimilated he gave the name of nutriment; to the similar material which is being
presented or becoming adherent, the name of
quasi-nutriment; and to everything else—that
is, contained in the stomach and veins—the
name of destined nutriment.

12. It is quite clear, therefore, that nutrition
must necessarily be a process of assimilation of
that which is nourishing to that which is being
nourished. Some, however, say that this assimilation does not occur in reality, but is merely
apparent; these are the people who think that
Nature is not artistic, that she does not show
forethought for the animal's welfare, and that
she has absolutely no native powers whereby

she alters some substances, attracts others, and discharges others.

Now, speaking generally, there have arisen the following two sects in medicine and philosophy among those who have made any definite pronouncement regarding Nature. I speak, of course, of such of them as know what they are talking about, and who realize the logical sequence of their hypotheses, and stand by them; as for those who cannot understand even this, but who simply talk any nonsense that comes to their tongues, and who do not remain definitely attached either to one sect or the other— such people are not even worth mentioning.

What, then, are these sects, and what are the logical consequences of their hypotheses? The one class supposes that all substance which is subject to genesis and destruction is at once continuous and susceptible of alteration. The other school assumes substance to be unchangeable, unalterable, and subdivided into fine particles, which are separated from one another by empty spaces.

All people, therefore, who can appreciate the logical sequence of an hypothesis hold that, according to the second teaching, there does not exist any substance or faculty peculiar either to Nature or to Soul, but that these result from the way in which the primary corpuscles, which are unaffected by change, come together. According to the first-mentioned teaching, on the other hand, Nature is not posterior to the corpuscles, but is a long way prior to them and older than they; and therefore in their view it is Nature which puts together the bodies both of plants and animals; and this she does by virtue of certain faculties which she possesses —these being, on the one hand, attractive and assimilative of what is appropriate, and, on the other, expulsive of what is foreign. Further, she skilfully moulds everything during the stage of genesis; and she also provides for the creatures after birth, employing here other faculties again, namely, one of affection and forethought for offspring, and one of sociability and friendship for kindred. According to the other school, none of these things exist in the natures [of living things], nor is there in the soul any original innate idea, whether of agreement or difference, of separation or synthesis, of justice or injustice, of the beautiful or ugly; all such things, they say, arise in us from sensation and through sensation, and animals are steered by certain images and memories.

Some of these people have even expressly declared that the soul possesses no reasoning faculty, but that we are led like cattle by the impression of our senses, and are unable to refuse or dissent from anything. In their view, obviously, courage, wisdom, temperance, and self-control are all mere nonsense, we do not love either each other or our offspring, nor do the gods care anything for us. This school also despises dreams, birds, omens, and the whole of astrology, subjects with which we have dealt at greater length in another work, in which we discuss the views of Asclepiades the physician. Those who wish to do so may familiarize themselves with these arguments, and they may also consider at this point which of the two roads lying before us is the better one to take. Hippocrates took the first-mentioned. According to this teaching, substance is one and is subject to alteration; there is a consensus in the movements of air and fluid throughout the whole body; Nature acts throughout in an artistic and equitable manner, having certain faculties, by virtue of which each part of the body draws to itself the juice which is proper to it, and, having done so, attaches it to every portion of itself, and completely assimilates it; while such part of the juice as has not been mastered, and is not capable of undergoing complete alteration and being assimilated to the part which is being nourished, is got rid of by yet another (an expulsive) faculty.

13. Now the extent of exactitude and truth in the doctrines of Hippocrates may be gauged, not merely from the way in which his opponents are at variance with obvious facts, but also from the various subjects of natural research themselves—the functions of animals, and the rest. For those people who do not believe that there exists in any part of the animal a faculty for attracting its own special quality are compelled repeatedly to deny obvious facts. For instance, Asclepiades, the physician, did this in the case of the kidneys. That these are organs for secreting [separating out] the urine, was the belief not only of Hippocrates, Diocles, Erasistratus, Praxagoras, and all other physicians of eminence, but practically every butcher is aware of this, from the fact that he daily observes both the position of the kidneys and the duct (termed the ureter) which runs from each kidney into the bladder, and from this arrangement he infers their characteristic use and faculty. But, even leaving the butchers aside, all people who suffer either from frequent dysuria or from retention of urine call themselves "nephritics," when they feel pain in the loins and pass sandy matter in their water.

I do not suppose that Asclepiades ever saw a stone which had been passed by one of these sufferers, or observed that this was preceded by a sharp pain in the region between kidneys and bladder as the stone traversed the ureter, or that, when the stone was passed, both the pain and the retention at once ceased. It is worth while, then, learning how his theory accounts for the presence of urine in the bladder, and one is forced to marvel at the ingenuity of a man who puts aside these broad, clearly visible routes,* and postulates others which are narrow, invisible—indeed, entirely imperceptible. His view, in fact, is that the fluid which we drink passes into the bladder by being resolved into vapours, and that, when these have been again condensed, it thus regains its previous form, and turns from vapour into fluid. He simply looks upon the bladder as a sponge or a piece of wool, and not as the perfectly compact and impervious body that it is, with two very strong coats. For if we say that the vapours pass through these coats, why should they not pass through the peritoneum and the diaphragm, thus filling the whole abdominal cavity and thorax with water? "But," says he, "of course the peritoneal coat is more impervious than the bladder, and this is why it keeps out the vapours, while the bladder admits them." Yet if he had ever practised anatomy, he might have known that the outer coat of the bladder springs from the peritoneum and is essentially the same as it, and that the inner coat, which is peculiar to the bladder, is more than twice as thick as the former.

Perhaps, however, it is not the thickness or thinness of the coats, but the situation of the bladder, which is the reason for the vapours being carried into it? On the contrary, even if it were probable for every other reason that the vapours accumulate there, yet the situation of the bladder would be enough in itself to prevent this. For the bladder is situated below, whereas vapours have a natural tendency to rise upwards; thus they would fill all the region of the thorax and lungs long before they came to the bladder.

But why do I mention the situation of the bladder, peritoneum, and thorax? For surely, when the vapours have passed through the coats of the stomach and intestines, it is in the space between these and the peritoneum that they will collect and become liquefied (just as in dropsical subjects it is in this region that most of the water gathers). Otherwise the va-

* The ureters.

pours must necessarily pass straight forward through everything which in any way comes in contact with them, and will never come to a standstill. But, if this be assumed, then they will traverse not merely the peritoneum but also the epigastrium, and will become dispersed into the surrounding air; otherwise they will certainly collect under the skin.

Even these considerations, however, our present-day Asclepiadeans attempt to answer, despite the fact that they always get soundly laughed at by all who happen to be present at their disputations on these subjects—so difficult an evil to get rid of is this sectarian partizanship, so excessively resistant to all cleansing processes, harder to heal than any itch!

Thus, one of our Sophists who is a thoroughly hardened disputer and as skilful a master of language as there ever was, once got into a discussion with me on this subject; so far from being put out of countenance by any of the above-mentioned considerations, he even expressed his surprise that I should try to overturn obvious facts by ridiculous arguments! "For," said he, "one may clearly observe any day in the case of any bladder, that, if one fills it with water or air and then ties up its neck and squeezes it all round, it does not let anything out at any point, but accurately retains all its contents. And surely," said he, "if there were any large and perceptible channels coming into it from the kidneys the liquid would run out through these when the bladder was squeezed, in the same way that it entered?" Having abruptly made these and similar remarks in precise and clear tones, he concluded by jumping up and departing—leaving me as though I were quite incapable of finding any plausible answer!

The fact is that those who are enslaved to their sects are not merely devoid of all sound knowledge, but they will not even stop to learn! Instead of listening, as they ought, to the reason why liquid can enter the bladder through the ureters, but is unable to go back again the same way,—instead of admiring Nature's artistic skill—they refuse to learn; they even go so far as to scoff, and maintain that the kidneys, as well as many other things, have been made by Nature for no purpose! And some of them who had allowed themselves to be shown the ureters coming from the kidneys and becoming implanted in the bladder, even had the audacity to say that these also existed for no purpose; and others said that they were spermatic ducts, and that this was why they were inserted into the neck of the bladder and not into its cavity. When, therefore, we had demonstrated to them the real spermatic ducts entering the neck of the bladder lower down than the ureters, we supposed that, if we had not done so before, we would now at least draw them away from their false assumptions, and convert them forthwith to the opposite view. But even this they presumed to dispute, and said that it was not to be wondered at that the semen should remain longer in these latter ducts, these being more constricted, and that it should flow quickly down the ducts which came from the kidneys, seeing that these were well dilated. We were, therefore, further compelled to show them in a still living animal, the urine plainly running out through the ureters into the bladder; even thus we hardly hoped to check their nonsensical talk.

Now the method of demonstration is as follows. One has to divide the peritoneum in front of the ureters, then secure these with ligatures, and next, having bandaged up the animal, let him go (for he will not continue to urinate). After this one loosens the external bandages and shows the bladder empty and the ureters quite full and distended—in fact almost on the point of rupturing; on removing the ligature from them, one then plainly sees the bladder becoming filled with urine.

When this has been made quite clear, then, before the animal urinates, one has to tie a ligature round his penis and then to squeeze the bladder all over; still nothing goes back through the ureters to the kidneys. Here, then, it becomes obvious that not only in a dead animal, but in one which is still living, the ureters are prevented from receiving back the urine from the bladder. These observations having been made, one now loosens the ligature from the animal's penis and allows him to urinate, then again ligatures one of the ureters and leaves the other to discharge into the bladder. Allowing, then, some time to elapse, one now demonstrates that the ureter which was ligatured is obviously full and distended on the side next to the kidneys, while the other one—that from which the ligature had been taken—is itself flaccid, but has filled the bladder with urine. Then, again, one must divide the full ureter, and demonstrate how the urine spurts out of it, like blood in the operation of venesection; and after this one cuts through the other also, and both being thus divided, one bandages up the animal externally. Then when enough time seems to have elapsed, one takes

off the bandages; the bladder will now be found empty, and the whole region between the intestines and the peritoneum full of urine, as if the animal were suffering from dropsy. Now, if anyone will but test this for himself on an animal, I think he will strongly condemn the rashness of Asclepiades, and if he also learns the reason why nothing regurgitates from the bladder into the ureters, I think he will be persuaded by this also of the forethought and art shown by Nature in relation to animals.

Now Hippocrates, who was the first known to us of all those who have been both physicians and philosophers inasmuch as he was the first to recognize what Nature effects, expresses his admiration of her, and is constantly singing her praises and calling her "just." Alone, he says, she suffices for the animal in every respect, performing of her own accord and without any teaching all that is required. Being such, she has, as he supposes, certain faculties, one attractive of what is appropriate, and another eliminative of what is foreign, and she nourishes the animal, makes it grow, and expels its diseases by crisis. Therefore he says that there is in our bodies a concordance in the movements of air and fluid, and that everything is in sympathy. According to Asclepiades, however, nothing is naturally in sympathy with anything else, all substance being divided and broken up into inharmonious elements and absurd "molecules." Necessarily, then, besides making countless other statements in opposition to plain fact, he was ignorant of Nature's faculties, both that attracting what is appropriate, and that expelling what is foreign. Thus he invented some wretched nonsense to explain blood-production and anadosis, and, being utterly unable to find anything to say regarding the clearing-out of superfluities, he did not hesitate to join issue with obvious facts, and, in this matter of urinary secretion, to deprive both the kidneys and the ureters of their activity, by assuming that there were certain invisible channels opening into the bladder. It was, of course, a grand and impressive thing to do, to mistrust the obvious, and to pin one's faith in things which could not be seen!

Also, in the matter of the yellow bile, he makes an even grander and more spirited venture; for he says this is actually generated in the bile-ducts, not merely separated out.

How comes it, then, that in cases of jaundice two things happen at the same time—that the dejections contain absolutely no bile, and that the whole body becomes full of it? He is forced here again to talk nonsense, just as he did in regard to the urine. He also talks no less nonsense about the black bile and the spleen, not understanding what was said by Hippocrates; and he attempts in stupid—I might say insane—language, to contradict what he knows nothing about.

And what profit did he derive from these opinions from the point of view of treatment? He neither was able to cure a kidney ailment, nor jaundice, nor a disease of black bile, nor would he agree with the view held not merely by Hippocrates but by all men regarding drugs —that some of them purge away yellow bile, and others black, some again phlegm, and others the thin and watery superfluity; he held that all the substances evacuated were produced by the drugs themselves, just as yellow bile is produced by the biliary passages! It matters nothing, according to this extraordinary man, whether we give a hydragogue or a cholagogue in a case of dropsy, for these all equally purge and dissolve the body, and produce a solution having such and such an appearance, which did not exist as such before!

Must we not, therefore, suppose he was either mad, or entirely unacquainted with practical medicine? For who does not know that if a drug for attracting phlegm be given in a case of jaundice it will not even evacuate four *cyathi** of phlegm? Similarly also if one of the hydragogues be given. A cholagogue, on the other hand, clears away a great quantity of bile, and the skin of patients so treated at once becomes clear. I myself have, in many cases, after treating the liver condition, then removed the disease by means of a single purgation; whereas, if one had employed a drug for removing phlegm one would have done no good.

Nor is Hippocrates the only one who knows this to be so, whilst those who take experience alone as their starting-point know otherwise; they, as well as all physicians who are engaged in the practice of medicine, are of this opinion. Asclepiades, however, is an exception; he would hold it a betrayal of his assumed "elements" to confess the truth about such matters. For if a single drug were to be discovered which attracted such and such a humour only, there would obviously be danger of the opinion gaining ground that there is in every body a faculty which attracts its own particular quality. He therefore says that safflower, the Cnidian berry, and Hippophaes, do not draw phlegm from the body, but actually make it. Moreover, he holds

* About 4 oz., or one-third of a pint.

that the flower and scales of bronze, and burnt bronze itself, and germander, and wild mastich dissolve the body into water, and that dropsical patients derive benefit from these substances, not because they are purged by them, but because they are rid of substances which actually help to increase the disease; for, if the medicine does not evacuate the dropsical fluid contained in the body, but generates it, it aggravates the condition further. Moreover, scammony, according to the Asclepiadean argument, not only fails to evacuate the bile from the bodies of jaundiced subjects, but actually turns the useful blood into bile, and dissolves the body; in fact it does all manner of evil and increases the disease.

And yet this drug may be clearly seen to do good to numbers of people! "Yes," says he, "they derive benefit certainly, but merely in proportion to the evacuation." . . . But if you give these cases a drug which draws off phlegm they will not be benefited. This is so obvious that even those who make experience alone their starting-point are aware of it; and these people make it a cardinal point of their teaching to trust to no arguments, but only to what can be clearly seen. In this, then, they show good sense; whereas Asclepiades goes far astray in bidding us distrust our senses where obvious facts plainly overturn his hypotheses. Much better would it have been for him not to assail obvious facts, but rather to devote himself entirely to these.

Is it, then, these facts only which are plainly irreconcilable with the views of Asclepiades? Is not also the fact that in summer yellow bile is evacuated in greater quantity by the same drugs, and in winter phlegm, and that in a young man more bile is evacuated, and in an old man more phlegm? Obviously each drug attracts something which already exists, and does not generate something previously non-existent. Thus if you give in the summer season a drug which attracts phlegm to a young man of a lean and warm habit, who has lived neither idly nor too luxuriously, you will with great difficulty evacuate a very small quantity of this humour, and you will do the man the utmost harm. On the other hand, if you give him a cholagogue, you will produce an abundant evacuation and not injure him at all.

Do we still, then, disbelieve that each drug attracts that humour which is proper to it? Possibly the adherents of Asclepiades will assent to this—or rather, they will—not possibly, but certainly—declare that they disbelieve it, lest they should betray their darling prejudices.

14. Let us pass on, then, again to another piece of nonsense; for the sophists do not allow one to engage in enquiries that are of any worth, albeit there are many such; they compel one to spend one's time in dissipating the fallacious arguments which they bring forward.

What, then, is this piece of nonsense? It has to do with the famous and far-renowned stone which draws iron [the lodestone]. It might be thought that this would draw their minds to a belief that there are in all bodies certain faculties by which they attract their own proper qualities.

Now Epicurus, despite the fact that he employs in his "Physics" elements similar to those of Asclepiades, yet allows that iron is attracted by the lodestone, and chaff by amber. He even tries to give the cause of the phenomenon. His view is that the atoms which flow from the stone are related in shape to those flowing from the iron, and so they become easily interlocked with one another; thus it is that, after colliding with each of the two compact masses (the stone and the iron) they then rebound into the middle and so become entangled with each other, and draw the iron after them. So far, then, as his hypotheses regarding causation go, he is perfectly unconvincing; nevertheless, he does grant that there is an attraction. Further, he says that it is on similar principles that there occur in the bodies of animals the dispersal of nutriment and the discharge of waste matters, as also the actions of cathartic drugs.

Asclepiades, however, who viewed with suspicion the incredible character of the cause mentioned, and who saw no other credible cause on the basis of his supposed elements, shamelessly had recourse to the statement that nothing is in any way attracted by anything else. Now, if he was dissatisfied with what Epicurus said, and had nothing better to say himself, he ought to have refrained from making hypotheses, and should have said that Nature is a constructive artist and that the substance of things is always tending towards unity and also towards alteration because its own parts act upon and are acted upon by one another. For, if he had assumed this, it would not have been difficult to allow that this constructive Nature has powers which attract appropriate and expel alien matter. For in no other way could she be constructive, preservative of the animal, and eliminative of its diseases, unless it be allowed that she conserves what is appropriate and discharges what is foreign.

But in this matter, too, Asclepiades realized the logical sequence of the principles he had assumed; he showed no scruples, however, in opposing plain fact; he joins issue in this matter also, not merely with all physicians, but with everyone else, and maintains that there is no such thing as a crisis, or critical day, and that Nature does absolutely nothing for the preservation of the animal. For his constant aim is to follow out logical consequences and to upset obvious fact, in this respect being opposed to Epicurus; for the latter always stated the observed fact, although he gives an ineffective explanation of it. For, that these small corpuscles belonging to the lodestone rebound, and become entangled with other similar particles of the iron, and that then, by means of this entanglement (which cannot be seen anywhere) such a heavy substance as iron is attracted—I fail to understand how anybody could believe this. Even if we admit this, the same principle will not explain the fact that, when the iron has another piece brought in contact with it, this becomes attached to it.

For what are we to say? That, forsooth, some of the particles that flow from the lodestone collide with the iron and then rebound back, and that it is by these that the iron becomes suspended? that others penetrate into it, and rapidly pass through it by way of its empty channels? that these then collide with the second piece of iron and are not able to penetrate it although they penetrated the first piece? and that they then course back to the first piece, and produce entanglements like the former ones?

The hypothesis here becomes clearly refuted by its absurdity. As a matter of fact, I have seen five writing-stylets of iron attached to one another in a line, only the first one being in contact with the lodestone, and the power being transmitted through it to the others. Moreover, it cannot be said that if you bring a second stylet into contact with the lower end of the first, it becomes held, attached, and suspended, whereas, if you apply it to any other part of the side it does not become attached. For the power of the lodestone is distributed in all directions; it merely needs to be in contact with the first stylet at any point; from this stylet again the power flows, as quick as a thought, all through the second, and from that again to the third. Now, if you imagine a small lodestone hanging in a house, and in contact with it all round a large number of pieces of iron, from them again others, from these others, and so on,—all these pieces of iron must surely become filled with the corpuscles which emanate from the stone; therefore, this first little stone is likely to become dissipated by disintegrating into these emanations. Further, even if there be no iron in contact with it, it still disperses into the air, particularly if this be also warm.

"Yes," says Epicurus, "but these corpuscles must be looked on as exceedingly small, so that some of them are a ten-thousandth part of the size of the very smallest particles carried in the air." Then do you venture to say that so great a weight of iron can be suspended by such small bodies? If each of them is a ten-thousandth part as large as the dust particles which are borne in the atmosphere, how big must we suppose the hook-like extremities by which they interlock with each other to be? For of course this is quite the smallest portion of the whole particle.

Then, again, when a small body becomes entangled with another small body, or when a body in motion becomes entangled with another also in motion, they do not rebound at once. For, further, there will of course be others which break in upon them from above, from below, from front and rear, from right and left, and which shake and agitate them and never let them rest. Moreover, we must perforce suppose that each of these small bodies has a large number of these hook-like extremities. For by one it attaches itself to its neighbours, by another—the topmost one—to the lodestone, and by the bottom one to the iron. For if it were attached to the stone above and not interlocked with the iron below, this would be of no use. Thus, the upper part of the superior extremity must hang from the lodestone, and the iron must be attached to the lower end of the inferior extremity; and, since they interlock with each other by their sides as well, they must, of course, have hooks there too. Keep in mind also, above everything, what small bodies these are which possess all these different kinds of outgrowths. Still more, remember how, in order that the second piece of iron may become attached to the first, the third to the second, and to that the fourth, these absurd little particles must both penetrate the passages in the first piece of iron and at the same time rebound from the piece coming next in the series, although this second piece is naturally in every way similar to the first.

Such an hypothesis, once again, is certainly not lacking in audacity; in fact, to tell the truth, it is far more shameless than the previous ones;

according to it, when five similar pieces of iron are arranged in a line, the particles of the lodestone which easily traverse the first piece of iron rebound from the second, and do not pass readily through it in the same way. Indeed, it is nonsense, whichever alternative is adopted. For, if they do rebound, how then do they pass through into the third piece? And if they do not rebound, how does the second piece become suspended to the first? For Epicurus himself looked on the rebound as the active agent in attraction.

But, as I have said, one is driven to talk nonsense whenever one gets into discussion with such men. Having, therefore, given a concise and summary statement of the matter, I wish to be done with it. For if one diligently familiarizes oneself with the writings of Asclepiades, one will see clearly their logical dependence on his first principles, but also their disagreement with observed facts. Thus, Epicurus, in his desire to adhere to the facts, cuts an awkward figure by aspiring to show that these agree with his principles, whereas Asclepiades safeguards the sequence of principles, but pays no attention to the obvious fact. Whoever, therefore, wishes to expose the absurdity of their hypotheses, must, if the argument be in answer to Asclepiades, keep in mind his disagreement with observed fact; or if in answer to Epicurus, his discordance with his principles. Almost all the other sects depending on similar principles are now entirely extinct, while these alone maintain a respectable existence still. Yet the tenets of Asclepiades have been unanswerably confuted by Menodotus the Empiricist, who draws his attention to their opposition to phenomena and to each other; and, again, those of Epicurus have been confuted by Asclepiades, who adhered always to logical sequence, about which Epicurus evidently cares little.

Now people of the present day do not begin by getting a clear comprehension of these sects, as well as of the better ones, thereafter devoting a long time to judging and testing the true and false in each of them; despite their ignorance, they style themselves, some "physicians" and others "philosophers." No wonder, then, that they honour the false equally with the true. For everyone becomes like the first teacher that he comes across, without waiting to learn anything from anybody else. And there are some of them, who, even if they meet with more than one teacher, are yet so unintelligent and slow-witted that even by the time they have reached old age they are still incapable of understanding the steps of an argument. . . . In the old days such people used to be set to menial tasks. . . . What will be the end of it God knows!

Now, we usually refrain from arguing with people whose principles are wrong from the outset. Still, having been compelled by the natural course of events to enter into some kind of a discussion with them, we must add this further to what was said—that it is not only cathartic drugs which naturally attract their special qualities, but also those which remove thorns and the points of arrows such as sometimes become deeply embedded in the flesh. Those drugs also which draw out animal poisons or poisons applied to arrows all show the same faculty as does the lodestone. Thus, I myself have seen a thorn which was embedded in a young man's foot fail to come out when we exerted forcible traction with our fingers, and yet come away painlessly and rapidly on the application of a medicament. Yet even to this some people will object, asserting that when the inflammation is dispersed from the part the thorn comes away of itself, without being pulled out by anything. But these people seem, in the first place, to be unaware that there are certain drugs for drawing out inflammation and different ones for drawing out embedded substances; and surely if it was on the cessation of an inflammation that the abnormal matters were expelled, then all drugs which disperse inflammations ought, ipso facto, to possess the power of extracting these substances as well.

And secondly, these people seem to be unaware of a still more surprising fact, namely, that not merely do certain medicaments draw out thorns and others poisons, but that of the latter there are some which attract the poison of the viper, others that of the sting-ray, and others that of some other animal; we can, in fact, plainly observe these poisons deposited on the medicaments. Here, then, we must praise Epicurus for the respect he shows towards obvious facts, but find fault with his views as to causation. For how can it be otherwise than extremely foolish to suppose that a thorn which we failed to remove by digital traction could be drawn out by these minute particles?

Have we now, therefore, convinced ourselves that everything which exists possesses a faculty by which it attracts its proper quality, and that some things do this more, and some less?

Or shall we also furnish our argument with the illustration afforded by corn? For those who refuse to admit that anything is attracted by anything else, will, I imagine, be here proved more ignorant regarding Nature than the very peasants. When, for my own part, I first learned of what happens, I was surprised, and felt anxious to see it with my own eyes. Afterwards, when experience also had confirmed its truth, I sought long among the various sects for an explanation, and, with the exception of that which gave the first place to attraction, I could find none which even approached plausibility, all the others being ridiculous and obviously quite untenable.

What happens, then, is the following. When our peasants are bringing corn from the country into the city in wagons, and wish to filch some away without being detected, they fill earthen jars with water and stand them among the corn; the corn then draws the moisture into itself through the jar and acquires additional bulk and weight, but the fact is never detected by the onlookers unless someone who knew about the trick before makes a more careful inspection. Yet, if you care to set down the same vessel in the very hot sun, you will find the daily loss to be very little indeed. Thus corn has a greater power than extreme solar heat of drawing to itself the moisture in its neighbourhood. Thus the theory that the water is carried towards the rarefied part of the air surrounding us (particularly when that is distinctly warm) is utter nonsense; for although it is much more rarefied there than it is amongst the corn, yet it does not take up a tenth part of the moisture which the corn does.

15. Since, then, we have talked sufficient nonsense—not willingly, but because we were forced, as the proverb says, "to behave madly among madmen"—let us return again to the subject of urinary secretion. Here let us forget the absurdities of Asclepiades, and, in company with those who are persuaded that the urine does pass through the kidneys, let us consider what is the character of this function. For, most assuredly, either the urine is conveyed by its own motion to the kidneys, considering this the better course (as do we when we go off to market!), or, if this be impossible, then some other reason for its conveyance must be found. What, then, is this? If we are not going to grant the kidneys a faculty for attracting this particular quality, as Hippocrates held, we shall discover no other reason. For, surely everyone sees that either the kidneys must attract the urine, or the veins must propel it—if, that is, it does not move of itself. But if the veins did exert a propulsive action when they contract, they would squeeze out into the kidneys not merely the urine, but

along with it the whole of the blood which they contain. And if this is impossible, as we shall show, the remaining explanation is that the kidneys do exert traction.

And how is propulsion by the veins impossible? The situation of the kidneys is against it. They do not occupy a position beneath the hollow vein [vena cava] as does the sieve-like [ethmoid] passage in the nose and palate in relation to the surplus matter from the brain; they are situated on both sides of it. Besides, if the kidneys are like sieves, and readily let the thinner serous [whey-like] portion through, and keep out the thicker portion, then the whole of the blood contained in the vena cava must go to them, just as the whole of the wine is thrown into the filters. Further, the example of milk being made into cheese will show clearly what I mean. For this, too, although it is all thrown into the wicker strainers, does not all percolate through; such part of it as is too fine in proportion to the width of the meshes passes downwards, and this is called whey [serum]; the remaining thick portion which is destined to become cheese cannot get down, since the pores of the strainers will not admit it. Thus it is that, if the blood-serum has similarly to percolate through the kidneys, the whole of the blood must come to them, and not merely one part of it.

What, then, is the appearance as found on dissection?

One division of the vena cava is carried upwards to the heart, and the other mounts upon the spine and extends along its whole length as far as the legs; thus one division does not even come near the kidneys, while the other approaches them but is certainly not inserted into them. Now, if the blood were destined to be purified by them as if they were sieves, the whole of it would have to fall into them, the thin part being thereafter conveyed downwards, and the thick part retained above. But, as a matter of fact, this is not so. For the kidneys lie on either side of the vena cava. They therefore do not act like sieves, filtering fluid sent to them by the vena cava, and themselves contributing no force. They obviously exert traction; for this is the only remaining alternative.

How, then, do they exert this traction? If, as Epicurus thinks, all attraction takes place by virtue of the rebounds and entanglements of atoms, it would be certainly better to maintain that the kidneys have no attractive action at all; for his theory, when examined, would be found as it stands to be much more ridiculous

even than the theory of the lodestone, mentioned a little while ago. Attraction occurs in the way that Hippocrates laid down; this will be stated more clearly as the discussion proceeds; for the present our task is not to demonstrate this, but to point out that no other cause of the secretion of urine can be given except that of attraction by the kidneys, and that this attraction does not take place in the way imagined by people who do not allow Nature a faculty of her own.

For if it be granted that there is any attractive faculty at all in those things which are governed by Nature, a person who attempted to say anything else about the absorption of nutriment would be considered a fool.

16. Now, while Erasistratus for some reason replied at great length to certain other foolish doctrines, he entirely passed over the view held by Hippocrates, not even thinking it worth while to mention it, as he did in his work "On Deglutition"; in that work, as may be seen, he did go so far as at least to make mention of the word attraction, writing somewhat as follows:

"Now, the stomach does not appear to exercise any attraction." But when he is dealing with anadosis he does not mention the Hippocratic view even to the extent of a single syllable. Yet we should have been satisfied if he had even merely written this: "Hippocrates lies in saying 'The flesh * attracts both from the stomach and from without,' for it cannot attract either from the stomach or from without." Or if he had thought it worth while to state that Hippocrates was wrong in criticizing the weakness of the neck of the uterus, "seeing that the orifice of the uterus has no power of attracting semen," or if he [Erasistratus] had thought proper to write any other similar opinion, then we in our turn would have defended ourselves in the following terms:

"My good sir, do not run us down in this rhetorical fashion without some proof; state some definite objection to our view, in order that either you may convince us by a brilliant refutation of the ancient doctrine, or that, on the other hand, we may convert you from your ignorance." Yet why do I say "rhetorical"? For we too are not to suppose that when certain rhetoricians pour ridicule upon that which they are quite incapable of refuting, without any attempt at argument, their words are really thereby constituted rhetoric. For rhetoric proceeds by persuasive reasoning; words without reason-

* i.e. the tissues.

ing are buffoonery rather than rhetoric. Therefore, the reply of Erasistratus in his treatise "On Deglutition" was neither rhetoric nor logic. For what is it that he says? "Now, the stomach does not appear to exercise any traction." Let us testify against him in return, and set our argument beside his in the same form. Now, there appears to be no peristalsis of the gullet. "And how does this appear?" one of his adherents may perchance ask. "For is it not indicative of peristalsis that always when the upper parts of the gullet contract the lower parts dilate?" Again, then, we say, "And in what way does the attraction of the stomach not appear? For is it not indicative of attraction that always when the lower parts of the gullet dilate the upper parts contract?" Now, if he would but be sensible and recognize that this phenomenon is not more indicative of the one than of the other view, but that it applies equally to both, we should then show him without further delay the proper way to the discovery of truth.

We will, however, speak about the stomach again. And the dispersal of nutriment [anadosis] need not make us have recourse to the theory regarding the natural tendency of a vacuum to become refilled, when once we have granted the attractive faculty of the kidneys. Now, although Erasistratus knew that this faculty most certainly existed, he neither mentioned it nor denied it, nor did he make any statement as to his views on the secretion of urine.

Why did he give notice at the very beginning of his "General Principles" that he was going to speak about natural activities—firstly what they are, how they take place, and in what situations—and then, in the case of urinary secretion, declared that this took place through the kidneys, but left out its method of occurrence? It must, then, have been for no purpose that he told us how digestion occurs, or spends time upon the secretion of biliary superfluities; for in these cases also it would have been sufficient to have named the parts through which the function takes place, and to have omitted the method. On the contrary, in these cases he was able to tell us not merely through what organs, but also in what way it occurs—as he also did, I think, in the case of anadosis; for he was not satisfied with saying that this took place through the veins, but he also considered fully the method, which he held to be from the tendency of a vacuum to become refilled. Concerning the secretion of urine, however, he writes that this occurs through the kidneys, but does not add

in what way it occurs. I do not think he could say that this was from the tendency of matter to fill a vacuum, for, if this were so, nobody would have ever died of retention of urine, since no more can flow into a vacuum than has run out. For, if no other factor comes into operation save only this tendency by which a vacuum becomes refilled, no more could ever flow in than had been evacuated. Nor could he suggest any other plausible cause, such, for example, as the expression of nutriment by the stomach which occurs in the process of anadosis; this had been entirely disproved in the case of blood in the vena cava; it is excluded, not merely owing to the long distance, but also from the fact that the overlying heart, at each diastole, robs the vena cava by violence of a considerable quantity of blood.

In relation to the lower part of the vena cava there would still remain, solitary and abandoned, the specious theory concerning the filling of a vacuum. This, however, is deprived of plausibility by the fact that people die of retention of urine, and also, no less, by the situation of the kidneys. For, if the whole of the blood were carried to the kidneys, one might properly maintain that it all undergoes purification there. But, as a matter of fact, the whole of it does not go to them, but only so much as can be contained in the veins going to the kidneys; this portion only, therefore, will be purified. Further, the thin serous part of this will pass through the kidneys as if through a sieve, while the thick sanguineous portion remaining in the veins will obstruct the blood flowing in from behind; this will first, therefore, have to run back to the vena cava, and so to empty the veins going to the kidneys; these veins will no longer be able to conduct a second quantity of unpurified blood to the kidneys—occupied as they are by the blood which had preceded, there is no passage left. What power have we, then, which will draw back the purified blood from the kidneys? And what power, in the next place, will bid this blood retire to the lower part of the vena cava, and will enjoin on another quantity coming from above not to proceed downwards before turning off into the kidneys?

Now Erasistratus realized that all these ideas were open to many objections, and he could only find one idea which held good in all respects —namely, that of attraction. Since, therefore, he did not wish either to get into difficulties or to mention the view of Hippocrates, he deemed it better to say nothing at all as to the manner in which secretion occurs.

But even if he kept silence, I am not going to do so. For I know that if one passes over the Hippocratic view and makes some other pronouncement about the function of the kidneys, one cannot fail to make oneself utterly ridiculous. It was for this reason that Erasistratus kept silence and Asclepiades lied; they are like slaves who have had plenty to say in the early part of their career, and have managed by excessive rascality to escape many and frequent accusations, but who, later, when caught in the act of thieving, cannot find any excuse; the more modest one then keeps silence, as though thunderstruck, whilst the more shameless continues to hide the missing article beneath his arm and denies on oath that he has ever seen it. For it was in this way also that Asclepiades, when all subtle excuses had failed him and there was no longer any room for nonsense about "conveyance towards the rarefied part [of the air]," and when it was impossible without incurring the greatest derision to say that this superfluity [i.e. the urine] is generated by the kidneys as is bile by the canals in the liver—he, then, I say, clearly lied when he swore that the urine does not reach the kidneys, and maintained that it passes, in the form of vapour, straight from the region of the vena cava, to collect in the bladder.

Like slaves, then, caught in the act of stealing, these two are quite bewildered, and while the one says nothing, the other indulges in shameless lying.

17. Now such of the younger men as have dignified themselves with the names of these two authorities by taking the appellations "Erasistrateans" or "Asclepiadeans" are like the Davi and Getae—the slaves introduced by the excellent Menander into his comedies. As these slaves held that they had done nothing fine unless they had cheated their master three times, so also the men I am discussing have taken their time over the construction of impudent sophisms, the one party striving to prevent the lies of Asclepiades from ever being refuted, and the other saying stupidly what Erasistratus had the sense to keep silence about.

But enough about the Asclepiadeans. The Erasistrateans, in attempting to say how the kidneys let the urine through, will do anything or suffer anything or try any shift in order to find some plausible explanation which does not demand the principle of attraction.

Now those near the times of Erasistratus maintain that the parts above the kidneys receive pure blood, whilst the watery residue, being heavy, tends to run downwards; that this, after percolating through the kidneys themselves, is thus rendered serviceable, and is sent, as blood, to all the parts below the kidneys.

For a certain period at least this view also found favour and flourished, and was held to be true; after a time, however, it became suspect to the Erasistrateans themselves, and at last they abandoned it. For apparently the following two points were assumed, neither of which is conceded by anyone, nor is even capable of being proved. The first is the heaviness of the serous fluid, which was said to be produced in the vena cava, and which did not exist, apparently, at the beginning, when this fluid was being carried up from the stomach to the liver. Why, then, did it not at once run downwards when it was in these situations? And if the watery fluid is so heavy, what plausibility can anyone find in the statement that it assists in the process of anadosis?

In the second place there is this absurdity, that even if it be agreed that all the watery fluid does fall downwards, and only when it is in the vena cava, still it is difficult, or, rather, impossible, to say through what means it is going to fall into the kidneys, seeing that these are not situated below, but on either side of the vena cava, and that the vena cava is not inserted into them, but merely sends a branch into each of them, as it also does into all the other parts.

What doctrine, then, took the place of this one when it was condemned? One which to me seems far more foolish than the first, although it also flourished at one time. For they say, that if oil be mixed with water and poured upon the ground, each will take a different route, the one flowing this way and the other that, and that, therefore, it is not surprising that the watery fluid runs into the kidneys, while the blood falls downwards along the vena cava. Now this doctrine also stands already condemned. For why, of the countless veins which spring from the vena cava, should blood flow into all the others, and the serous fluid be diverted to those going to the kidneys? They have not answered the question which was asked; they merely state what happens and imagine they have thereby assigned the reason.

Once again, then (the third cup to the Saviour!),* let us now speak of the worst doctrine of all, lately invented by Lycus of Macedonia, but which is popular owing to its novelty. This Lycus, then, maintains, as though uttering an

* In a toast, the third cup was drunk to Zeus Sôtêr (the Saviour).

oracle from the inner sanctuary, that urine is residual matter from the nutrition of the kidneys! Now, the amount of urine passed every day shows clearly that it is the whole of the fluid drunk which becomes urine, except for that which comes away with the dejections or passes off as sweat or insensible perspiration. This is most easily recognized in winter in those who are doing no work but are carousing, especially if the wine be thin and diffusible; these people rapidly pass almost the same quantity as they drink. And that even Erasistratus was aware of this is known to those who have read the first book of his "General Principles." Thus Lycus is speaking neither good Erasistratism, nor good Asclepiadism, far less good Hippocratism. He is, therefore, as the saying is, like a white crow, which cannot mix with the genuine crows owing to its colour, nor with the pigeons owing to its size. For all this, however, he is not to be disregarded; he may, perhaps, be stating some wonderful truth, unknown to any of his predecessors.

Now it is agreed that all parts which are undergoing nutrition produce a certain amount of residue, but it is neither agreed nor is it likely, that the kidneys alone, small bodies as they are, could hold four whole *congii,* * and sometimes even more, of residual matter. For this surplus must necessarily be greater in quantity in each of the larger viscera; thus, for example, that of the lung, if it corresponds in amount to the size of the viscus, will obviously be many times more than that in the kidneys, and thus the whole of the thorax will become filled, and the animal

* About twelve quarts.

will be at once suffocated. But if it be said that the residual matter is equal in amount in each of the other parts, where are the bladders, one may ask, through which it is excreted? For, if the kidneys produce in drinkers three and sometimes four congii of superflous matter, that of each of the other viscera will be much more, and thus an enormous barrel will be needed to contain the waste products of them all. Yet one often urinates practically the same quantity as one has drunk, which would show that the whole of what one drinks goes to the kidneys.

Thus the author of this third piece of trickery would appear to have achieved nothing, but to have been at once detected, and there still remains the original difficulty which was insoluble by Erasistratus and by all others except Hippocrates. I dwell purposely on this topic, knowing well that nobody else has anything to say about the function of the kidneys, but that either we must prove more foolish than the very butchers if we do not agree that the urine passes through the kidneys; or, if one acknowledges this, that then one cannot possibly give any other reason for the secretion than the principle of attraction.

Now, if the movement of urine does not depend on the tendency of a vacuum to become refilled, it is clear that neither does that of the blood nor that of the bile; or if that of these latter does so, then so also does that of the former. For they must all be accomplished in one and the same way, even according to Erasistratus himself.

This matter, however, will be discussed more fully in the book following this.

Book Two

1. In the previous book we demonstrated that not only Erasistratus, but also all others who would say anything to the purpose about urinary secretion, must acknowledge that the kidneys possess some faculty which attracts to them this particular quality existing in the urine. Besides this we drew attention to the fact that the urine is not carried through the kidneys into the bladder by one method, the blood into parts of the animal by another, and the yellow bile separated out on yet another principle. For when once there has been demonstrated in any one organ, the drawing, or so-called epispastic faculty, there is then no difficulty in transferring it to the rest. Certainly Nature did not give a

power such as this to the kidneys without giving it also to the vessels which abstract the biliary fluid,* nor did she give it to the latter without also giving it to each of the other parts. And, assuredly, if this is true, we must marvel that Erasistratus should make statements concerning the delivery of nutriment from the food-canal which are so false as to be detected even by Asclepiades. Now, Erasistratus considers it absolutely certain that, if anything flows from the veins, one of two things must happen: either a completely empty space will result, or

* The radicles of the hepatic ducts in the liver were supposed to be the active agents in extracting bile from the blood.

the contiguous quantum of fluid will run in and take the place of that which has been evacuated. Asclepiades, however, holds that not one of two, but one of three things must be said to result in the emptied vessels: either there will be an entirely empty space, or the contiguous portion will flow in, or the vessel will contract. For whereas, in the case of reeds and tubes it is true to say that, if these be submerged in water, and are emptied of the air which they contain in their lumens, then either a completely empty space will be left, or the contiguous portion will move onwards; in the case of veins this no longer holds, since their coats can collapse and so fall in upon the interior cavity. It may be seen, then, how false this hypothesis—by Zeus, I cannot call it a demonstration!—of Erasistratus is.

And, from another point of view, even if it were true, it is superfluous, if the stomach has the power of compressing the veins, as he himself supposed, and the veins again of contracting upon their contents and propelling them forwards. For, apart from other considerations, no plethora would ever take place in the body, if delivery of nutriment resulted merely from the tendency of a vacuum to become refilled. Now, if the compression of the stomach becomes weaker the further it goes, and cannot reach to an indefinite distance, and if, therefore, there is need of some other mechanism to explain why the blood is conveyed in all directions, then the principle of the refilling of a vacuum may be looked on as a necessary addition; there will not, however, be a plethora in any of the parts coming after the liver, or, if there be, it will be in the region of the heart and lungs; for the heart alone of the parts which come after the liver draws the nutriment into its right ventricle, thereafter sending it through the arterioid vein* to the lungs (for Erasistratus himself will have it that, owing to the membranous excrescences, no other parts save the lungs receive nourishment from the heart). If, however, in order to explain how plethora comes about, we suppose the force of compression by the stomach to persist indefinitely, we have no further need of the principle of the refilling of a vacuum, especially if we assume contraction of the veins in addition—as is, again, agreeable to Erasistratus himself.

2. Let me draw his attention, then, once again, even if he does not wish it, to the kidneys, and let me state that these confute in the very clearest manner such people as object to the principle of attraction. Nobody has ever said anything plausible, nor, as we previously showed, has anyone been able to discover, by any means, any other cause for the secretion of urine; we necessarily appear mad if we maintain that the urine passes into the kidneys in the form of vapour, and we certainly cut a poor figure when we talk about the tendency of a vacuum to become refilled; this idea is foolish in the case of blood, and impossible, nay, perfectly nonsensical, in the case of the urine.

This, then, is one blunder made by those who dissociate themselves from the principle of attraction. Another is that which they make about the secretion of yellow bile. For in this case, too, it is not a fact that when the blood runs past the mouths [stomata] of the bile-ducts there will be a thorough separation out [secretion] of biliary waste-matter. "Well," say they, "let us suppose that it is not secreted but carried with the blood all over the body." But, you sapient folk, Erasistratus himself supposed that Nature took thought for the animals' future, and was workmanlike in her method; and at the same time he maintained that the biliary fluid was useless in every way for the animals. Now these two things are incompatible. For how could Nature be still looked on as exercising forethought for the animal when she allowed a noxious humour such as this to be carried off and distributed with the blood? . . .

This, however, is a small matter. I shall again point out here the greatest and most obvious error. For if the yellow bile adjusts itself to the narrower vessels and stomata, and the blood to the wider ones, for no other reason than that blood is thicker and bile thinner, and that the stomata of the veins are wider and those of the bile-ducts narrower, then it is clear that this watery and serous superfluity,† too, will run out into the bile-ducts quicker than does the bile, exactly in proportion as it is thinner than the bile! How is it, then, that it does not run out? "Because," it may be said, "urine is thicker than bile!" This was what one of our Erasistrateans ventured to say, herein clearly disregarding the evidence of his senses, although he had trusted these in the case of the bile and blood. For, if it be that we are to look on bile as thinner than blood because it runs more, then, since the serous residue † passes through fine linen or lint or a sieve more easily even than does bile, by these tokens bile must also be thicker than the watery fluid. For here, again, there is no argument which will demonstrate that bile is thinner than the serous superfluities.

* What we now call the pulmonary artery.

† Urine, or, more exactly, blood-serum.

But when a man shamelessly goes on using circumlocutions, and never acknowledges when he has had a fall, he is like the amateur wrestlers, who, when they have been overthrown by the experts and are lying on their backs on the ground, so far from recognizing their fall, actually seize their victorious adversaries by the necks and prevent them from getting away, thus supposing themselves to be the winners!

3. Thus, every hypothesis of channels as an explanation of natural functioning is perfect nonsense. For, if there were not an inborn faculty given by Nature to each one of the organs at the very beginning, then animals could not continue to live even for a few days, far less for the number of years which they actually do. For let us suppose they were under no guardianship, lacking in creative ingenuity and forethought; let us suppose they were steered only by material forces, and not by any special faculties (the one attracting what is proper to it, another rejecting what is foreign, and yet another causing alteration and adhesion of the matter destined to nourish it); if we suppose this, I am sure it would be ridiculous for us to discuss natural, or, still more, psychical, activities—or, in fact, life as a whole.

For there is not a single animal which could live or endure for the shortest time if, possessing within itself so many different parts, it did not employ faculties which were attractive of what is appropriate, eliminative of what is foreign, and alterative of what is destined for nutrition. On the other hand, if we have these faculties, we no longer need channels, little or big, resting on an unproven hypothesis, for explaining the secretion of urine and bile, and the conception of some favourable situation (in which point alone Erasistratus shows some common sense, since he does regard all the parts of the body as having been well and truly placed and shaped by Nature).

But let us suppose he remained true to his own statement that Nature is "artistic"—this Nature which, at the beginning, well and truly shaped and disposed all the parts of the animal, and, after carrying out this function (for she left nothing undone), brought it forward to the light of day, endowed with certain faculties necessary for its very existence, and, thereafter, gradually increased it until it reached its due size. If he argued consistently on this principle, I fail to see how he can continue to refer natural functions to the smallness or largeness of canals, or to any other similarly absurd hypothesis. For this Nature which shapes and gradu-

ally adds to the parts is most certainly extended throughout their whole substance. Yes indeed, she shapes and nourishes and increases them through and through, not on the outside only. For Praxiteles and Phidias and all the other statuaries used merely to decorate their material on the outside, in so far as they were able to touch it; but its inner parts they left unembellished, unwrought, unaffected by art or forethought, since they were unable to penetrate therein and to reach and handle all portions of the material. It is not so, however, with Nature. Every part of a bone she makes bone, every part of the flesh she makes flesh, and so with fat and all the rest; there is no part which she has not touched, elaborated, and embellished. Phidias, on the other hand, could not turn wax into ivory and gold, nor yet gold into wax: for each of these remains as it was at the commencement, and becomes a perfect statue simply by being clothed externally in a form and artificial shape. But Nature does not preserve the original character of any kind of matter; if she did so, then all parts of the animal would be blood—that blood, namely, which flows to the semen from the impregnated female and which is, so to speak, like the statuary's wax, a single uniform matter, subjected to the artificer. From this blood there arises no part of the animal which is as red and moist [as blood is], for bone, artery, vein, nerve, cartilage, fat, gland, membrane, and marrow are not blood, though they arise from it.

I would then ask Erasistratus himself to inform me what the altering, coagulating, and shaping agent is. He would doubtless say, "Either Nature or the semen," meaning the same thing in both cases, but explaining it by different devices. For that which was previously semen, when it begins to procreate and to shape the animal, becomes, so to say, a special nature. For in the same way that Phidias possessed the faculties of his art even before touching his material, and then activated these in connection with this material (for every faculty remains inoperative in the absence of its proper material), so it is with the semen: its faculties it possessed from the beginning,* while its activities it does not receive from its material, but it manifests them in connection therewith.

And, of course, if it were to be overwhelmed with a great quantity of blood, it would perish, while if it were to be entirely deprived of blood it would remain inoperative and would not turn into a nature. Therefore, in order that it may

* Galen attributed to the semen what we should to the fertilized ovum.

not perish, but may become a nature in place of semen, there must be an afflux to it of a little blood—or, rather, one should not say a little, but a quantity commensurate with that of the semen. What is it then that measures the quantity of this afflux? What prevents more from coming? What ensures against a deficiency? What is this third overseer of animal generation that we are to look for, which will furnish the semen with a due amount of blood? What would Erasistratus have said if he had been alive, and had been asked this question? Obviously, the semen itself. This, in fact, is the artificer analogous with Phidias, whilst the blood corresponds to the statuary's wax.

Now, it is not for the wax to discover for itself how much of it is required; that is the business of Phidias. Accordingly the artificer will draw to itself as much blood as it needs. Here, however, we must pay attention and take care not unwittingly to credit the semen with reason and intelligence; if we were to do this, we would be making neither semen nor a nature, but an actual living animal. And if we retain these two principles—that of proportionate attraction and that of the non-participation of intelligence—we shall ascribe to the semen a faculty for attracting blood similar to that possessed by the lodestone for iron. Here, then, again, in the case of the semen, as in so many previous instances, we have been compelled to acknowledge some kind of attractive faculty.

And what is the semen? Clearly the active principle of the animal, the material principle being the menstrual blood. Next, seeing that the active principle employs this faculty primarily, therefore, in order that any one of the things fashioned by it may come into existence, it [the principle] must necessarily be possessed of its own faculty. How, then, was Erasistratus unaware of it, if the primary function of the semen be to draw to itself a due proportion of blood? Now, this fluid would be in due proportion if it were so thin and vaporous, that, as soon as it was drawn like dew into every part of the semen, it would everywhere cease to display its own particular character; for so the semen will easily dominate and quickly assimilate it—in fact, will use it as food. It will then, I imagine, draw to itself a second and a third quantum, and thus by feeding it acquires for itself considerable bulk and quantity. In fact, the alterative faculty has now been discovered as well, although about this also Erasistratus has not written a word. And, thirdly the shaping faculty will become evident, by virtue of which the semen firstly surrounds itself with a thin membrane like a kind of superficial condensation; this is what was described by Hippocrates in the sixth-day birth, which, according to his statement, fell from the singing-girl and resembled the pellicle of an egg. And following this all the other stages will occur, such as are described by him in his work "On the Child's Nature."

But if each of the parts formed were to remain as small as when it first came into existence, of what use would that be? They have, then, to grow. Now, how will they grow? By becoming extended in all directions and at the same time receiving nourishment. And if you will recall what I previously said about the bladder which the children blew up and rubbed, you will also understand my meaning better as expressed in what I am now about to say.

Imagine the heart to be, at the beginning, so small as to differ in no respect from a millet-seed, or, if you will, a bean; and consider how otherwise it is to become large than by being extended in all directions and acquiring nourishment throughout its whole substance, in the way that, as I showed a short while ago, the semen is nourished. But even this was unknown to Erasistratus—the man who sings the artistic skill of Nature! He imagines that animals grow like webs, ropes, sacks, or baskets, each of which has, woven on to its end or margin, other material similar to that of which it was originally composed.

But this, most sapient sir, is not growth, but genesis! For a bag, sack, garment, house, ship, or the like is said to be still coming into existence [undergoing genesis] so long as the appropriate form for the sake of which it is being constructed by the artificer is still incomplete. Then, when does it grow? Only when the basket, being complete, with a bottom, a mouth, and a belly, as it were, as well as the intermediate parts, now becomes larger in all these respects. "And how can this happen?" someone will ask. Only by our basket suddenly becoming an animal or a plant; for growth belongs to living things alone. Possibly you imagine that a house grows when it is being built, or a basket when being plaited, or a garment when being woven? It is not so, however. Growth belongs to that which has already been completed in respect to its form, whereas the process by which that which is still becoming attains its form is termed not growth but genesis. That which is, grows, while that which is not, becomes.

4. This also was unknown to Erasistratus, whom nothing escaped, if his followers speak

in any way truly in maintaining that he was familiar with the Peripatetic philosophers. Now, in so far as he acclaims Nature as being an artist in construction, even I recognize the Peripatetic teachings, but in other respects he does not come near them. For if anyone will make himself acquainted with the writings of Aristotle and Theophrastus, these will appear to him to consist of commentaries on the Nature-lore [physiology] of Hippocrates—according to which the principles of heat, cold, dryness and moisture act upon and are acted upon by one another, the hot principle being the most active, and the cold coming next to it in power; all this was stated in the first place by Hippocrates and secondly by Aristotle. Further, it is at once the Hippocratic and the Aristotelian teaching that the parts which are being nourished receive that nourishment throughout their whole substance, and that, similarly, processes of mingling and alteration involve the entire substance. Moreover, that digestion is a species of alteration—a transmutation of the nutriment into the proper quality of the thing receiving it; that blood-production also is an alteration, and nutrition as well; that growth results from extension in all directions, combined with nutrition; that alteration is effected mainly by the warm principle, and that therefore digestion, nutrition, and the generation of the various humours, as well as the qualities of the surplus substances, result from the innate heat; all these and many other points besides in regard to the aforesaid faculties, the origin of diseases, and the discovery of remedies, were correctly stated first by Hippocrates of all writers whom we know, and were in the second place correctly expounded by Aristotle. Now, if all these views meet with the approval of the Peripatetics, as they undoubtedly do, and if none of them satisfy Erasistratus, what can the Erasistrateans possibly mean by claiming that their leader was associated with these philosophers? The fact is, they revere him as a god, and think that everything he says is true. If this be so, then we must suppose the Peripatetics to have strayed very far from truth, since they approve of none of the ideas of Erasistratus. And, indeed, the disciples of the latter produce his connection with the Peripatetics in order to furnish his Nature-lore with a respectable pedigree.

Now, let us reverse our argument and put it in a different way from that which we have just employed. For if the Peripatetics were correct in their teaching about Nature, there could be nothing more absurd than the contentions of Erasistratus. And, I will leave it to the Erasistrateans themselves to decide; they must either advance the one proposition or the other. According to the former one the Peripatetics had no accurate acquaintance with Nature, and according to the second, Erasistratus. It is my task, then, to point out the opposition between the two doctrines, and theirs to make the choice. . . .

But they certainly will not abandon their reverence for Erasistratus. Very well, then; let them stop talking about the Peripatetic philosophers. For among the numerous physiological teachings regarding the genesis and destruction of animals, their health, their diseases, and the methods of treating these, there will be found one only which is common to Erasistratus and the Peripatetics—namely, the view that Nature does everything for some purpose, and nothing in vain.

But even as regards this doctrine their agreement is only verbal; in practice Erasistratus makes havoc of it a thousand times over. For, according to him, the spleen was made for no purpose, as also the omentum; similarly, too, the arteries which are inserted into kidneys— although these are practically the largest of all those that spring from the great artery [aorta]! And to judge by the Erasistratean argument, there must be countless other useless structures; for, if he knows nothing at all about these structures, he has little more anatomical knowledge than a butcher, while, if he is acquainted with them and yet does not state their use, he clearly imagines that they were made for no purpose, like the spleen. Why, however, should I discuss these structures fully, belonging as they do to the treatise "On the Use of Parts," which I am personally about to complete?

Let us, then, sum up again this same argument, and, having said a few words more in answer to the Erasistrateans, proceed to our next topic. The fact is, these people seem to me to have read none of Aristotle's writings, but to have heard from others how great an authority he was on "Nature," and that those of the Porch follow in the steps of his Nature-lore; apparently they then discovered a single one of the current ideas which is common to Aristotle and Erasistratus, and made up some story of a connection between Erasistratus and these people. That Erasistratus, however, has no share in the Nature-lore of Aristotle is shown by an enumeration of the aforesaid doctrines, which emanated first from Hippocrates, secondly from Aristotle, thirdly from the Stoics (with a single modification, namely, that for them the qualities are bodies). Perhaps, however, they will maintain that it was in the matter of logic that Erasistratus associated himself with the Peripatetic philosophers? Here they show ignorance of the fact that these philosophers never brought forward false or inconclusive arguments, while the Erasistratean books are full of them.

So perhaps somebody may already be asking, in some surprise, what possessed Erasistratus that he turned so completely from the doctrines of Hippocrates, and why it is that he takes away the attractive faculty from the biliary passages in the liver—for we have sufficiently discussed the kidneys—alleging [as the cause of bile-secretion] a favourable situation, the narrowness of vessels, and a common space into which the veins from the gateway [of the liver] conduct the unpurified blood, and from which, in the first place, the [biliary] passages take over the bile, and secondly, the [branches] of the vena cava take over the purified blood. For it would not only have done him no harm to have mentioned the idea of attraction, but he would thereby have been able to get rid of countless other disputed questions.

5. At the actual moment, however, the Erasistrateans are engaged in a considerable battle, not only with others but also amongst themselves, and so they cannot explain the passage from the first book of the "General Principles," in which Erasistratus says, "Since there are two kinds of vessels opening at the same place, the one kind extending to the gall-bladder and the other to the vena cava, the result is that, of the nutriment carried up from the alimentary canal, that part which fits both kinds of stomata is received into both kinds of vessels, some being carried into the gall-bladder, and the rest passing over into the vena cava." For it is difficult to say what we are to understand by the words "opening at the same place" which are written at the beginning of this passage. Either they mean there is a junction between the termination of the vein which is on the concave surface of the liver and two other vascular terminations (that of the vessel on the convex surface of the liver and that of the bile-duct), or, if not, then we must suppose that there is, as it were, a common space for all three vessels, which becomes filled from the lower vein,* and empties itself both into the bile-duct and into the branches of the vena cava. Now, there are many difficulties in both of these explanations, but if I were to state them all, I should find myself inadvertent-

* The portal vein.

ly writing an exposition of the teaching of Erasistratus, instead of carrying out my original undertaking. There is, however, one difficulty common to both these explanations, namely, that the whole of the blood does not become purified. For it ought to fall into the bile-duct as into a kind of sieve, instead of going (running, in fact, rapidly) past it, into the larger stoma, by virtue of the impulse of anadosis.

Are these, then, the only inevitable difficulties in which the argument of Erasistratus becomes involved through his disinclination to make any use of the attractive faculty, or is it that the difficulty is greatest here, and also so obvious that even a child could not avoid seeing it?

6. And if one looks carefully into the matter one will find that even Erasistratus' reasoning on the subject of nutrition, which he takes up in the second book of his "General Principles," fails to escape this same difficulty. For, having conceded one premise to the principle that matter tends to fill a vacuum, as we previously showed, he was only able to draw a conclusion in the case of the veins and their contained blood. That is to say, when blood is running away through the stomata of the veins, and is being dispersed, then, since an absolutely empty space cannot result, and the veins cannot collapse (for this was what he overlooked), it was therefore shown to be necessary that the adjoining quantum of fluid should flow in and fill the place of the fluid evacuated. It is in this way that we may suppose the veins to be nourished; they get the benefit of the blood which they contain. But how about the nerves? For they do not also contain blood. One might obviously say that they draw their supply from the veins. But Erasistratus will not have it so. What further contrivance, then, does he suppose? He says that a nerve has within itself veins and arteries, like a rope woven by Nature out of three different strands. By means of this hypothesis he imagined that his theory would escape from the idea of attraction. For if the nerve contain within itself a blood-vessel it will no longer need the adventitious flow of other blood from the real vein lying adjacent; this fictitious vessel, perceptible only in theory, will suffice it for nourishment.

But this, again, is succeeded by another similar difficulty. For this small vessel will nourish itself, but it will not be able to nourish this adjacent simple nerve or artery, unless these possess some innate proclivity for attracting nutriment. For how could the nerve, being simple, attract its nourishment, as do the composite veins, by virtue of the tendency of a vacuum to become refilled? For, although according to Erasistratus, it contains within itself a cavity of sorts, this is not occupied with blood, but with psychic pneuma, and we are required to imagine the nutriment introduced, not into this cavity, but into the vessel containing it, whether it needs merely to be nourished, or to grow as well. How, then, are we to imagine it introduced? For this simple vessel [i.e. nerve] is so small—as are also the other two—that if you prick it at any part with the finest needle you will tear the whole three of them at once. Thus there could never be in it a perceptible space entirely empty. And an emptied space which merely existed in theory could not compel the adjacent fluid to come and fill it.

At this point, again, I should like Erasistratus himself to answer regarding this small elementary nerve, whether it is actually one and definitely continuous, or whether it consists of many small bodies, such as those assumed by Epicurus, Leucippus, and Democritus. For I see that the Erasistrateans are at variance on this subject. Some of them consider it one and continuous, for otherwise, as they say, he would not have called it simple; and some venture to resolve it into yet other elementary bodies. But if it be one and continuous, then what is evacuated from it in the so-called insensible transpiration of the physicians will leave no empty space in it; otherwise it would not be one body but many, separated by empty spaces. But if it consists of many bodies, then we have "escaped by the back door," as the saying is, to Asclepiades, seeing that we have postulated certain inharmonious elements. Once again, then, we must call Nature "inartistic"; for this necessarily follows the assumption of such elements.

For this reason some of the Erasistrateans seem to me to have done very foolishly in reducing the simple vessels to elements such as these. Yet it makes no difference to me, since the theory of both parties regarding nutrition will be shown to be absurd. For in these minute simple vessels constituting the large perceptible nerves, it is impossible, according to the theory of those who would keep the former continuous, that any "refilling of a vacuum" should take place, since no vacuum can occur in a continuum even if anything does run away; for the parts left come together (as is seen in the case of water) and again become one, taking up the whole space of that which previously separated them. Nor will any "refilling" occur if we accept the

argument of the other Erasistrateans, since none of their elements need it. For this principle only holds of things which are perceptible, and not of those which exist merely in theory; this Erasistratus expressly acknowledges, for he states that it is not a vacuum such as this, interspersed in small portions among the corpuscles, that his various treatises deal with, but a vacuum which is clear, perceptible, complete in itself, large in size, evident, or however else one cares to term it (for, what Erasistratus himself says is, that "there cannot be a perceptible space which is entirely empty"; while I, for my part, being abundantly equipped with terms which are equally elucidatory, at least in relation to the present topic of discussion, have added them as well).

Thus it seems to me better that we also should help the Erasistrateans with some contribution, since we are on the subject, and should advise those who reduce the vessel called primary and simple by Erasistratus into other elementary bodies to give up their opinion; for not only do they gain nothing by it, but they are also at variance with Erasistratus in this matter. That they gain nothing by it has been clearly demonstrated; for this hypothesis could not escape the difficulty regarding nutrition. And it also seems perfectly evident to me that this hypothesis is not in consonance with the view of Erasistratus, when it declares that what he calls simple and primary is composite, and when it destroys the principle of Nature's artistic skill. For, if we do not grant a certain unity of substance to these simple structures as well, and if we arrive eventually at inharmonious and indivisible elements, we shall most assuredly deprive Nature of her artistic skill, as do all the physicians and philosophers who start from this hypothesis. For, according to such a hypothesis, Nature does not precede, but is secondary to the parts of the animal. Now, it is not the province of what comes secondarily, but of what pre-exists, to shape and to construct. Thus we must necessarily suppose that the faculties of Nature, by which she shapes the animal, and makes it grow and receive nourishment, are present from the seed onwards; whereas none of these inharmonious and non-partite corpuscles contains within itself any formative, incremental, nutritive, or, in a word, any artistic power; it is, by hypothesis, unimpressionable and untransformable, whereas, as we have previously shown, none of the processes mentioned takes place without transformation, alteration, and complete intermixture. And, owing to this necessity, those who belong to these sects are unable to follow out the consequences of their supposed elements, and they are all therefore forced to declare Nature devoid of art. It is not from us, however, that the Erasistrateans should have learnt this, but from those very philosophers who lay most stress on a preliminary investigation into the elements of all existing things.

Now, one can hardly be right in supposing that Erasistratus could reach such a pitch of foolishness as to be incapable of recognizing the logical consequences of this theory, and that, while assuming Nature to be artistically creative, he would at the same time break up substance into insensible, inharmonious, and untransformable elements. If, however, he will grant that there occurs in the elements a process of alteration and transformation, and that there exists in them unity and continuity, then that simple vessel of his (as he himself names it) will turn out to be single and uncompounded. And the simple vein will receive nourishment from itself, and the nerve and artery from the vein. How, and in what way? For, when we were at this point before, we drew attention to the disagreement among the Erasistrateans, and we showed that the nutrition of these simple vessels was impraticable according to the teachings of both parties, although we did not hesitate to adjudicate in their quarrel and to do Erasistratus the honour of placing him in the better sect.

Let our argument, then, be transferred again to the doctrine which assumes this elementary nerve to be a single, simple, and entirely unified structure, and let us consider how it is to be nourished; for what is discovered here will at once be found to be common also to the school of Hippocrates.

It seems to me that our enquiry can be most rigorously pursued in subjects who are suffering from illness and have become very emaciated, since in these people all parts of the body are obviously atrophied and thin, and in need of additional substance and feeding-up; for the same reason the ordinary perceptible nerve, regarding which we originally began this discussion, has become thin, and requires nourishment. Now, this contains within itself various parts, namely, a great many of these primary, invisible, minute nerves, a few simple arteries, and similarly also veins. Thus, all its elementary nerves have themselves also obviously become emaciated; for, if they had not, neither would the nerve as a whole; and of course, in such a case, the whole nerve cannot require

nourishment without each of these requiring it too. Now, if on the one hand they stand in need of feeding-up, and if on the other the principle of the refilling of a vacuum can give them no help—both by reason of the difficulties previously mentioned and the actual thinness, as I shall show—we must then seek another cause for nutrition.

How is it, then, that the tendency of a vacuum to become refilled is unable to afford nourishment to one in such a condition? Because its rule is that only so much of the contiguous matter should succeed as has flowed away. Now this is sufficient for nourishment in the case of those who are in good condition, for, in them, what is presented must be equal to what has flowed away. But in the case of those who are very emaciated and who need a great restoration of nutrition, unless what was presented were many times greater than what has been emptied out, they would never be able to regain their original habit. It is clear, therefore, that these parts will have to exert a greater amount of attraction, in so far as their requirements are greater. And I fail to understand how Erasistratus does not perceive that here again he is putting the cart before the horse. Because, in the case of the sick, there must be a large amount of presentation in order to feed them up, he argues that the factor of "refilling" must play an equally large part. And how could much presentation take place if it were not preceded by an abundant delivery of nutriment? And if he calls the conveyance of food through the veins delivery, and its assumption by each of these simple and visible nerves and arteries not delivery but distribution, as some people have thought fit to name it, and then ascribes conveyance through the veins to the principle of vacuum-refilling alone, let him explain to us the assumption of food by the hypothetical elements. For it has been shown that at least in relation to these there is no question of the refilling of a vacuum being in operation, and especially where the parts are very attenuated. It is worth while listening to what Erasistratus says about these cases in the second book of his "General Principles": "In the ultimate simple [vessels], which are thin and narrow, presentation takes place from the adjacent vessels, the nutriment being attracted through the sides of the vessels and deposited in the empty spaces left by the matter which has been carried away." Now, in this statement firstly I admit and accept the words "through the sides." For, if the simple nerve were actually to take in the food through its mouth, it could not distribute it through its whole substance; for the mouth is dedicated to the psychic pneuma. It can, however, take it in through its sides from the adjacent simple vein. Secondly, I also accept in Erasistratus' statement the expression which precedes "through the sides." What does this say? "The nutriment being attracted through the sides of the vessels." Now I, too, agree that it is attracted, but it has been previously shown that this is not through the tendency of evacuated matter to be replaced.

7. Let us, then, consider together how it is attracted. How else than in the way that iron is attracted by the lodestone, the latter having a faculty attractive of this particular quality [existing in iron]? But if the beginning of anadosis depends on the squeezing action of the stomach, and the whole movement thereafter on the peristalsis and propulsive action of the veins, as well as on the traction exerted by each of the parts which are undergoing nourishment, then we can abandon the principle of replacement of evacuated matter, as not being suitable for a man who assumes Nature to be a skilled artist; thus we shall also have avoided the contradiction of Asclepiades though we cannot refute it: for the disjunctive argument used for the purposes of demonstration is, in reality, disjunctive not of two but of three alternatives; now, if we treat the disjunction as a disjunction of two alternatives, one of the two propositions assumed in constructing our proof must be false; and if as a disjunctive of three alternatives, no conclusion will be arrived at.

8. Now Erasistratus ought not to have been ignorant of this if he had ever had anything to do with the Peripatetics—even in a dream. Nor, similarly, should he have been unacquainted with the genesis of the humours, about which, not having even anything moderately plausible to say, he thinks to deceive us by the excuse that the consideration of such matters is not the least useful. Then, in Heaven's name, is it useful to know how food is digested in the stomach, but unnecessary to know how bile comes into existence in the veins? Are we to pay attention merely to the evacuation of this humour, and not to its genesis? As though it were not far better to prevent its excessive development from the beginning than to give ourselves all the trouble of expelling it! And it is a strange thing to be entirely unaware as to whether its genesis is to be looked on as taking place in the body, or whether it comes from without and is contained in the food. For, if it was right to raise this problem, why should we not make in-

vestigations concerning the blood as well—whether it takes its origin in the body, or is distributed through the food as is maintained by those who postulate homœomeries? Assuredly it would be much more useful to investigate what kinds of food are suited, and what kinds unsuited, to the process of blood-production rather than to enquire into what articles of diet are easily mastered by the activity of the stomach, and what resist and contend with it. For the choice of the latter bears reference merely to digestion, while that of the former is of importance in regard to the generation of useful blood. For it is not equally important whether the aliment be imperfectly chylified in the stomach or whether it fail to be turned into useful blood. Why is Erasistratus not ashamed to distinguish all the various kinds of digestive failure and all the occasions which give rise to them, whilst in reference to the errors of blood-production he does not utter a single word—nay, not a syllable? Now, there is certainly to be found in the veins both thick and thin blood; in some people it is redder, in others yellower, in some blacker, in others more of the nature of phlegm. And one who realizes that it may smell offensively not in one way only, but in a great many different respects (which cannot be put into words, although perfectly appreciable to the senses), would, I imagine, condemn in no measured terms the carelessness of Erasistratus in omitting a consideration so essential to the practice of our art.

Thus it is clear what errors in regard to the subject of dropsies logically follow this carelessness. For, does it not show the most extreme carelessness to suppose that the blood is prevented from going forward into the liver owing to the narrowness of the passages, and that dropsy can never occur in any other way? For, to imagine that dropsy is never caused by the spleen or any other part, but always by induration of the liver,* is the standpoint of a man whose intelligence is perfectly torpid and who is quite out of touch with things that happen every day. For, not merely once or twice, but frequently, we have observed dropsy produced by chronic haemorrhoids which have been suppressed, or which, through immoderate bleeding, have given the patient a severe chill; similarly, in women, the complete disappearance of the monthly discharge, or an undue evacuation such as is caused by violent bleeding from the womb, often provoke dropsy; and in some of them the so-called female flux ends in this disorder. I leave

* Cirrhosis of the liver.

out of account the dropsy which begins in the flanks or in any other susceptible part; this clearly confutes Erasistratus' assumption, although not so obviously as does that kind of dropsy which is brought about by an excessive chilling of the whole constitution; this, which is the primary reason for the occurrence of dropsy, results from a failure of blood-production, very much like the diarrhoea which follows imperfect digestion of food; certainly in this kind of dropsy neither the liver nor any other viscus becomes indurated.

The learned Erasistratus, however, overlooks —nay, despises—what neither Hippocrates, Diocles, Praxagoras, nor Philistion despised, nor indeed any of the best philosophers, whether Plato, Aristotle, or Theophrastus; he passes by whole functions as though it were but a trifling and casual department of medicine which he was neglecting, without deigning to argue whether or not these authorities are right in saying that the bodily parts of all animals are governed by the Warm, the Cold, the Dry and the Moist, the one pair being active and the other passive, and that among these the Warm has most power in connection with all functions, but especially with the genesis of the humours. Now, one cannot be blamed for not agreeing with all these great men, nor for imagining that one knows more than they; but not to consider such distinguished teaching worthy either of contradiction or even mention shows an extraordinary arrogance.

Now, Erasistratus is thoroughly small-minded and petty to the last degree in all his disputations—when, for instance, in his treatise "On Digestion," he argues jealously with those who consider that this is a process of putrefaction of the food; and, in his work "On Anadosis," with those who think that the anadosis of blood through the veins results from the contiguity of the arteries; also, in his work "On Respiration," with those who maintain that the air is forced along by contraction. Nay, he did not even hesitate to contradict those who maintain that the urine passes into the bladder in a vaporous state, as also those who say that imbibed fluids are carried into the lung. Thus he delights to choose always the most valueless doctrines, and to spend his time more and more in contradicting these; whereas on the subject of the origin of blood (which is in no way less important than the chylification of food in the stomach) he did not deign to dispute with any of the ancients, nor did he himself venture to bring forward any other opinion, despite the fact that at the beginning of his treatise on "General Principles" he undertook to say how all the various natural functions take place, and through what parts of the animal! Now, is it possible that, when the faculty which naturally digests food is weak, the animal's digestion fails, whereas the faculty which turns the digested food into blood cannot suffer any kind of impairment? Are we to suppose this latter faculty alone to be as tough as steel and unaffected by circumstances? Or is it that weakness of this faculty will result in something else than dropsy? The fact, therefore, that Erasistratus, in regard to other matters, did not hesitate to attack even the most trivial views, whilst in this case he neither dared to contradict his predecessors nor to advance any new view of his own, proves plainly that he recognized the fallacy of his own way of thinking.

For what could a man possibly say about blood who had no use for innate heat? What could he say about yellow or black bile, or phlegm? Well, of course, he might say that the bile could come directly from without, mingled with the food! Thus Erasistratus practically says so in the following words: "It is of no value in practical medicine to find out whether a fluid of this kind * arises from the elaboration of food in the stomach-region, or whether it reaches the body because it is mixed with the food taken in from outside." But my very good Sir, you most certainly maintain also that this humour has to be evacuated from the animal, and that it causes great pain if it be not evacuated. How, then, if you suppose that no good comes from the bile, do you venture to say that an investigation into its origin is of no value in medicine?

Well, let us suppose that it is contained in the food, and not specifically secreted in the liver (for you hold these two things possible). In this case, it will certainly make a considerable difference whether the ingested food contains a minimum or a maximum of bile; for the one kind is harmless, whereas that containing a large quantity of bile, owing to the fact that it cannot be properly purified in the liver, will result in the various affections—particularly jaundice—which Erasistratus himself states to occur where there is much bile. Surely, then, it is most essential for the physician to know in the first place, that the bile is contained in the food itself from outside, and, secondly, that for example, beet contains a great deal of bile, and bread very little, while olive oil contains most, and wine least of all, and all the other articles

* Bile.

of diet different quantities. Would it not be absurd for any one to choose voluntarily those articles which contain more bile, rather than those containing less?

What, however, if the bile is not contained in the food, but comes into existence in the animal's body? Will it not also be useful to know what state of the body is followed by a greater, and what by a smaller occurrence of bile? For obviously it is in our power to alter and transmute morbid states of the body—in fact, to give them a turn for the better. But if we did not know in what respect they were morbid or in what way they diverged from the normal, how should we be able to ameliorate them?

Therefore it is not useless in treatment, as Erasistratus says, to know the actual truth about the genesis of bile. Certainly it is not impossible, or even difficult to discover that the reason why honey produces yellow bile is not that it contains a large quantity of this within itself, but because it [the honey] undergoes change, becoming altered and transmuted into bile. For it would be bitter to the taste if it contained bile from the outset, and it would produce an equal quantity of bile in every person who took it. The facts, however, are not so. For in those who are in the prime of life, especially if they are warm by nature and are leading a life of toil, the honey changes entirely into yellow bile. Old people, however, it suits well enough, inasmuch as the alteration which it undergoes is not into bile, but into blood. Erasistratus, however, in addition to knowing nothing about this, shows no intelligence even in the division of his argument; he says that it is of no practical importance to investigate whether the bile is contained in the food from the beginning or comes into existence as a result of gastric digestion. He ought surely to have added something about its genesis in liver and veins, seeing that the old physicians and philosophers declare that it along with the blood is generated in these organs. But it is inevitable that people who, from the very outset, go astray, and wander from the right road, should talk such nonsense, and should, over and above this, neglect to search for the factors of most practical importance in medicine.

Having come to this point in the argument, I should like to ask those who declare that Erasistratus was very familiar with the Peripatetics, whether they know what Aristotle stated and demonstrated with regard to our bodies being compounded out of the Warm, the Cold, the Dry and the Moist, and how he says that among these the Warm is the most active, and that

those animals which are by nature warmest have abundance of blood, whilst those that are colder are entirely lacking in blood, and consequently in winter lie idle and motionless, lurking in holes like corpses. Further, the question of the colour of the blood has been dealt with not only by Aristotle but also by Plato. Now I, for my part, as I have already said, did not set before myself the task of stating what has been so well demonstrated by the Ancients, since I cannot surpass these men either in my views or in my method of giving them expression. Doctrines, however, which they either stated without demonstration, as being self-evident (since they never suspected that there could be sophists so degraded as to contemn the truth in these matters), or else which they actually omitted to mention at all—these I propose to discover and prove.

Now in reference to the genesis of the humours, I do not know that any one could add anything wiser than what has been said by Hippocrates, Aristotle, Praxagoras, Philotimus and many other among the Ancients. These men demonstrated that when the nutriment becomes altered in the veins by the innate heat, blood is produced when it is in moderation, and the other humours when it is not in proper proportion. And all the observed facts agree with this argument. Thus, those articles of food, which are by nature warmer are more productive of bile, while those which are colder produce more phlegm. Similarly of the periods of life, those which are naturally warmer tend more to bile, and the colder more to phlegm. Of occupations also, localities and seasons, and, above all, of natures themselves, the colder are more phlegmatic, and the warmer more bilious. Also cold diseases result from phlegm, and warmer ones from yellow bile. There is not a single thing to be found which does not bear witness to the truth of this account. How could it be otherwise? For, seeing that every part functions in its own special way because of the manner in which the four qualities are compounded, it is absolutely necessary that the function [activity] should be either completely destroyed, or, at least hampered, by any damage to the qualities, and that thus the animal should fall ill, either as a whole, or in certain of its parts.

Also the diseases which are primary and most generic are four in number, and differ from each other in warmth, cold, dryness and moisture. Now, Erasistratus himself confesses this, albeit unintentionally; for when he says that the digestion of food becomes worse in fever, not because the innate heat has ceased to be in due proportion, as people previously supposed, but because the stomach, with its activity impaired, cannot contract and triturate as before—then, I say, one may justly ask him what it is that has impaired the activity of the stomach.

Thus, for example, when a bubo develops following an accidental wound gastric digestion does not become impaired until after the patient has become fevered; neither the bubo nor the sore of itself impedes in any way or damages the activity of the stomach. But if fever occurs, the digestion at once deteriorates, and we are also right in saying that the activity of the stomach at once becomes impaired. We must add, however, by what it has been impaired. For the wound was not capable of impairing it, nor yet the bubo, for, if they had been, then they would have caused this damage before the fever as well. If it was not these that caused it, then it was the excess of heat (for these two symptoms occurred besides the bubo—an alteration in the arterial and cardiac movements and an excessive development of natural heat). Now the alteration of these movements will not merely not impair the function of the stomach in any way: it will actually prove an additional help among those animals in which, according to Erasistratus, the pneuma, which is propelled through the arteries and into the alimentary canal, is of great service in digestion; there is only left, then, the disproportionate heat to account for the damage to the gastric activity. For the pneuma is driven in more vigorously and continuously, and in greater quantity now than before; thus in this case, the animal whose digestion is promoted by pneuma will digest more, whereas the remaining factor—abnormal heat—will give them indigestion. For to say, on the one hand, that the pneuma has a certain property by virtue of which it promotes digestion, and then to say that this property disappears in cases of fever, is simply to admit the absurdity. For when they are again asked what it is that has altered the pneuma, they will only be able to reply, "the abnormal heat," and particularly if it be the pneuma in the food canal which is in question (since this does not come in any way near the bubo).

Yet why do I mention those animals in which the property of the pneuma plays an important part, when it is possible to base one's argument upon human beings, in whom it is either of no importance at all, or acts quite faintly and feebly? But Erasistratus himself agrees that human beings digest badly in fevers, adding as

the cause that the activity of the stomach has been impaired. He cannot, however, advance any other cause of this impairment than abnormal heat. But if it is not by accident that the abnormal heat impairs this activity, but by virtue of its own essence and power, then this abnormal heat must belong to the primary diseases. But, indeed, if disproportion of heat belongs to the primary diseases, it cannot but be that a proportionate blending [eucrasia] of the qualities produces the normal activity. For a disproportionate blend [dyscrasia] can only become a cause of the primary diseases through derangement of the eucrasia. That is to say, it is because the [normal] activities arise from the eucrasia that the primary impairments of these activities necessarily arise from its derangement.

I think, then, it has been proved to the satisfaction of those people who are capable of seeing logical consequences, that, even according to Erasistratus' own argument, the cause of the normal functions is eucrasia of the Warm. Now, this being so, there is nothing further to prevent us from saying that, in the case of each function, eucrasia is followed by the more, and dyscrasia by the less favourable alternative. And, therefore, if this be the case, we must suppose blood to be the outcome of proportionate, and yellow bile of disproportionate heat. So we naturally find yellow bile appearing in greatest quantity in ourselves at the warm periods of life, in warm countries, at warm seasons of the year, and when we are in a warm condition; similarly in people of warm temperaments, and in connection with warm occupations, modes of life, or diseases.

And to be in doubt as to whether this humour has its genesis in the human body or is contained in the food is what you would expect from one who has—I will not say failed to see that, when those who are perfectly healthy have, under the compulsion of circumstances, to fast contrary to custom, their mouths become bitter and their urine bile-coloured, while they suffer from gnawing pains in the stomach—but has, as it were, just made a sudden entrance into the world, and is not yet familiar with the phenomena which occur there. Who, in fact, does not know that anything which is overcooked grows at first salt and afterwards bitter? And if you will boil honey itself, far the sweetest of all things, you can demonstrate that even this becomes quite bitter. For what may occur as a result of boiling in the case of other articles which are not warm by nature, exists naturally in honey; for this reason it does not become sweeter on being boiled, since exactly the same quantity of heat as is needed for the production of sweetness exists from beforehand in the honey. Therefore the external heat, which would be useful for insufficiently warm substances, becomes in the honey a source of damage, in fact an excess; and it is for this reason that honey, when boiled, can be demonstrated to become bitter sooner than the others. For the same reason it is easily transmuted into bile in those people who are naturally warm, or in their prime, since warm when associated with warm becomes readily changed into a disproportionate combination and turns into bile sooner than into blood. Thus we need a cold temperament and a cold period of life if we would have honey brought to the nature of blood. Therefore Hippocrates not improperly advised those who were naturally bilious not to take honey, since they were obviously of too warm a temperament. So also, not only Hippocrates, but all physicians say that honey is bad in bilious diseases but good in old age; some of them having discovered this through the indications afforded by its nature, and others simply through experiment, for the Empiricist physicians too have made precisely the same observation, namely, that honey is good for an old man and not for a young one, that it is harmful for those who are naturally bilious, and serviceable for those who are phlegmatic. In a word, in bodies which are warm either through nature, disease, time of life, season of the year, locality, or occupation, honey is productive of bile, whereas in opposite circumstances it produces blood.

But surely it is impossible that the same article of diet can produce in certain persons bile and in others blood, if it be not that the genesis of these humours is accomplished in the body. For if all articles of food contained bile from the beginning and of themselves, and did not produce it by undergoing change in the animal body, then they would produce it similarly in all bodies; the food which was bitter to the taste would, I take it, be productive of bile, while that which tasted good and sweet would not generate even the smallest quantity of bile. Moreover, not only honey but all other sweet substances are readily converted into bile in the aforesaid bodies which are warm for any of the reasons mentioned.

Well, I have somehow or other been led into this discussion,—not in accordance with my plan, but compelled by the course of the argument. This subject has been treated at great length by Aristotle and Praxagoras, who have correctly expounded the view of Hippocrates and Plato.

9. For this reason the things that we have said are not to be looked upon as proofs but rather as indications of the dulness of those who think differently, and who do not even recognise what is agreed on by everyone and is a matter of daily observation. As for the scientific proofs of all this, they are to be drawn from these principles of which I have already spoken—namely, that bodies act upon and are acted upon by each other in virtue of the Warm, Cold, Moist and Dry. And if one is speaking of any activity, whether it be exercised by vein, liver, arteries, heart, alimentary canal, or any part, one will be inevitably compelled to acknowledge that this activity depends upon the way in which the four qualities are blended. Thus I should like to ask the Erasistrateans why it is that the stomach contracts upon the food, and why the veins generate blood. There is no use in recognizing the mere fact of contraction, without also knowing the cause; if we know this, we shall also be able to rectify the failures of function. "This is no concern of ours," they say; "we do not occupy ourselves with such causes as these; they are outside the sphere of the practitioner, and belong to that of the scientific investigator." Are you, then, going to oppose those who maintain that the cause of the function of every organ is a natural eucrasia, that the dyscrasia is itself known as a disease, and that it is certainly by this that the activity becomes impaired? Or, on the other hand, will you be convinced by the proofs which the ancient writers furnished? Or will you take a midway course between these two, neither perforce accepting these arguments as true nor contradicting them as false, but suddenly becoming sceptics—Pyrrhonists, in fact? But if you do this you will have to shelter yourselves behind the Empiricist teaching. For how are you going to be successful in treatment, if you do not understand the real essence of each disease? Why, then, did you not call yourselves Empiricists from the beginning? Why do you confuse us by announcing that you are investigating natural activities with a view to treatment? If the stomach is, in a particular case, unable to exercise its peristaltic and grinding functions, how are we going to bring it back to the normal if we do not know the cause of its disability? What I say is that we must cool the over-heated stomach and warm the chilled one; so also we must moisten the one which has become dried up, and conversely; so, too, in combinations of these conditions; if the stom-

ach becomes at the same time warmer and drier than normally, the first principle of treatment is at once to chill and moisten it; and if it become colder and moister, it must be warmed and dried; so also in other cases. But how on earth are the followers of Erasistratus going to act, confessing as they do that they make no sort of investigation into the cause of disease? For the fruit of the enquiry into activities is that by knowing the causes of the dyscrasiae one may bring them back to the normal, since it is of no use for the purposes of treatment merely to know what the activity of each organ is.

Now, it seems to me that Erasistratus is unaware of this fact also, that the actual disease is that condition of the body which, not accidentally, but primarily and of itself, impairs the normal function. How, then, is he going to diagnose or cure diseases if he is entirely ignorant of what they are, and of what kind and number? As regards the stomach, certainly, Erasistratus held that one should at least investigate how it digests the food. But why was not investigation also made as to the primary originative cause of this? And, as regards the veins and the blood, he omitted even to ask the question "how?"

Yet neither Hippocrates nor any of the other physicians or philosophers whom I mentioned a short while ago thought it right to omit this; they say that when the heat which exists naturally in every animal is well blended and moderately moist it generates blood; for this reason they also say that the blood is a virtually warm and moist humour, and similarly also that yellow bile is warm and dry, even though for the most part it appears moist. (For in them the apparently dry would seem to differ from the virtually dry.) Who does not know that brine and sea-water preserve meat and keep it uncorrupted, whilst all other water—the drinkable kind—readily spoils and rots it? And who does not know that when yellow bile is contained in large quantity in the stomach, we are troubled with an unquenchable thirst, and that when we vomit this up, we at once become much freer from thirst than if we had drunk very large quantities of fluid? Therefore this humour has been very properly termed warm, and also virtually dry. And, similarly, phlegm has been called cold and moist; for about this also clear proofs have been given by Hippocrates and the other Ancients.

Prodicus also, when in his book "On the Nature of Man" he gives the name "phlegm" (from the verb πεφλέχθαι) to that element in the humours which has been burned or, as it were, over-roasted, while using a different terminology, still keeps to the fact just as the others do; this man's innovations in nomenclature have also been amply done justice to by Plato. Thus, the white-coloured substance which everyone else calls phlegm, and which Prodicus calls blenna [mucus], is the well-known cold, moist humour which collects mostly in old people and in those who have been chilled in some way, and not even a lunatic could say that this was anything else than cold and moist.

If, then, there is a warm and moist humour, and another which is warm and dry, and yet another which is moist and cold, is there none which is virtually cold and dry? Is the fourth combination of temperaments, which exists in all other things, non-existent in the humours alone? No; the black bile is such a humour. This, according to intelligent physicians and philosophers, tends to be in excess, as regards seasons, mainly in the fall of the year, and, as regards ages, mainly after the prime of life. And, similarly, also they say that there are cold and dry modes of life, regions, constitutions, and diseases. Nature, they suppose, is not defective in this single combination; like the three other combinations, it extends everywhere.

At this point, also, I would gladly have been able to ask Erasistratus whether his "artistic" Nature has not constructed any organ for clearing away a humour such as this. For whilst there are two organs for the excretion of urine, and another of considerable size for that of yellow bile, does the humour which is more pernicious than these wander about persistently in the veins mingled with the blood? Yet Hippocrates says, "Dysentery is a fatal condition if it proceeds from black bile"; while that proceeding from yellow bile is by no means deadly, and most people recover from it; this proves how much more pernicious and acrid in its potentialities is black than yellow bile. Has Erasistratus, then, not read the book, "On the Nature of Man," any more than any of the rest of Hippocrates' writings, that he so carelessly passes over the consideration of the humours? Or, does he know it, and yet voluntarily neglect one of the finest studies in medicine? Thus he ought not to have said anything about the spleen, nor have stultified himself by holding that an artistic Nature would have prepared so large an organ for no purpose. As a matter of fact, not only Hippocrates and Plato—who are no less authorities on Nature than is Erasistratus—say that this viscus also is one of those which cleanse

the blood, but there are thousands of the ancient physicians and philosophers as well who
are in agreement with them. Now, all of these
the high and mighty Erasistratus affected to despise, and he neither contradicted them nor
even so much as mentioned their opinion. Hippocrates, indeed, says that the spleen wastes in
those people in whom the body is in good condition, and all those physicians also who base
themselves on experience agree with this. Again,
in those cases in which the spleen is large and is
increasing from internal suppuration, it destroys
the body and fills it with evil humours; this
again is agreed on, not only by Hippocrates, but
also by Plato and many others, including the
Empiric physicians. And the jaundice which
occurs when the spleen is out of order is darker in colour, and the cicatrices of ulcers are
dark. For, generally speaking, when the spleen
is drawing the atrabiliary humour into itself to
a less degree than is proper, the blood is unpurified, and the whole body takes on a bad
colour. And when does it draw this in to a less
degree than proper? Obviously, when it [the
spleen] is in a bad condition. Thus, just as the
kidneys, whose function it is to attract the urine,
do this badly when they are out or order, so also the spleen, which has in itself a native power
of attracting an atrabiliary quality, if it ever happens to be weak, must necessarily exercise this
attraction badly, with the result that the blood
becomes thicker and darker.

Now all these points, affording as they do the
greatest help in the diagnosis and in the cure of
disease were entirely passed over by Erasistratus, and he pretended to despise these great men
—he who does not despise ordinary people, but
always jealously attacks the most absurd doctrines. Hence, it was clearly because he had nothing to say against the statements made by the
Ancients regarding the function and utility of
the spleen, and also because he could discover
nothing new himself, that he ended by saying
nothing at all. I, however, for my part, have
demonstrated, firstly from the causes by which
everything throughout nature is governed (by
the causes I mean the Warm, Cold, Dry and
Moist) and secondly, from obvious bodily phenomena, that there must needs be a cold and
dry humour. And having in the next place
drawn attention to the fact that this humour is
black bile [atrabiliary] and that the viscus which
clears it away is the spleen—having pointed this
out by help of as few as possible of the proofs
given by ancient writers, I shall now proceed to
what remains of the subject in hand.

What else, then, remains but to explain clearly what it is that happens in the generation of
the humours, according to the belief and demonstration of the Ancients? This will be more
clearly understood from a comparison. Imagine,
then, some new wine which has been not long
ago pressed from the grape, and which is fer-
menting and undergoing alteration through the
agency of its contained heat. Imagine next two
residual substances produced during this process of alteration, the one tending to be light
and air-like and the other to be heavy and more
of the nature of earth; of these the one, as I
understand, they call the flower and the other
the lees. Now you may correctly compare yellow bile to the first of these, and black bile to
the latter, although these humours have not the
the same appearance when the animal is in normal health as that which they often show when
it is not so; for then the yellow bile becomes
vitelline, being so termed because it becomes
like the yolk of an egg, both in colour and density; and again, even the black bile itself becomes much more malignant than when in its
normal condition, but no particular name has
been given to [such a condition of] the humour,
except that some people have called it corrosive
or acetose, because it also becomes sharp like
vinegar and corrodes the animal's body—as also the earth, if it be poured out upon it—and
it produces a kind of fermentation and seething,
accompanied by bubbles—an abnormal putrefaction having become added to the natural
condition of the black humour. It seems to me
also that most of the ancient physicians give the
name black humour and not black bile to the
normal portion of this humour, which is discharged from the bowel and which also frequently rises to the top [of the stomach-con-
tents]; and they call black bile that part which,
through a kind of combustion and putrefaction,
has had its quality changed to acid. There is no
need, however, to dispute about names, but we
must realise the facts, which are as follow:—

In the genesis of blood, everything in the nutriment which belongs naturally to the thick
and earth-like part of the food, and which does
not take on well the alteration produced by the
innate heat—all this the spleen draws into itself. On the other hand, that part of the nutriment which is roasted, so to speak, or burnt
(this will be the warmest and sweetest part of
it, like honey and fat), becomes yellow bile, and
is cleared away through the so-called biliary
vessels; now, this is thin, moist, and fluid, not
like what it is when, having been roasted to an

excessive degree, it becomes yellow, fiery, and thick, like the yolk of eggs; for this latter is already abnormal, while the previously mentioned state is natural. Similarly with the black humour: that which does not yet produce, as I say, this seething and fermentation on the ground, is natural, while that which has taken over this character and faculty is unnatural; it has assumed an acridity owing to the combustion caused by abnormal heat, and has practically become transformed into ashes. In somewhat the same way burned lees differ from unburned. The former is a warm substance, able to burn, dissolve, and destroy the flesh. The other kind, which has not yet undergone combustion, one may find the physicians employing for the same purposes that one uses the so-called potter's earth and other substances which have naturally a combined drying and chilling action.

Now the vitelline bile also may take on the appearance of this combusted black bile, if ever it chance to be roasted, so to say, by fiery heat. And all the other forms of bile are produced, some from a blending of those mentioned, others being, as it were, transition-stages in the genesis of these or in their conversion into one another. And they differ in that those first mentioned are unmixed and unique, while the latter forms are diluted with various kinds of serum. And all the serums in the humours are waste substances, and the animal body needs to be purified from them. There is, however, a natural use for the humours first mentioned, both thick and thin; the blood is purified both by the spleen and by the bladder beside the liver, and a part of each of the two humours is put away, of such quantity and quality that, if it were carried all over the body, it would do a certain amount of harm. For that which is decidedly thick and earthy in nature, and has entirely escaped alteration in the liver, is drawn by the spleen into itself; the other part which is only moderately thick, after being elaborated [in the liver], is carried all over the body. For the blood in many parts of the body has need of a certain amount of thickening, as also, I take it, of the fibres which it contains. And the use of these has been discussed by Plato, and it will also be discussed by me in such of my treatises as may deal with the use of parts. And the blood also needs, not least, the yellow humour, which has as yet not reached the extreme stage of combustion; in the treatises mentioned it will be pointed out what purpose is subserved by this.

Now Nature has made no organ for clearing away phlegm, this being cold and moist, and, as it were, half-digested nutriment; such a substance, therefore, does not need to be evacuated, but remains in the body and undergoes alteration there. And perhaps one cannot properly give the name of phlegm to the surplus-substance which runs down from the brain, but one should call it mucus [blenna] or coryza—as, in fact, it is actually termed; in any case it will be pointed out, in the treatise "On the Use of Parts," how Nature has provided for the evacuation of this substance. Further, the device provided by Nature which ensures that the phlegm which forms in the stomach and intestines may be evacuated in the most rapid and effective way possible—this also will be described in that commentary. As to that portion of the phlegm which is carried in the veins, seeing that this is of service to the animal, it requires no evacuation. Here too, then, we must pay attention and recognise that, just as in the case of each of the two kinds of bile, there is one part which is useful to the animal and in accordance with its nature, while the other part is useless and contrary to nature, so also is it with the phlegm; such of it as is sweet is useful to the animal and according to nature, while, as to such of it as has become bitter or salt, that part which is bitter is completely undigested, while that part which is salt has undergone putrefaction. And the term "complete indigestion" refers of course to the second digestion—that which takes place in the veins; it is not a failure of the first digestion—that in the alimentary canal—for it would not have become a humour at the outset if it had escaped this digestion also.

It seems to me that I have made enough reference to what has been said regarding the genesis and destruction of humours by Hippocrates, Plato, Aristotle, Praxagoras, and Diocles, and many others among the Ancients; I did not deem it right to transport the whole of their final pronouncements into this treatise. I have said only so much regarding each of the humours as will stir up the reader, unless he be absolutely inept, to make himself familiar with the writings of the Ancients, and will help him to gain more easy access to them. In another treatise I have written on the humours according to Praxagoras, son of Nicarchus; although this authority makes as many as ten humours, not including the blood (the blood itself being an eleventh), this is not a departure from the teaching of Hippocrates; for Praxagoras divides into species and varieties the humours which Hippocrates first mentioned, with the demonstration proper to each.

Those, then, are to be praised who explain the points which have been duly mentioned, as also those who add what has been left out; for it is not possible for the same man to make both a beginning and an end. Those, on the other hand, deserve censure who are so impatient that they will not wait to learn any of the things which have been duly mentioned, as do also those who are so ambitious that, in their lust after novel doctrines, they are always attempting some fraudulent sophistry, either purposely neglecting certain subjects, as Erasistratus does in the case of the humours, or unscrupulously attacking other people, as does this same writer, as well as many of the more recent authorities.

But let this discussion come to an end here, and I shall add in the third book all that remains.

Book Three

1. It has been made clear in the preceding discussion that nutrition occurs by an alteration or assimilation of that which nourishes to that which receives nourishment, and that there exists in every part of the animal a faculty which in view of its activity we call, in general terms, alterative, or, more specifically, assimilative and nutritive. It was also shown that a sufficient supply of the matter which the part being nourished makes into nutriment for itself is ensured by virtue of another faculty which naturally attracts its proper juice [humour] that that juice is proper to each part which is adapted for assimilation, and that the faculty which attracts the juice is called, by reason of its activity, attractive or epispastic. It has also been shown that assimilation is preceded by adhesion, and this, again, by presentation, the latter stage being, as one might say, the end or goal of the activity corresponding to the attractive faculty. For the actual bringing up of nutriment from the veins into each of the parts takes place through the activation of the attractive faculty, whilst to have been finally brought up and presented to the part is the actual end for which we desired such an activity; it is attracted in order that it may be presented. After this, considerable time is needed for the nutrition of the animal; whilst a thing may be even rapidly attracted, on the other hand to become adherent, altered, and entirely assimilated to the part which is being nourished and to become a part of it, cannot take place suddenly, but requires a considerable amount of time. But if the nutritive juice, so presented, does not remain in the part, but withdraws to another one, and keeps flowing away, and constantly changing and shifting its position, neither adhesion nor complete assimilation will take place in any of them. Here too, then, the [animal's] nature has need of some other faculty for ensuring a prolonged stay of the presented juice at the part, and this not a faculty which comes in from somewhere outside but one which is resident in the part which is to be nourished. This faculty, again, in view of its activity our predecessors were obliged to call retentive.

Thus our argument has clearly shown the necessity for the genesis of such a faculty, and whoever has an appreciation of logical sequence must be firmly persuaded from what we have said that, if it be laid down and proved by previous demonstration that Nature is artistic and solicitous for the animal's welfare, it necessarily follows that she must also possess a faculty of this kind.

2. Since, however, it is not our habit to employ this kind of demonstration alone, but to add thereto cogent and compelling proofs drawn from obvious facts, we will also proceed to the latter kind in the present instance: we will demonstrate that in certain parts of the body the retentive faculty is so obvious that its operation can be actually recognised by the senses, whilst in other parts it is less obvious to the senses, but is capable even here of being detected by the argument.

Let us begin our exposition, then, by first dealing systematically for a while with certain definite parts of the body, in reference to which we may accurately test and enquire what sort of thing the retentive faculty is.

Now, could one begin the enquiry in any better way than with the largest and hollowest organs? Personally I do not think one could. It is to be expected that in these, owing to their size, the activities will show quite clearly, whereas with respect to the small organs, even if they possess a strong faculty of this kind, its activation will not at once be recognisable to sense.

Now those parts of the animal which are especially hollow and large are the stomach and the organ which is called the womb or uterus. What prevents us, then, from taking up these first and considering their activities, conducting the enquiry on our own persons in regard to those activities which are obvious without dissection, and, in the case of those which are more obscure, dissecting animals which are near to man; not that even animals unlike him will not show, in a general way, the faculty in question, but because in this manner we may find out at once what is common to all and what is peculiar to ourselves, and so may become more resourceful in the diagnosis and treatment of disease.

Now it is impossible to speak of both organs at once, so we shall deal with each in turn, beginning with the one which is capable of demonstrating the retentive faculty most plainly. For the stomach retains the food until it has quite digested it, and the uterus retains the embryo until it brings it to completion, but the time taken for the completion of the embryo is many times more than that for the digestion of food.

3. We may expect, then, to detect the retentive faculty in the uterus more clearly in proportion to the longer duration of its activity as compared with that of the stomach. For, as we know, it takes nine months in most women for the foetus to attain maturity in the womb, this organ having its neck quite closed, and entirely surrounding the embryo together with the chorion. Further, it is the utility of the function which determines the closure of the os and the stay of the foetus in the uterus. For it is not casually nor without reason that Nature has made the uterus capable of contracting upon, and of retaining the embryo, but in order that the latter may arrive at a proper size. When, therefore, the object for which the uterus brought its retentive faculty into play has been fulfilled, it then stops this faculty and brings it back to a state of rest, and employs instead of it another faculty hitherto quiescent—the propulsive faculty. In this case again the quiescent and active states are both determined by utility; when this calls, there is activity; when it does not, there is rest.

Here, then, once more, we must observe well the Art [artistic tendency] of Nature—how she has not merely placed in each organ the capabilities of useful activities, but has also foreordained the times both of rest and movement. For when everything connected with the pregnancy proceeds properly, the eliminative faculty remains quiescent as though it did not exist, but if anything goes wrong in connection either with the chorion or any of the other membranes or with the foetus itself, and its completion is

entirely despaired of, then the uterus no longer awaits the nine-months period, but the retentive faculty forthwith ceases and allows the heretofore inoperative faculty to come into action. Now it is that something is done—in fact, useful work effected—by the eliminative or propulsive faculty (for so it, too, has been called, receiving, like the rest, its names from the corresponding activities).

Further, our theory can, I think, demonstrate both together; for seeing that they succeed each other, and that the one keeps giving place to the other according as utility demands, it seems not unreasonable to accept a common demonstration also for both. Thus it is the work of the retentive faculty to make the uterus contract upon the foetus at every point, so that, naturally enough, when the midwives palpate it, the os is found to be closed, whilst the pregnant women themselves, during the first days—and particularly on that on which conception takes place—experience a sensation as if the uterus were moving and contracting upon itself. Now, if both of these things occur—if the os closes apart from inflammation or any other disease, and if this is accompanied by a feeling of movement in the uterus—then the women believe that they have received the semen which comes from the male, and that they are retaining it.

Now we are not inventing this for ourselves: one may say the statement is based on prolonged experience of those who occupy themselves with such matters. Thus Herophilus does not hesitate to state in his writings that up to the time of labour the os uteri will not admit so much as the tip of a probe, that it no longer opens to the slightest degree if pregnancy has begun—that, in fact, it dilates more widely at the times of the menstrual flow. With him are in agreement all the others who have applied themselves to this subject; and particularly Hippocrates, who was the first of all physicians and philosophers to declare that the os uteri closes during pregnancy and inflammation, albeit in pregnancy it does not depart from its own nature, whilst in inflammation it becomes hard.

In the case of the opposite (the eliminative) faculty, the os opens, whilst the whole fundus approaches as near as possible to the os, expelling the embryo as it does so; and along with the fundus the contiguous parts—which form as it were a girdle round the whole organ—cooperate in the work; they squeeze upon the embryo and propel it bodily outwards. And, in many women who exercise such a faculty immoderately, violent pains cause forcible prolapse of the whole womb; here almost the same thing happens as frequently occurs in wrestling-bouts and struggles, when in our eagerness to overturn and throw others we are ourselves upset along with them; for similarly when the uterus is forcing the embryo forward it sometimes becomes entirely prolapsed, and particularly when the ligaments connecting it with the spine happen to be naturally lax.

A wonderful device of Nature's also is this—that, when the foetus is alive, the os uteri is closed with perfect accuracy, but if it dies, the os at once opens up to the extent which is necessary for the foetus to make its exit. The midwife, however, does not make the parturient woman get up at once and sit down on the [obstetric] chair, but she begins by palpating the os as it gradually dilates, and the first thing she says is that it has dilated "enough to admit the little finger," then that "it is bigger now," and as we make enquiries from time to time, she answers that the size of the dilatation is increasing. And when it is sufficient to allow of the transit of the foetus, she then makes the patient get up from her bed and sit on the chair, and bids her make every effort to expel the child. Now, this additional work which the patient does of herself is no longer the work of the uterus but of the epigastric muscles, which also help us in defaecation and micturition.

4. Thus the two faculties are clearly to be seen in the case of the uterus; in the case of the stomach they appear as follows:—Firstly in the condition of gurgling, which physicians are persuaded, and with reason, to be a symptom of weakness of the stomach; for sometimes when the very smallest quantity of food has been ingested this does not occur, owing to the fact that the stomach is contracting accurately upon the food and constricting it at every point; sometimes when the stomach is full the gurglings yet make themselves heard as though it were empty. For if it be in a natural condition, employing its contractile faculty in the ordinary way, then, even if its contents be very small, it grasps the whole of them and does not leave any empty space. When it is weak, however, being unable to lay hold of its contents accurately, it produces a certain amount of vacant space, and allows the liquid contents to flow about in different directions in accordance with its changes of shape, and so to produce gurglings.

Thus those who are troubled with this symptom expect, with good reason, that they will also be unable to digest adequately; proper digestion cannot take place in a weak stomach. In such people also, the mass of food may be plainly seen to remain an abnormally long time in the stomach, as would be natural if their digestion were slow. Indeed, the chief way in which these people will surprise one is in the length of time that not food alone but even fluids will remain in their stomachs. Now, the actual cause of this is not, as one would imagine, that the lower outlet of the stomach, being fairly narrow, will allow nothing to pass before being reduced to a fine state of division. There are a great many people who frequently swallow large quantities of big fruit-stones; one person, who was holding a gold ring in his mouth, inadvertently swallowed it; another swallowed a coin, and various people have swallowed various hard and indigestible objects; yet all these people easily passed by the bowel what they had swallowed, without there being any subsequent symptoms. Now surely if narrowness of the gastric outlet were the cause of untriturated food remaining for an abnormally long time, none of these articles I have mentioned would ever have escaped. Furthermore, the fact that it is liquids which remain longest in these people's stomachs is sufficient to put the idea of narrowness of the outlet out of court. For, supposing a rapid descent were dependent upon emulsification, then soups, milk, and barley-emulsion would at once pass along in every case. But as a matter of fact this is not so. For in people who are extremely asthenic it is just these fluids which remain undigested, which accumulate and produce gurglings, and which oppress and overload the stomach, whereas in strong persons not merely do none of these things happen, but even a large quantity of bread or meat passes rapidly down.

And it is not only because the stomach is distended and loaded and because the fluid runs from one part of it to another accompanied by gurglings—it is not only for these reasons that one would judge that there was an unduly long continuance of the food in it, in those people who are so disposed, but also from the vomiting. Thus, there are some who vomit up every particle of what they have eaten, not after three or four hours, but actually in the middle of the night, a lengthy period having elapsed since their meal.

Suppose you fill any animal whatsoever with liquid food—an experiment I have often carried out in pigs, to whom I give a sort of mess of wheaten flour and water, thereafter cutting them open after three or four hours; if you will do this yourself, you will find the food still in the stomach. For it is not chylification which determines the length of its stay here—since this can also be effected outside the stomach; the determining factor is digestion which is a different thing from chylification, as are blood-production and nutrition. For, just as it has been shown that these two processes depend upon a change of qualities, similarly also the digestion of food in the stomach involves a transmutation of it into the quality proper to that which is receiving nourishment. Then, when it is completely digested, the lower outlet opens and the food is quickly ejected through it, even if there should be amongst it abundance of stones, bones, grape-pips, or other things which cannot be reduced to chyle. And you may observe this yourself in an animal, if you will try to hit upon the time at which the descent of food from the stomach takes place. But even if you should fail to discover the time, and nothing was yet passing down, and the food was still undergoing digestion in the stomach, still even then you would find dissection not without its uses. You will observe, as we have just said, that the pylorus is accurately closed, and that the whole stomach is in a state of contraction upon the food very much as the womb contracts upon the foetus. For it is never possible to find a vacant space in the uterus, the stomach, or in either of the two bladders—that is, either in that called bile-receiving or in the other; whether their contents be abundant or scanty, their cavities are seen to be replete and full, owing to the fact that their coats contract constantly upon the contents—so long, at least, as the animal is in a natural condition.

Now Erasistratus for some reason declares that it is the contractions of the stomach which are the cause of everything—that is to say, of the softening of the food, the removal of waste matter, and the absorption of the food when chylified [emulsified].

Now I have personally, on countless occasions, divided the peritoneum of a still living animal and have always found all the intestines contracting peristaltically upon their contents. The condition of the stomach, however, is found less simple; as regards the substances freshly swallowed, it had grasped these accurately both above and below, in fact at every point, and was as devoid of movement as though it had grown round and become united with the food. At the same time I found the pylorus persistently closed and accurately shut, like the os uteri on the foetus.

In the cases, however, where digestion had been completed the pylorus had opened, and the stomach was undergoing peristaltic movements, similar to those of the intestines.

5. Thus all these facts agree that the stomach, uterus, and bladders possess certain inborn faculties which are retentive of their own proper qualities and eliminative of those that are foreign. For it has been already shown that the bladder by the liver draws bile into itself, while it is also quite obvious that it eliminates this daily into the stomach. Now, of course, if the eliminative were to succeed the attractive faculty and there were not a retentive faculty between the two, there would be found, on every occasion that animals were dissected, an equal quantity of bile in the gall-bladder. This however, we do not find. For the bladder is sometimes observed to be very full, sometimes quite empty, while at other times you find in it various intermediate degrees of fulness, just as is the case with the other bladder—that which receives the urine; for even without resorting to anatomy we may observe that the urinary bladder continues to collect urine up to the time that it becomes uncomfortable through the increasing quantity of urine or the irritation caused by its acidity—the presumption thus being that here, too, there is a retentive faculty.

Similarly, too, the stomach, when, as often happens, it is irritated by acidity, gets rid of the food, although still undigested, earlier than proper; or again, when oppressed by the quantity of its contents, or disordered from the co-existence of both conditions, it is seized with diarrhoea. Vomiting also is an affection of the upper [part of the] stomach analogous to diarrhoea, and it occurs when the stomach is overloaded or is unable to stand the quality of food or surplus substances which it contains. Thus, when such a condition develops in the lower parts of the stomach, while the parts about the inlet are normal, it ends in diarrhoea, whereas if this condition is in the upper stomach, the lower parts being normal, it ends in vomiting.

6. This may often be clearly observed in those who are disinclined for food; when obliged to eat, they have not the strength to swallow, and, even if they force themselves to do so, they cannot retain the food, but at once vomit it up. And those especially who have a dislike to some particular kind of food, sometimes take it under compulsion, and then promptly bring it up; or, if they force themselves to keep it down, they are nauseated and feel their stomach turned up, and endeavouring to relieve itself of its discomfort.

Thus, as was said at the beginning, all the observed facts testify that there must exist in almost all parts of the animal a certain inclination towards, or, so to speak, an appetite for their own special quality, and an aversion to, or, as it were, a hatred of the foreign quality. And it is natural that when they feel an inclination they should attract, and that when they feel aversion they should expel.

From these facts, then, again, both the attractive and the propulsive faculties have been demonstrated to exist in everything.

But if there be an inclination or attraction, there will also be some benefit derived; for no existing thing attracts anything else for the mere sake of attracting, but in order to benefit by what is acquired by the attraction. And of course it cannot benefit by it if it cannot retain it. Herein, then, again, the retentive faculty is shown to have its necessary origin: for the stomach obviously inclines towards its own proper qualities and turns away from those that are foreign to it. *

But if it aims at and attracts its food and benefits by it while retaining and contracting upon it, we may also expect that there will be some termination to the benefit received, and that thereafter will come the time for the exercise of the eliminative faculty.

7. But if the stomach both retains and benefits by its food, then it employs it for the end for which it [the stomach] naturally exists. And it exists to partake of that which is of a quality befitting and proper to it. Thus it attracts all the most useful parts of the food in a vaporous and finely divided condition, storing this up in its own coats, and applying it to them. And when it is sufficiently full it puts away from it, as one might something troublesome, the rest of the food, this having itself meanwhile obtained some profit from its association with the stomach. For it is impossible for two bodies which are adapted for acting and being acted upon to come together without either both acting or being acted upon, or else one acting and the other being acted upon. For if their forces are equal they will act and be acted upon equally, and if the one be much superior in strength, it will exert its activity upon its passive neighbour; thus, while producing a great and appreciable effect, it will itself be acted upon either little or not at all. But it is herein also that the

main difference lies between nourishing food and a deleterious drug; the latter masters the forces of the body, whereas the former is mastered by them.

There cannot, then, be food which is suited for the animal which is not also correspondingly subdued by the qualities existing in the animal. And to be subdued means to undergo alteration. Now, some parts are stronger in power and others weaker; therefore, while all will subdue the nutriment which is proper to the animal, they will not all do so equally. Thus the stomach will subdue and alter its food, but not to the same extent as will the liver, veins, arteries, and heart.

We must therefore observe to what extent it does alter it. The alteration is more than that which occurs in the mouth, but less than that in the liver and veins. For the latter alteration changes the nutriment into the substance of blood, whereas that in the mouth obviously changes it into a new form, but certainly does not completely transmute it. This you may discover in the food which is left in the intervals between the teeth, and which remains there all night; the bread is not exactly bread, nor the meat meat, for they have a smell similar to that of the animal's mouth, and have been disintegrated and dissolved, and have had the qualities of the animal's flesh impressed upon them. And you may observe the extent of the alteration which occurs to food in the mouth if you will chew some corn and then apply it to an unripe [undigested] boil: you will see it rapidly transmuting—in fact entirely digesting—the boil, though it cannot do anything of the kind if you mix it with water. And do not let this surprise you; this phlegm [saliva] in the mouth is also a cure for lichens†; it even rapidly destroys scorpions; while, as regards the animals which emit venom, some it kills at once, and others after an interval; to all of them in any case it does great damage. Now, the masticated food is all, firstly, soaked in and mixed up with this phlegm; and secondly, it is brought into contact with the actual skin of the mouth; thus it undergoes more change than the food which is wedged into the vacant spaces between the teeth.

But just as masticated food is more altered than the latter kind, so is food which has been swallowed more altered than that which has been merely masticated. Indeed, there is no comparison between these two processes; we have

---

* Galen confuses the nutrition of organs with that of the ultimate living elements or cells; the stomach does not, of course, feed itself in the way a cell does.

† Apparently skin-diseases in which a superficial crust (resembling the lichen on a tree-trunk) forms—e.g. psoriasis.

only to consider what the stomach contains—phlegm, bile, pneuma, [innate] heat, and, indeed the whole substance of the stomach. And if one considers along with this the adjacent viscera, like a lot of burning hearths around a great cauldron—to the right the liver, to the left the spleen, the heart above, and along with it the diaphragm (suspended and in a state of constant movement), and the omentum sheltering them all—you may believe what an extraordinary alteration it is which occurs in the food taken into the stomach.

How could it easily become blood if it were not previously prepared by means of a change of this kind? It has already been shown that nothing is altered all at once from one quality to its opposite. How then could bread, beef, beans, or any other food turn into blood if they had not previously undergone some other alteration? And how could the faeces be generated right away in the small intestine? For what is there in this organ more potent in producing alteration than the factors in the stomach? Is it the number of the coats, or the way it is surrounded by neighbouring viscera, or the time that the food remains in it, or some kind of innate heat which it contains? Most assuredly the intestines have the advantage of the stomach in none of these respects. For what possible reason, then, will objectors have it that bread may often remain a whole night in the stomach and still preserve its original qualities, whereas when once it is projected into the intestines, it straightway becomes ordure? For, if such a long period of time is incapable of altering it, neither will the short period be sufficient, or, if the latter is enough, surely the longer time will be much more so! Well, then, can it be that, while the nutriment does undergo an alteration in the stomach, this is a different kind of alteration and one which is not dependent on the nature of the organ which alters it? Or if it be an alteration of this latter kind, yet one perhaps which is not proper to the body of the animal? This is still more impossible. Digestion was shown to be nothing else than an alteration to the quality proper to that which is receiving nourishment. Since, then, this is what digestion means and since the nutriment has been shown to take on in the stomach a quality appropriate to the animal which is about to be nourished by it, it has been demonstrated adequately that nutriment does undergo digestion in the stomach.

And Asclepiades is absurd when he states that the quality of the digested food never shows itself either in eructations or in the vomited matter, or on dissection. For of course the mere fact that the food smells of the body shows that it has undergone gastric digestion. But this man is so foolish that, when he hears the Ancients saying that the food is converted in the stomach into something "good," he thinks it proper to look out not for what is good in its possible effects, but for what is good to the taste: this is like saying that apples (for so one has to argue with him) become more apple-like [in flavour] in the stomach, or honey more honey-like!

Erasistratus, however, is still more foolish and absurd, either through not perceiving in what sense the Ancients said that digestion is similar to the process of boiling, or because he purposely confused himself with sophistries. It is, he says, inconceivable that digestion, involving as it does such trifling warmth, should be related to the boiling process. This is as if we were to suppose that it was necessary to put the fires of Etna under the stomach before it could manage to alter the food; or else that, while it was capable of altering the food, it did not do this by virtue of its innate heat, which of course was moist, so that the word boil was used instead of bake.

What he ought to have done, if it was facts that he wished to dispute about, was to have tried to show, first and foremost, that the food is not transmuted or altered in quality by the stomach at all, and secondly, if he could not be confident of this, he ought to have tried to show that this alteration was not of any advantage to the animal. If, again, he were unable even to make this misrepresentation, he ought to have attempted to confute the postulate concerning the active principles—to show, in fact, that the functions taking place in the various parts do not depend on the way in which the Warm, Cold, Dry, and Moist are mixed, but on some other factor. And if he had not the audacity to misrepresent facts even so far as this, still he should have tried at least to show that the Warm is not the most active of all the principles which play a part in things governed by Nature. But if he was unable to demonstrate this any more than any of the previous propositions, then he ought not to have made himself ridiculous by quarrelling uselessly with a mere name—as though Aristotle had not clearly stated in the fourth book of his "Meteorology," as well as in many other passages, in what way digestion can be said to be allied to boiling, and also that the latter expression is not used in its primitive or strict sense.

But, as has been frequently said already, the

one starting-point of all this is a thorough-going enquiry into the question of the Warm, Cold, Dry and Moist; this Aristotle carried out in the second of his books "On Genesis and Destruction," where he shows that all the transmutations and alterations throughout the body take place as a result of these principles. Erasistratus, however, advanced nothing against these or anything else that has been said above, but occupied himself merely with the word "boiling."

8. Thus, as regards digestion, even though he neglected everything else, he did at least attempt to prove his point—namely, that digestion in animals differs from boiling carried on outside; in regard to the question of deglutition, however, he did not go even so far as this. What are his words?

"The stomach does not appear to exercise any traction."

Now the fact is that the stomach possesses two coats, which certainly exist for some purpose; they extend as far as the mouth, the internal one remaining throughout similar to what it is in the stomach, and the other one tending to become of a more fleshy nature in the gullet. Now simple observation will testify that these coats * have their fibres inserted in contrary directions. And, although Erasistratus did not attempt to say for what reason they are like this, I am going to do so.

The inner coat has its fibres straight, since it exists for the purpose of traction. The outer coat has its fibres transverse, for the purpose of peristalsis. In fact, the movements of each of the mobile organs of the body depend on the setting of the fibres. Now please test this assertion first in the muscles themselves; in these the fibres are most distinct, and their movements visible owing to their vigour. And after the muscles, pass to the physical organs, and you will see that they all move in correspondence with their fibres. This is why the fibres throughout the intestines are circular in both coats—they only contract peristaltically, they do not exercise traction. The stomach, again, has some of its fibres longitudinal for the purpose of traction and the others transverse for the purpose of peristalsis. For just as the movements in the muscles take place when each of the fibres becomes tightened and drawn towards its origin, such also is what happens in the stomach; when the transverse fibres tighten, the breadth of the cavity contained by them becomes less; and when the longitudinal fibres contract and draw in upon

* The mucous and the muscular coats.

themselves, the length must necessarily be curtailed. This curtailment of length, indeed, is well seen in the act of swallowing: the larynx is seen to rise upwards to exactly the same degree that the gullet is drawn downwards; while, after the process of swallowing has been completed and the gullet is released from tension, the larynx can be clearly seen to sink down again. This is because the inner coat of the stomach, which has the longitudinal fibres and which also lines the gullet and the mouth, extends to the interior of the larynx, and it is thus impossible for it to be drawn down by the stomach without the larynx being involved in the traction.

Further, it will be found acknowledged in Erasistratus's own writings that the circular fibres (by which the stomach as well as other parts performs its contractions) do not curtail its length, but contract and lessen its breadth. For he says that the stomach contracts peristaltically round the food during the whole period of digestion. But if it contracts, without in any way being diminished in length, this is because downward traction of the gullet is not a property of the movement of circular peristalsis. For what alone happens, as Erasistratus himself said, is that when the upper parts contract the lower ones dilate. And everyone knows that this can be plainly seen happening even in a dead man, if water be poured down his throat; this symptom results from the passage of matter through a narrow channel; it would be extraordinary if the channel did not dilate when a mass was passing through it. Obviously then the dilatation of the lower parts along with the contraction of the upper is common both to dead bodies, when anything whatsoever is passing through them, and to living ones, whether they contract peristaltically round their contents or attract them.

Curtailment of length, on the other hand, is peculiar to organs which possess longitudinal fibres for the purpose of attraction. But the gullet was shown to be pulled down; for otherwise it would not have drawn upon the larynx. It is therefore clear that the stomach attracts food by the gullet.

Further, in vomiting, the mere passive conveyance of rejected matter up to the mouth will certainly itself suffice to keep open those parts of the oesophagus which are distended by the returned food; as it occupies each part in front [above], it first dilates this, and of course leaves the part behind [below] contracted. Thus, in this respect at least, the condition of the gullet is precisely similar to what it is in the act of swallowing. But there being no traction, the whole length remains equal in such cases.

And for this reason it is easier to swallow than to vomit, for deglutition results from both coats of the stomach being brought into action, the inner one exerting a pull and the outer one helping by peristalsis and propulsion, whereas emesis occurs from the outer coat alone functioning, without there being any kind of pull towards the mouth. For, although the swallowing of food is ordinarily preceded by a feeling of desire on the part of the stomach, there is in the case of vomiting no corresponding desire from the mouth-parts for the experience; the two are opposite dispositions of the stomach itself; it yearns after and tends towards what is advantageous and proper to it, it loathes and rids itself of what is foreign. Thus the actual process of swallowing occurs very quickly in those who have a good appetite for such foods as are proper to the stomach; this organ obviously draws them in and down before they are masticated; whereas in the case of those who are forced to take a medicinal draught or who take food as medicine, the swallowing of these articles is accomplished with distress and difficulty.

From what has been said, then, it is clear that the inner coat of the stomach (that containing longitudinal fibres) exists for the purpose of exerting a pull from mouth to stomach, and that it is only in deglutition that it is active, whereas the external coat, which contains transverse fibres, has been so constituted in order that it may contract upon its contents and propel them forward; this coat furthermore, functions in vomiting no less than in swallowing. The truth of my statement is also borne out by what happens in the case of the *channae* and *synodonts;** the stomachs of these animals are sometimes found in their mouths, as also Aristotle writes in his "History of Animals"; he also adds the cause of this: he says that it is owing to their voracity.

The facts are as follows. In all animals, when the appetite is very intense, the stomach rises up, so that some people who have a clear perception of this condition say that their stomach "creeps out" of them; in others, who are still masticating their food and have not yet worked it up properly in the mouth, the stomach obviously snatches away the food from them against their will. In those animals, therefore, which are naturally voracious, in whom the mouth cavity is of generous proportions, and the stom-

* The *channa* is a kind of sea-perch; the *synodont* is supposed to be an edible Mediterranean perch.

ach situated close to it (as in the case of the synodont and channa), it is in no way surprising that, when they are sufficiently hungry and are pursuing one of the smaller animals, and are just on the point of catching it, the stomach should, under the impulse of desire, spring into the mouth. And this cannot possibly take place in any other way than by the stomach drawing the food to itself by means of the gullet, as though by a hand. In fact, just as we ourselves, in our eagerness to grasp more quickly something lying before us, sometimes stretch out our whole bodies along with our hands, so also the stomach stretches itself forward along with the gullet, which is, as it were, its hand. And thus, in these animals in whom those three factors co-exist—an excessive propensity for food, a small gullet, and ample mouth proportions— in these, any slight tendency to movement forwards brings the whole stomach into the mouth.

Now the constitution of the organs might itself suffice to give a naturalist an indication of their functions. For Nature would never have purposelessly constructed the oesophagus of two coats with contrary dispositions; they must also have each been meant to have a different action. The Erasistratean school, however, are capable of anything rather than of recognizing the effects of Nature. Come, therefore, let us demonstrate to them by animal dissection as well that each of the two coats does exercise the activity which I have stated. Take an animal, then; lay bare the structures surrounding the gullet, without severing any of the nerves, arteries, or veins which are there situated; next divide with vertical incisions, from the lower jaw to the thorax, the outer coat of the oesophagus (that containing transverse fibres); then give the animal food and you will see that it still swallows although the peristaltic function has been abolished. If, again, in another animal, you cut through both coats with transverse incisions, you will observe that this animal also swallows although the inner coat is no longer functioning. From this it is clear that the animal can also swallow by either of the two coats, although not so well as by both. For the following also, in addition to other points, may be distinctly observed in the dissection which I have described—that during deglutition the gullet becomes slightly filled with air which is swallowed along with the food, and that, when the outer coat is contracting, this air is easily forced with the food into the stomach, but that, when there only exists an inner coat, the air impedes the conveyance of food, by distending this coat and hindering its action.

But Erasistratus said nothing about this, nor did he point out that the oblique situation of the gullet clearly confutes the teaching of those who hold that it is simply by virtue of the impulse from above that food which is swallowed reaches the stomach. The only correct thing he said was that many of the longnecked animals bend down to swallow. Hence, clearly, the observed fact does not show how we swallow but how we do not swallow. For from this observation it is clear that swallowing is not due merely to the impulse from above; it is yet, however, not clear whether it results from the food being attracted by the stomach, or conducted by the gullet. For our part, however, having enumerated all the different considerations—those based on the constitution of the organs, as well as those based on the other symptoms which, as just mentioned, occur both before and after the gullet has been exposed—we have thus sufficiently proved that the inner coast exists for the purpose of attraction and the outer for the purpose of propulsion.

Now the original task we set before ourselves was to demonstrate that the retentive faculty exists in every one of the organs, just as in the previous book we proved the existence of the attractive, and, over and above this, the alterative faculty. Thus, in the natural course of our argument, we have demonstrated these four faculties existing in the stomach—the attractive faculty in connection with swallowing, the retentive with digestion, the expulsive with vomiting and with the descent of digested food into the small intestine—and digestion itself we have shown to be a process of alteration.

9. Concerning the spleen, also, we shall therefore have no further doubts as to whether it attracts what is proper to it, rejects what is foreign, and has a natural power of altering and retaining all that it attracts; nor shall we be in any doubt as to the liver, veins, arteries, heart, or any other organ. For these four faculties have been shown to be necessary for every part which is to be nourished; this is why we have called these faculties the handmaids of nutrition. For just as human faeces are most pleasing to dogs, so the residual matters from the liver are, some of them, proper to the spleen, others to the gall-bladder, and others to the kidneys.

10. I should not have cared to say anything further as to the origin of these [surplus substances] after Hippocrates, Plato, Aristotle, Diocles, Praxagoras, and Philotimus, nor indeed should I even have said anything about the faculties, if any of our predecessors had worked out this subject thoroughly.

While, however, the statements which the Ancients made on these points were correct, they yet omitted to defend their arguments with logical proofs; of course they never suspected that there could be sophists so shameless as to try to contradict obvious facts. More recent physicians, again, have been partly conquered by the sophistries of these fellows and have given credence to them; whilst others who attempted to argue with them appear to me to lack to a great extent the power of the Ancients. For this reason I have attempted to put together my arguments in the way in which it seems to me the Ancients, had any of them been still alive, would have done, in opposition to those who would overturn the finest doctrines of our art.

I am not, however, unaware that I shall achieve either nothing at all or else very little. For I find that a great many things which have been conclusively demonstrated by the Ancients are unintelligible to the bulk of the Moderns owing to their ignorance—nay, that, by reason of their laziness, they will not even make an attempt to comprehend them; and even if any of them have understood them, they have not given them impartial examination.

The fact is that he whose purpose is to know anything better than the multitude do must far surpass all others both as regards his nature and his early training. And when he reaches early adolescence he must become possessed with an ardent love for truth, like one inspired; neither day nor night may he cease to urge and strain himself in order to learn thoroughly all that has been said by the most illustrious of the Ancients. And when he has learnt this, then for a prolonged period he must test and prove it, observing what part of it is in agreement, and what in disagreement with obvious fact; thus he will choose this and turn away from that. To such an one my hope has been that my treatise would prove of the very greatest assistance. . . . Still, such people may be expected to be quite few in number, while, as for the others, this book will be as superfluous to them as a tale told to an ass.

11. For the sake, then, of those who are aiming at truth, we must complete this treatise by adding what is still wanting in it. Now, in people who are very hungry, the stomach obviously attracts or draws down the food before it has been thoroughly softened in the mouth, whilst in those who have no appetite or who

are being forced to eat, the stomach is displeased and rejects the food. And in a similar way each of the other organs possesses both faculties—that of attracting what is proper to it, and that of rejecting what is foreign. Thus, even if there be any organ which consists of only one coat (such as the two bladders, the uterus, and the veins), it yet possesses both kinds of fibres, the longitudinal and the transverse.

But further, there are fibres of a third kind—the oblique—which are much fewer in number than the two kinds already spoken of. In the organs consisting of two coats this kind of fibre is found in the one coat only, mixed with the longitudinal fibres; but in the organs composed of one coat it is found along with the other two kinds. Now, these are of the greatest help to the action of the faculty which we have named retentive. For during this period the part needs to be tightly contracted and stretched over its contents at every point—the stomach during the whole period of digestion, and the uterus during that of gestation.

Thus too, the coat of a vein, being single, consists of various kinds of fibres; whilst the outer coat of an artery consists of circular fibres, and its inner coat mostly of longitudinal fibres, but with a few oblique ones also amongst them. Veins thus resemble the uterus or the bladder as regards the arrangement of their fibres, even though they are deficient in thickness; similarly arteries resemble the stomach. Alone of all organs the intestines consist of two coats of which both have their fibres transverse. Now the proof that it was for the best that all the organs should be naturally such as they are (that, for instance, the intestines should be composed of two coats) belongs to the subject of the use of parts; thus we must not now desire to hear about matters of this kind nor why the anatomists are at variance regarding the number of coats in each organ. For these questions have been sufficiently discussed in the treatise "On Disagreement in Anatomy." And the problem as to why each organ has such and such a character will be discussed in the treatise "On the Use of Parts."

12. It is not, however, our business to discuss either of these questions here, but to consider duly the natural faculties, which, to the number of four, exist in each organ. Returning then, to this point, let us recall what has already been said, and set a crown to the whole subject by adding what is still wanting. For when every part of the animal has been shewn to draw into itself the juice which is proper to it (this being practically the first of the natural faculties), the next point to realise is that the part does not get rid either of this attracted nutriment as a whole, or even of any superfluous portion of it, until either the organ itself, or the major part of its contents also have their condition reversed. Thus, when the stomach is sufficiently filled with the food and has absorbed and stored away the most useful part of it in its own coats, it then rejects the rest like an alien burden. The same happens to the bladders, when the matter attracted into them begins to give trouble either because it distends them through its quantity or irritates them by its quality.

And this also happens in the case of the uterus; for it is either because it can no longer bear to be stretched that it strives to relieve itself of its annoyance, or else because it is irritated by the quality of the fluids poured out into it. Now both of these conditions sometimes occur with actual violence, and then miscarriage takes place. But for the most part they happen in a normal way, this being then called not miscarriage but delivery or parturition. Now abortifacient drugs or certain other conditions which destroy the embryo or rupture certain of its membranes are followed by abortion, and similarly also when the uterus is in pain from being in a bad state of tension; and, as has been well said by Hippocrates, excessive movement on the part of the embryo itself brings on labour. Now pain is common to all these conditions, and of this there are three possible causes—either excessive bulk, or weight, or irritation; bulk when the uterus can no longer support the stretching, weight when the contents surpass its strength, and irritation when the fluids which had previously been pent up in the membranes, flow out, on the rupture of these, into the uterus itself, or else when the whole foetus perishes, putrefies, and is resolved into pernicious ichors, and so irritates and bites the coat of the uterus.

In all organs, then, both their natural effects and their disorders and maladies plainly take place on analogous lines, some so clearly and manifestly as to need no demonstration, and others less plainly, although not entirely unrecognizable to those who are willing to pay attention.

Thus, to take the case of the stomach: the irritation is evident here because this organ possesses most sensibility, and among its other affections those producing nausea and the so-called heartburn clearly demonstrate the eliminative faculty which expels foreign matter. So also in the case of the uterus and the urinary bladder; this latter also may be plainly observed to receive and accumulate fluid until it is so stretched by the amount of this as to be incapable of enduring the pain; or it may be the quality of the urine which irritates it; for every superfluous substance which lingers in the body must obviously putrefy, some in a shorter, and some in a longer time, and thus it becomes pungent, acrid, and burdensome to the organ which contains it. This does not apply, however, in the case of the bladder alongside the liver, whence it is clear that it possesses fewer nerves than do the other organs. Here too, however, at least the physiologist must discover an analogy. For since it was shown that the gall-bladder attracts its own special juice, so as to be often found full, and that it discharges it soon after, this desire to discharge must be either due to the fact that it is burdened by the quantity or that the bile has changed in quality to pungent and acrid. For while food does not change its original quality so fast that it is already ordure as soon as it falls into the small intestine, on the other hand the bile even more readily than the urine becomes altered in quality as soon as ever it leaves the veins, and rapidly undergoes change and putrefaction. Now, if there be clear evidence in relation to the uterus, stomach, and intestines, as well as to the urinary bladder, that there is either some distention, irritation, or burden inciting each of these organs to elimination, there is no difficulty in imagining this in the case of the gall-bladder also, as well as in the other organs,—to which obviously the arteries and veins also belong.

13. Nor is there any further difficulty in ascertaining that it is through the same channel that both attraction and discharge take place at different times. For obviously the inlet to the stomach does not merely conduct food and drink into this organ, but in the condition of nausea it performs the opposite service. Further, the neck of the bladder which is beside the liver, albeit single, both fills and empties the bladder. Similarly the canal of the uterus affords an entrance to the semen and an exit to the foetus.

But in this latter case, again, whilst the eliminative faculty is evident, the attractive faculty is not so obvious to most people. It is, however, the cervix which Hippocrates blames for inertia of the uterus when he says:—"Its orifice has no power of attracting semen."

Erasistratus, however, and Asclepiades reached such heights of wisdom that they deprived not merely the stomach and the womb of this faculty but also the bladder by the liver, and the kidneys as well. I have, however, pointed out in the first book that it is impossible to assign any other cause for the secretion of urine or bile.

Now, when we find that the uterus, the stomach and the bladder by the liver carry out attraction and expulsion through one and the same duct, we need no longer feel surprised that Nature should also frequently discharge waste-substances into the stomach through the veins. Still less need we be astonished if a certain amount of the food should, during long fasts, be drawn back from the liver into the stomach through the same veins by which it was yielded up to the liver during absorption of nutriment. To disbelieve such things would of course be like refusing to believe that purgative drugs draw their appropriate humours from all over the body by the same stomata through which absorption previously takes place, and to look for separate stomata for absorption and purgation respectively. As a matter of fact one and the same stoma subserves two distinct faculties, and these exercise their pull at different times in opposite directions—first it subserves the pull of the liver and, during catharsis, that of the drug. What is there surprising, then, in the fact that the veins situated between the liver and the region of the stomach* fulfil a double service or purpose? Thus, when there is abundance of nutriment contained in the food-canal, it is carried up to the liver by the veins mentioned; and when the canal is empty and in need of nutriment, this is again attracted from the liver by the same veins.

For everything appears to attract from and to go shares with everything else, and, as the most divine Hippocrates has said, there would seem to be a consensus in the movements of fluids and vapours. Thus the stronger draws and the weaker is evacuated.

Now, one part is weaker or stronger than another either absolutely, by nature, and in all cases, or else it becomes so in such and such a particular instance. Thus, by nature and in all men alike, the heart is stronger than the liver at attracting what is serviceable to it and rejecting what is not so; similarly the liver is stronger than the intestines and stomach, and the arteries than the veins. In each of us personally, however, the liver has stronger drawing power at one time, and the stomach at another. For when there is much nutriment contained in the alimentary canal and the appetite and craving of the liver is violent, then the viscus exerts far

* The mesenteric veins.

the strongest traction. Again, when the liver is full and distended and the stomach empty and in need, then the force of the traction shifts to the latter.

Suppose we had some food in our hands and were snatching it from one another; if we were equally in want, the stronger would be likely to prevail, but if he had satisfied his appetite, and was holding what was over carelessly, or was anxious to share it with somebody, and if the weaker was excessively desirous of it, there would be nothing to prevent the latter from getting it all. In a similar manner the stomach easily attracts nutriment from the liver when it [the stomach] has a sufficiently strong craving for it, and the appetite of the viscus is satisfied. And sometimes the surplusage of nutriment in the liver is a reason why the animal is not hungry; for when the stomach has better and more available food it requires nothing from extraneous sources, but if ever it is in need and is at a loss how to supply the need, it becomes filled with waste-matters; these are certain biliary, phlegmatic [mucous] and serous fluids, and are the only substances that the liver yields in response to the traction of the stomach, on the occasions when the latter too is in want of nutriment.

Now, just as the parts draw food from each other, so also they sometimes deposit their excess substances in each other, and just as the stronger prevailed when the two were exercising traction, so it is also when they are depositing; this is the cause of the so-called fluxions, for every part has a definite inborn tension, by virtue of which it expels its superfluities, and, therefore, when one of these parts,—owing, of course, to some special condition—becomes weaker, there will necessarily be a confluence into it of the superfluities from all the other parts. The strongest part deposits its surplus matter in all the parts near it; these again in other parts which are weaker; these next into yet others; and this goes on for a long time, until the superfluity, being driven from one part into another, comes to rest in one of the weakest of all; it cannot flow from this into another part, because none of the stronger ones will receive it, while the affected part is unable to drive it away.

When, however, we come to deal again with the origin and cure of disease, it will be possible to find there also abundant proofs of all that we have correctly indicated in this book. For the present, however, let us resume again the task that lay before us, i.e. to show that there is noth-

ing surprising in nutriment coming from the liver to the intestines and stomach by way of the very veins through which it had previously been yielded up from these organs into the liver. And in many people who have suddenly and completely given up active exercise, or who have had a limb cut off, there occurs at certain periods an evacuation of blood by way of the intestines—as Hippocrates has also pointed out somewhere. This causes no further trouble but sharply purges the whole body and evacuates the plethoras; the passage of the superfluities is effected, of course, through the same veins by which absorption took place.

Frequently also in disease Nature purges the animal through these same veins—although in this case the discharge is not sanguineous, but corresponds to the humour which is at fault. Thus in cholera the entire body is evacuated by way of the veins leading to the intestines and stomach.

To imagine that matter of different kinds is carried in one direction only would characterise a man who was entirely ignorant of all the natural faculties, and particularly of the eliminative faculty, which is the opposite of the attractive. For opposite movements of matter, active and passive, must necessarily follow opposite faculties; that is to say, every part, after it has attracted its special nutrient juice and has retained and taken the benefit of it hastens to get rid of all the surplusage as quickly and effectively as possible, and this it does in accordance with the mechanical tendency of this surplus matter.

Hence the stomach clears away by vomiting those superfluities which come to the surface of its contents, whilst the sediment it clears away by diarrhœa. And when the animal becomes sick, this means that the stomach is striving to be evacuated by vomiting. And the expulsive faculty has in it so violent and forcible an element that in cases of ileus [volvulus], when the lower exit is completely closed, vomiting of faeces occurs; yet such surplus matter could not be emitted from the mouth without having first traversed the whole of the small intestine, the jejunum, the pylorus, the stomach, and the oesophagus. What is there to wonder at, then, if something should also be transferred from the extreme skin-surface and so reach the intestines and stomach? This also was pointed out to us by Hippocrates, who maintained that not merely pneuma or excess-matter, but actual nutriment is brought down from the outer surface to the original place from which it was

taken up. For the slightest mechanical movements determine this expulsive faculty, which
apparently acts through the transverse fibres,
and which is very rapidly transmitted from the
source of motion to the opposite extremities. It
is, therefore, neither unlikely nor impossible
that, when the part adjoining the skin becomes
suddenly oppressed by an unwonted cold, it
should at once be weakened and should find
that the liquid previously deposited beside it
without discomfort had now become more of
a burden than a source of nutrition, and should
therefore strive to put it away. Finally, seeing
that the passage outwards was shut off by the
condensation [of tissue], it would turn to the
remaining exit and would thus forcibly expel
all the waste-matter at once into the adjacent
part; this would do the same to the part following it; and the process would not cease until the
transference finally terminated at the inner ends
of the veins.

Now, movements like these come to an end
fairly soon, but those resulting from internal
irritants (e.g., in the administration of purgative drugs or in cholera) become much stronger
and more lasting; they persist as long as the
condition of things about the mouths of the
veins continues, that is, so long as these continue to attract what is adjacent. For this condition causes evacuation of the contiguous part,
and that again of the part next to it, and this
never stops until the extreme surface is reached;
thus, as each part keeps passing on matter to its
neighbour, the original affection very quickly
arrives at the extreme termination. Now this is
also the case in ileus; the inflamed intestine is
unable to support either the weight or the acridity of the waste substances and so does its best
to excrete them, in fact to drive them as far
away as possible. And, being prevented from
effecting an expulsion downwards when the
severest part of the inflammation is there, it expels the matter into the adjoining part of the
intestines situated above. Thus the tendency of
the eliminative faculty is step by step upwards,
until the superfluities reach the mouth.

Now this will be also spoken of at greater
length in my treatise on disease. For the present,
however, I think I have shown clearly that there
is a universal conveyance or transference from
one thing into another, and that, as Hippocrates
used to say, there exists in everything a consensus in the movement of air and fluids. And
I do not think that anyone, however slow his
intellect, will now be at a loss to understand any
of these points,—how, for instance, the stomach

or intestines get nourished, or in what manner
anything makes its way inwards from the outer surface of the body. Seeing that all parts
have the faculty of attracting what is suitable
or well-disposed and of eliminating what is
troublesome or irritating, it is not surprising
that opposite movements should occur in them
consecutively—as may be clearly seen in the
case of the heart, in the various arteries, in the
thorax, and lungs. In all these the active movements of the organs and therewith the passive
movements of [their contained] matters may
be seen taking place almost every second in opposite directions. Now, you are not astonished
when the trachea-artery alternately draws air
into the lungs and gives it out, and when the
nostrils and the whole mouth act similarly; nor
do you think it strange or paradoxical that the
air is dismissed through the very channel by
which it was admitted just before. Do you, then,
feel a difficulty in the case of the veins which
pass down from the liver into the stomach and
intestines, and do you think it strange that nutriment should at once be yielded up to the liver
and drawn back from it into the stomach by the
same veins? You must define what you mean
by this expression "at once." If you mean "at
the same time" this is not what we ourselves
say; for just as we take in a breath at one moment and give it out again at another, so at one
time the liver draws nutriment from the stomach, and at another the stomach from the liver.
But if your expression "at once" means that in
one and the same animal a single organ subserves the transport of matter in opposite directions, and if it is this which disturbs you, consider inspiration and expiration. For of course
these also take place through the same organs,
albeit they differ in their manner of movement,
and in the way in which the matter is conveyed
through them.

Now the lungs, the thorax, the arteries rough
and smooth, the heart, the mouth, and the nostrils reverse their movements at very short intervals and change the direction of the matters
they contain. On the other hand, the veins
which pass down from the liver to the intestines
and stomach reverse the direction of their movements not at such short intervals, but sometimes once in many days.

The whole matter, in fact, is as follows:—
Each of the organs draws into itself the nutriment alongside it, and devours all the useful
fluid in it, until it is thoroughly satisfied; this
nutriment, as I have already shown, it stores
up in itself, afterwards making it adhere and

then assimilating it—that is, it becomes nourished by it. For it has been demonstrated with sufficient clearness already that there is something which necessarily precedes actual nutrition, namely adhesion, and that before this again comes presentation. Thus as in the case of the animals themselves the end of eating is that the stomach should be filled, similarly in the case of each of the parts, the end of presentation is the filling of this part with its appropriate liquid. Since, therefore, every part has, like the stomach, a craving to be nourished, it too envelops its nutriment and clasps it all round as the stomach does. And this [action of the stomach], as has been already said, is necessarily followed by the digestion of the food, although it is not to make it suitable for the other parts that the stomach contracts upon it; if it did so, it would no longer be a physiological organ, but an animal possessing reason and intelligence, with the power of choosing the better [of two alternatives].

But while the stomach contracts for the reason that the whole body possesses a power of attracting and of utilising appropriate qualities, as has already been explained, it also happens that, in this process, the food undergoes alteration; further, when filled and saturated with the fluid pabulum from the food, it thereafter looks on the food as a burden; thus it at once gets rid of the excess—that is to say, drives it downwards—itself turning to another task, namely that of causing adhesion. And during this time, while the nutriment is passing along the whole length of the intestine, it is caught up by the vessels which pass into the intestine; as we shall shortly demonstrate, most of it is seized by the veins, but a little also by the arteries; at this stage also it becomes presented to the coats of the intestines.

Now imagine the whole economy of nutrition divided into three periods. Suppose that in the first period the nutriment remains in the stomach and is digested and presented to the stomach until satiety is reached, also that some of it is taken up from the stomach to the liver.

During the second period it passes along the intestines and becomes presented both to them and to the liver—again until the stage of satiety —while a small part of it is carried all over the body. During this period, also imagine that what was presented to the stomach in the first period becomes now adherent to it.

During the third period the stomach has reached the stage of receiving nourishment; it now entirely assimilates everything that had become adherent to it: at the same time in the intestines and liver there takes place adhesion of what had been before presented, while dispersal [anadosis] is taking place to all parts of the body, as also presentation. Now, if the animal takes food immediately after these [three stages] then, during the time that the stomach is again digesting and getting the benefit of this by presenting all the useful part of it to its own coats, the intestines will be engaged in final assimilation of the juices which have adhered to them, and so also will the liver: while in the various parts of the body there will be taking place adhesion of the portions of nutriment presented. And if the stomach is forced to remain without food during this time, it will draw its nutriment from the veins in the mesentery and liver; for it will not do so from the actual body of the liver (by body of the liver I mean first and foremost its flesh proper, and after this all the vessels contained in it), for it is irrational to suppose that one part would draw away from another part the juice already contained in it, especially when adhesion and final assimilation of that juice were already taking place; the juice, however, that is in the cavity of the veins will be abstracted by the part which is stronger and more in need.

It is in this way, therefore, that the stomach, when it is in need of nourishment and the animal has nothing to eat, seizes it from the veins in the liver. Also in the case of the spleen we have shown in a former passage how it draws all material from the liver that tends to be thick, and by working it up converts it into more useful matter. There is nothing surprising, therefore, if, in the present instance also, some of this should be drawn from the spleen into such organs as communicate with it by veins, e.g. the omentum, mesentery, small intestine, colon, and the stomach itself. Nor is it surprising that the spleen should disgorge its surplus matters into the stomach at one time, while at another time it should draw some of its appropriate nutriment from the stomach.

For, as has already been said, speaking generally, everything has the power at different times of attracting from and of adding to everything else. What happens is just as if you might imagine a number of animals helping themselves at will to a plentiful common stock of food; some will naturally be eating when others have stopped, some will be on the point of stopping when others are beginning, some eating together, and others in succession. Yes, by Zeus! and one will often be plundering another, if he be in need while the other has an abundant supply ready to hand. Thus it is in no way surprising that matter should make its way back from the outer surface of the body to the interior, or should be carried from the liver and spleen into the stomach by the same vessels by which it was carried in the reverse direction.

In the case of the arteries this is clear enough, as also in the case of heart, thorax, and lungs; for, since all of these dilate and contract alternately, it must needs be that matter is subsequently discharged back into the parts from which it was previously drawn. Now Nature foresaw this necessity, and provided the cardiac openings of the vessels with membranous attachments, to prevent their contents from being carried backwards. How and in what manner this takes place will be stated in my work "On the Use of Parts," where among other things I show that it is impossible for the openings of the vessels to be closed so accurately that nothing at all can run back. Thus it is inevitable that the reflux into the venous artery (as will also be made clear in the work mentioned) should be much greater than through the other openings. But what it is important for our present purpose to recognise is that every kind possessing a large and appreciable cavity must, when it dilates, abstract matter from all its neighbours, and, when it contracts, must squeeze matter back into them. This should all be clear from what has already been said in this treatise and from what Erasistratus and I myself have demonstrated elsewhere respecting the tendency of a vacuum to become refilled.

14. And further, it has been shown in other treatises that all the arteries possess a power which derives from the heart, and by virtue of which they dilate and contract.

Put together, therefore, the two facts—that the arteries have this motion, and that everything, when it dilates, draws neighbouring matter into itself—and you will find nothing strange in the fact that those arteries which reach the skin draw in the outer air when they dilate, while those which anastomose at any point with the veins attract the thinnest and most vaporous part of the blood which these contain, and as for those arteries which are near the heart, it is on the heart itself that they exert their traction. For, by virtue of the tendency by which a vacuum becomes refilled, the lightest and thinnest part obeys the tendency before that which is heavier and thicker. Now the lightest and thinnest of anything in the body is firstly pneuma, secondly vapour, and in the third place

that part of the blood which has been accurately elaborated and refined.

These, then, are what the arteries draw into themselves on every side; those arteries which reach the skin draw in the outer air (this being near them and one of the lightest of things); as to the other arteries, those which pass up from the heart into the neck, and that which lies along the spine, as also such arteries as are near these—draw mostly from the heart itself; and those which are farther from the heart and skin necessarily draw the lightest part of the blood out of the veins. So also the traction exercised by the diastole of the arteries which go to the stomach and intestines takes place at the expense of the heart itself and the numerous veins in its neighbourhood; for these arteries cannot get anything worth speaking of from the thick heavy nutriment contained in the intestines and stomach, since they first become filled with lighter elements. For if you let down a tube into a vessel full of water and sand, and suck the air out of the tube with your mouth, the sand cannot come up to you before the water, for in accordance with the principle of the refilling of a vacuum the lighter matter is always the first to succeed to the evacuation.

15. It is not to be wondered at, therefore, that only a very little [nutrient matter] such, namely, as has been accurately elaborated—gets from the stomach into the arteries, since these first become filled with lighter matter. We must understand that there are two kinds of attraction, that by which a vacuum becomes refilled and that caused by appropriateness of quality; air is drawn into bellows in one way, and iron by the lodestone in another. And we must also understand that the traction which results from evacuation acts primarily on what is light, whilst that from appropriateness of quality acts frequently, it may be, on what is heavier (if this should be naturally more nearly related). Therefore, in the case of the heart and the arteries, it is in so far as they are hollow organs, capable of diastole, that they always attract the lighter matter first, while, in so far as they require nourishment, it is actually into their coats (which are the real bodies of these organs) that the appropriate matter is drawn. Of the blood, then, which is taken into their cavities when they dilate, that part which is most proper to them and most able to afford nourishment is attracted by their actual coats.

Now, apart from what has been said, the following is sufficient proof that something is taken over from the veins into the arteries. If you will kill an animal by cutting through a number of its large arteries, you will find the veins becoming empty along with the arteries: now, this could never occur if there were not anastomoses between them. Similarly, also, in the heart itself, the thinnest portion of the blood is drawn from the right ventricle into the left, owing to there being perforations in the septum between them: these can be seen for a great part [of their length]; they are like a kind of fossae [pits] with wide mouths, and they get constantly narrower; it is not possible, however, actually to observe their extreme terminations, owing both to the smallness of these and to the fact that when the animal is dead all the parts are chilled and shrunken. Here, too, however, our argument, starting from the principle that nothing is done by Nature in vain, discovers these anastomoses between the ventricles of the heart; for it could not be at random and by chance that there occurred fossae ending thus in narrow terminations.

And secondly [the presence of these anastomoses has been assumed] from the fact that, of the two orifices in the right ventricle, the one conducting blood in and the other out, the former * is much the larger. For, the fact that the insertion of the vena cava into the heart is larger than the vein which is inserted into the lungs suggests that not all the blood which the vena cava gives to the heart is driven away again from the heart to the lungs. Nor can it be said that any of the blood is expended in the nourishment of the actual body of the heart, since there is another vein ** which breaks up in it and which does not take its origin nor get its share of blood from the heart itself. And even if a certain amount is so expended, still the vein leading to the lungs is not to such a slight extent smaller than that inserted into the heart as to make it likely that the blood is used as nutriment for the heart: the disparity is much too great for such an explanation. It is, therefore, clear that something is taken over into the left ventricle. †

Moreover, of the two vessels connected with it, that which brings pneuma into it from the lungs is much smaller than the great outgrowing artery from which the arteries all over the body originate; this would suggest that it not merely gets pneuma from the lungs, but that it also gets blood from the right ventricle through the anastomoses mentioned.

Now it belongs to the treatise "On the Use of Parts" to show that it was best that some parts of the body should be nourished by pure, thin, and vaporous blood, and others by thick, turbid blood, and that in this matter also Nature has overlooked nothing. Thus it is not desirable that these matters should be further discussed. Having mentioned, however, that there are two kinds of attraction, certain bodies exerting attraction along wide channels during diastole (by virtue of the principle by which a vacuum becomes refilled) and others exerting it by virtue of their appropriateness of quality, we must next remark that the former bodies can attract even from a distance, while the latter can only do so from among things which are quite close to them; the very longest tube let down into water can easily draw up the liquid into the mouth, but if you withdraw iron to a distance from the lodestone or corn from the jar (an instance of this kind has in fact been already given) no further attraction can take place. This you can observe most clearly in connection with garden conduits. For a certain amount of moisture is distributed from these into every part lying close at hand but it cannot reach those lying farther off: therefore one has to arrange the flow of water into all parts of the garden by cutting a number of small channels leading from the large one. The intervening spaces between these small channels are made of such a size as will, presumably, best allow them [the spaces] to satisfy their needs by drawing from the liquid which flows to them from every side. So also is it in the bodies of animals. Numerous conduits distributed through the various limbs bring them pure blood, much like the garden water-supply, and, further, the intervals between these conduits have been wonderfully arranged by Nature from the outset so that the intervening parts should be plentifully provided for when absorbing blood, and that they should never be deluged by a quantity of superfluous fluid running in at unsuitable times.

For the way in which they obtain nourishment is somewhat as follows. In the body‡ which is continuous throughout, such as Erasistratus supposes his simple vessel to be, it is

* The tricuspid orifice.
** The coronary vein.
† Galen's conclusion, of course, is, so far, correct, but he has substituted an imaginary direct communication between the ventricles for the actual and more round about pulmonary circulation of whose existence he apparently had no idea. His views were eventually corrected by the Renascence anatomists.

‡ Or we may render it "corpuscle"; Galen practically means the cell.

the superficial parts which are the first to make use of the nutriment with which they are brought into contact; then the parts coming next draw their share from these by virtue of their contiguity; and again others from these; and this does not stop until the quality of the nutrient substance has been distributed among all parts of the corpuscle in question. And for such parts as need the humour which is destined to nourish them to be altered still further, Nature has provided a kind of storehouse, either in the form of a central cavity or else as separate caverns, or something analogous to caverns. Thus the flesh of the viscera and of the muscles is nourished from the blood directly, this having undergone merely a slight alteration; the bones, however, in order to be nourished, require very great change, and what blood is to flesh marrow is to bone; in the case of the small bones, which do not possess central cavities, this marrow is distributed in their caverns, whereas in the larger bones which do contain central cavities the marrow is all concentrated in these.

For, as was pointed out in the first book, things having a similar substance can easily change into one another, whereas it is impossible for those which are very different to be assimilated to one another without intermediate stages. Such a one in respect to cartilage is the myxoid substance which surrounds it, and in respect to ligaments, membranes, and nerves the viscous liquid dispersed inside them; for each of these consists of numerous fibres, which are homogeneous—in fact, actual sensible elements; and in the intervals between these fibres is dispersed the humour most suited for nutrition; this they have drawn from the blood in the veins, choosing the most appropriate possible, and now they are assimilating it step by step and changing it into their own substance.

All these considerations, then, agree with one another, and bear sufficient witness to the truth of what has been already demonstrated; there is thus no need to prolong the discussion further. For, from what has been said, anyone can readily discover in what way all the particular [vital activities] come about. For instance, we could in this way ascertain why it is that in the case of many people who are partaking freely of wine, the fluid which they have drunk is rapidly absorbed through the body and almost the whole of it is passed by the kidneys within a very short time. For here, too, the rapidity with which the fluid is absorbed depends on appropriateness of quality, on the thinness of the fluid, on the width of the vessels and their mouths, and on the efficiency of the attractive faculty. The parts situated near the alimentary canal, by virtue of their appropriateness of quality, draw in the imbibed food for their own purposes, then the parts next to them in their turn snatch it away, then those next again take it from these, until it reaches the vena cava, whence finally the kidneys attract that part of it which is proper to them. Thus it is in no way surprising that wine is taken up more rapidly than water, owing to its appropriateness of quality, and, further, that the white clear kind of wine is absorbed more rapidly owing to its thinness, while black turbid wine is checked on the way and retarded because of its thickness.

These facts, also, will afford abundant proof of what has already been said about the arteries; everywhere, in fact, such blood as is both specifically appropriate and at the same time thin in consistency answers more readily to their traction than does blood which is not so; this is why the arteries which, in their diastole, absorb vapour, pneuma, and thin blood attract either none at all or very little of the juices contained in the stomach and intestines.

THE GREAT IDEAS, *Volumes 2 and 3*